Course 1

FLORIDA

D1288360

elevate science

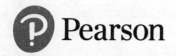 **Pearson**

Boston, Massachusetts   Chandler, Arizona
Glenview, Illinois   New York, New York

AUTHORS

You're an author!

As you write in this science book, your answers and personal discoveries will be recorded for you to keep, making this book unique to you. That is why you are one of the primary authors of this book.

✏ In the space below, print your name, school, town, and state. Then write a short autobiography that includes your interests and accomplishments.

YOUR NAME ....

SCHOOL ....

TOWN, STATE ....

AUTOBIOGRAPHY ....

....

....

....

....

....

....

Your Photo

The cover photo shows lava entering the sea from an active volcano in Kilauea, Hawaii.

Pearson Education, Inc. 330 Hudson Street, New York, NY 10013

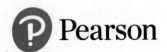

ISBN-13: 978-0-328-94859-8
ISBN-10: 0-328-94859-4
5   20

Program Authors

ZIPPORAH MILLER, EdD
Coordinator for K-12 Science Programs, Anne Arundel County Public Schools
Dr. Zipporah Miller currently serves as the Senior Manager for Organizational Learning with the Anne Arundel County Public School System. Prior to that she served as the K-12 Coordinator for science in Anne Arundel County. She conducts national training to science stakeholders on the Next Generation Science Standards. Dr. Miller also served as the Associate Executive Director for Professional Development Programs and conferences at the National Science Teachers Association (NSTA) and served as a reviewer during the development of Next Generation Science Standards. Dr. Miller holds a doctor's degree from the University of Maryland College Park, a master's degree in school administration and supervision from Bowie State University and a bachelor's degree from Chadron State College.

MICHAEL J. PADILLA, PhD
Professor Emeritus, Eugene P. Moore School of Education, Clemson University, Clemson, South Carolina
Michael J. Padilla taught science in middle and secondary schools, has more than 30 years of experience educating middle-school science teachers, and served as one of the writers of the 1996 U.S. National Science Education Standards. In recent years Mike has focused on teaching science to English Language Learners. His extensive experience as Principal Investigator on numerous National Science Foundation and U.S. Department of Education grants resulted in more than $35 million in funding to improve science education. He served as president of the National Science Teachers Association, the world's largest science teaching organization, in 2005–6.

MICHAEL E. WYSESSION, PhD
Professor of Earth and Planetary Sciences, Washington University, St. Louis, Missouri
Author of more than 100 science and science education publications, Dr. Wysession was awarded the prestigious National Science Foundation Presidential Faculty Fellowship and Packard Foundation Fellowship for his research in geophysics, primarily focused on using seismic tomography to determine the forces driving plate tectonics. Dr. Wysession is also a leader in geoscience literacy and education; he is the chair of the Earth Science Literacy Initiative, the author of several popular video lectures on geology in the *Great Courses* series, and a lead writer of the *Next Generation Science Standards**.

REVIEWERS

Program Consultants

Carol Baker
Science Curriculum

Dr. Carol K. Baker is superintendent for Lyons Elementary K-8 School District in Lyons, Illinois. Prior to this, she was Director of Curriculum for Science and Music in Oak Lawn, Illinois. Before this she taught Physics and Earth Science for 18 years. In the recent past, Dr. Baker also wrote assessment questions for ACT (EXPLORE and PLAN), was elected president of the Illinois Science Teachers Association from 2011–2013, and served as a member of the Museum of Science and Industry (Chicago) advisory board. She is a writer of the Next Generation Science Standards. Dr. Baker received her B.S. in Physics and a science teaching certification. She completed her master's of Educational Administration (K-12) and earned her doctorate in Educational Leadership.

Jim Cummins
ELL

Dr. Cummins's research focuses on literacy development in multilingual schools and the role technology plays in learning across the curriculum. *Elevate Science* incorporates research-based principles for integrating language with the teaching of academic content based on Dr. Cummins's work.

Elfrieda Hiebert
Literacy

Dr. Hiebert, a former primary-school teacher, is President and CEO of TextProject, a non-profit aimed at providing open-access resources for instruction of beginning and struggling readers. She is also a research associate at the University of California Santa Cruz. Her research addresses how fluency, vocabulary, and knowledge can be fostered through appropriate texts, and her contributions have been recognized through awards such as the Oscar Causey Award for Outstanding Contributions to Reading Research (Literacy Research Association, 2015), Research to Practice award (American Educational Research Association, 2013), and the William S. Gray Citation of Merit Award for Outstanding Contributions to Reading Research (International Reading Association, 2008).

Content Reviewers

Alex Blom, Ph.D.
Associate Professor
Department Of Physical Sciences
Alverno College
Milwaukee, Wisconsin

Joy Branlund, Ph.D.
Department of Physical Science
Southwestern Illinois College
Granite City, Illinois

Judy Calhoun
Associate Professor
Physical Sciences
Alverno College
Milwaukee, Wisconsin

Stefan Debbert
Associate Professor of Chemistry
Lawrence University
Appleton, Wisconsin

Diane Doser
Professor
Department of Geological Sciences
University of Texas at El Paso
El Paso, Texas

Rick Duhrkopf, Ph.D.
Department of Biology
Baylor University
Waco, Texas

Jennifer Liang
University of Minnesota Duluth
Duluth, Minnesota

Heather Mernitz, Ph.D.
Associate Professor of Physical Sciences
Alverno College
Milwaukee, Wisconsin

Joseph McCullough, Ph.D.
Cabrillo College
Aptos, California

Katie M. Nemeth, Ph.D.
Assistant Professor
College of Science and Engineering
University of Minnesota Duluth
Duluth, Minnesota

Maik Pertermann
Department of Geology
Western Wyoming Community College
Rock Springs, Wyoming

Scott Rochette
Department of the Earth Sciences
The College at Brockport
State University of New York
Brockport, New York

David Schuster
Washington University in St Louis
St. Louis, Missouri

Shannon Stevenson
Department of Biology
University of Minnesota Duluth
Duluth, Minnesota

Paul Stoddard, Ph.D.
Department of Geology and Environmental Geosciences
Northern Illinois University
DeKalb, Illinois

Nancy Taylor
American Public University
Charles Town, West Virginia

Teacher Reviewers

Jennifer Bennett, M.A.
Memorial Middle School
Tampa, Florida

Sonia Blackstone
Lake County Schools
Howey In the Hills, Florida

Teresa Bode
Roosevelt Elementary
Tampa, Florida

Tyler C. Britt, Ed.S.
Curriculum & Instructional
 Practice Coordinator
Raytown Quality Schools
Raytown, Missouri

A. Colleen Campos
Grandview High School
Aurora, Colorado

Ronald Davis
Riverview Elementary
Riverview, Florida

Coleen Doulk
Challenger School
Spring Hill, Florida

Mary D. Dube
Burnett Middle School
Seffner, Florida

Sandra Galpin
Adams Middle School
Tampa, Florida

Rhonda Graham
Science Supervisor
Pittsburgh Public Schools
Pittsburgh, Pennsylvania

Margaret Henry
Lebanon Junior High School
Lebanon, Ohio

Christina Hill
Beth Shields Middle School
Ruskin, Florida

Judy Johnis
Gorden Burnett Middle School
Seffner, Florida

Karen Y. Johnson
Beth Shields Middle School
Ruskin, Florida

Jane Kemp
Lockhart Elementary School
Tampa, Florida

Denise Kuhling
Adams Middle School
Tampa, Florida

Esther Leonard, M.Ed. and L.M.T.
Gifted and talented Implementation Specialist
San Antonio Independent School District
San Antonio, Texas

Kelly Maharaj
Challenger K–8 School of Science
 and Mathematics
Spring Hill, Florida

Kevin J. Maser, Ed.D.
H. Frank Carey Jr/Sr High School
Franklin Square, New York

Angie L. Matamoros, Ph.D.
ALM Science Consultant
Weston, Florida

Corey Mayle
Brogden Middle School
Durham, North Carolina

Keith McCarthy
George Washington Middle School
Wayne, New Jersey

Yolanda O. Peña
John F. Kennedy Junior High School
West Valley City, Utah

Kathleen M. Poe
Jacksonville Beach Elementary School
Jacksonville Beach, Florida

Wendy Rauld
Monroe Middle School
Tampa, Florida

Anne Rice
Woodland Middle School
Gurnee, Illinois

Pat (Patricia) Shane, Ph.D.
STEM & ELA Education Consultant
Chapel Hill, North Carolina

Diana Shelton
Burnett Middle School
Seffner, Florida

Nakia Sturrup
Jennings Middle School
Seffner, Florida

Melissa Triebwasser
Walden Lake Elementary
Plant City, Florida

Michele Bubley Wiehagen
Science Coach
Miles Elementary School
Tampa, Florida

Pauline Wilcox
Instructional Science Coach
Fox Chapel Middle School
Spring Hill, Florida

Safety Reviewers

Douglas Mandt, M.S.
Science Education Consultant
Edgewood, Washington

Juliana Textley, Ph.D.
Author, NSTA books on school science safety
Adjunct Professor
Lesley University
Cambridge, Massachusetts

TOPIC

1 Energy

The Essential Question How does energy cause change?

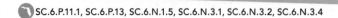
SC.6.P.11.1, SC.6.P.13, SC.6.N.1.5, SC.6.N.3.1, SC.6.N.3.2, SC.6.N.3.4

Go to PearsonRealize.com to access your digital course.

▶ VIDEO
• Energy Engineer

INTERACTIVITY
• Get the Ball Rolling • Understanding Machines • Levers • Force and Energy • Interpret Kinetic Energy Graphs • Racing for Kinetic Energy • Roller Coasters and Potential Energy • Prosthetics in Motion • Types of Energy • Forms of Energy • Energy Transformations • Take It to the Extreme

VIRTUAL LAB

ASSESSMENT

eTEXT

APP

HANDS-ON LABS

иConnect What Would Make a Card Jump?

иInvestigate
• What Work Is
• Mass, Velocity, and Kinetic Energy
• Energy, Magnetism, and Electricity
• Making a Flashlight Shine
• Law of Conservation of Energy

иDemonstrate
3, 2, 1...Liftoff!

TOPIC
2

Forces and Motion 50

The Essential Question How is the motion of an object affected by forces that act on it?

Quest KICKOFF Build a Better Bumper Car 52

SC.6.P.12.1, SC.6.P.13.1, SC.6.P.13.2, SC.6.P.13.3, SC.6.N.3.2, SC.6.N.3.3, SC.6.N.3.4

Go to PearsonRealize.com to access your digital course.

▶ VIDEO
• Mechanical Engineer

👆 INTERACTIVITY
• Relative Motion • Balanced and Unbalanced Forces • Explore Forces • Falling for Velocity • Motion Graphs • How Forces Affect Motion • How are Mass, Motion, and Force Related? • Going, Going, Gone! • Fuel Efficient Vehicles • Exploring Gravity • The Pull of the Tides

📱 VIRTUAL LAB

☑ ASSESSMENT

📖 eTEXT

📱 APP

HANDS-ON LABS

Connect Identifying Motion

Investigate
• Motion Commotion
• Walking the Walk
• Newton Scooters
• Observing Friction
• Sticky Sneakers

Demonstrate
Stopping on a Dime

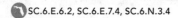

Go to PearsonRealize.com
to access your digital course.

▶ **VIDEO**
• Aquaculture Manager

👆 **INTERACTIVITY**
• Describing Systems
• Thermal Energy and the Cycling of Matter
• Maps and Methods
• Constructive and Destructive Forces
• The Water Cycle
• Siting a Fish Farm
• Floridan Aquifer System

VIRTUAL LAB

ASSESSMENT

eTEXT

APP

HANDS-ON LABS

иConnect What Interactions Occur Within the Earth System?

иInvestigate
• Where Heat Flows
• Surface Features
• Water on Earth

иDemonstrate
Modeling a Watershed

TOPIC

4

Energy in the Atmosphere and Ocean 146

The Essential Question How does energy move throughout Earth's atmosphere and ocean?

Quest KICKOFF **Crossing the Atlantic**.............. 148

SC.6.E.7.1, SC.6.E.7.3, SC.6.E.7.5, SC.6.E.7.8, SC.6.E.7.9, SC.6.N.1.1, SC.6.N.3.4

Go to PearsonRealize.com to access your digital course.

▶ **VIDEO**
• Ship Captain

👆 **INTERACTIVITY**
• Fluids on the Move
• Patterns in the Wind
• Where the Wind Blows
• Winds Across the Globe
• Currents and Climate
• Ocean Habitats
• Keeping Current on Currents

📖 **VIRTUAL LAB**

☑ **ASSESSMENT**

📖 **eTEXT**

📱 **APP**

HANDS-ON LABS

иConnect Does a Plastic Bag Trap Heat?

иInvestigate
• Heating Earth's Surface
• United States Precipitation
• Modeling Ocean Current Formation

иDemonstrate
Not All Heating Is Equal

Weather and Climate 188

The Essential Question What determines weather and climate on Earth?

Quest KICKOFF Preparing a Plan 190

SC.6.E.7.2, SC.6.E.7.3, SC.6.E.7.6, SC.6.E.7.7, SC.6.E.7.8, SC.6.N.1.1, SC.6.N.1.4, SC.6.N.1.5

Go to PearsonRealize.com to access your digital course.

▶ **VIDEO**
• Meteorologist

INTERACTIVITY
• Ways That Water Moves • Water Cycle • Interruptions in the Water Cycle • Clean Drinking Water • When Air Masses Collide • Mapping Out the Weather • Using Air Masses to Predict Weather • Weather Predicting • Not in Kansas Anymore • Tinkering with Technology • Two Sides of the Mountain • Olympic Choices

VIRTUAL LAB
• Create a Snow Day

☑ **ASSESSMENT**

📖 **eTEXT**

📱 **APP**

HANDS-ON LABS

иConnect Puddle Befuddlement

иInvestigate
• How Clouds and Fog Form
• Weather Fronts
• Tracking Weather
• Predicting Hurricanes
• Classifying Climates

иDemonstrate
Water from Trees

TOPIC 6

Earth's Surface Systems 248

The Essential Question What processes change Earth's surface?

Quest KICKOFF Ingenious Island 250

 SC.6.E.6.1, SC.6.N.3.4

Go to PearsonRealize.com
to access your digital course.

▶ VIDEO
• Civil Engineer

👆 INTERACTIVITY
• Colors of the Sand
• Dating Using Weathering Rates
• Classify the Force of Weathering
• Predicting Disasters
• Material Slope Angle
• Changing Landscapes
• Karst Topography
• Carving a Canyon
• Mammoth Caves
• Effects of Glaciers
• Glacial Ice
• Coastline Management

📱 VIRTUAL LAB

☑ ASSESSMENT

📖 eTEXT

📱 APP

HANDS-ON LABS

uConnect How Does Gravity Affect
Materials on a Slope?

uInvestigate
• Freezing and Thawing
• Small, Medium, and Large
• Raindrops Falling
• Changing Coastlines

uDemonstrate
Materials on a Slope

TOPIC 7

Living Things in the Biosphere 300

The Essential Question How do scientists define and organize living things?

Quest KICKOFF Sort Out Those Organisms 302

SC.6.L.14.6, SC.6.L.15.1, SC.6.N.1.5, SC.6.N.2.2

📶 Go to **PearsonRealize.com** to access your digital course.

▶ **VIDEO**
- Public Health Advisor

👆 **INTERACTIVITY**
- What All Living Things Have in Common
- Mom's Car Must Be Alive
- Classify It
- Life as a Single Cell
- Viruses by the Numbers
- Vaccines and Populations
- Bacteriophage Treatments
- There's Something Going Around
- Modifying a Virus

📱 **VIRTUAL LAB**

☑ **ASSESSMENT**

📖 **eTEXT**

📱 **APP**

HANDS-ON LABS

uConnect Is It an Animal?

uInvestigate
- Cheek Cells
- Living Mysteries
- A Mystery Organism No More!
- Life In a Drop of Pond Water

uDemonstrate
It's Alive!

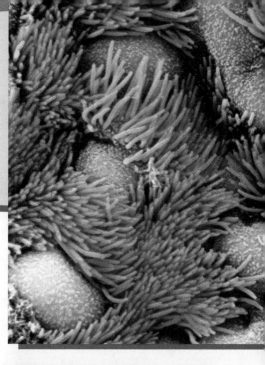

Go to PearsonRealize.com to access your digital course.

▶ VIDEO
• Illustrator

👆 INTERACTIVITY
• Through a Microscope • Functions of All Cells • A Strange Specimen • Structure Function Junction • Build a Cell • Specialized Cells • Cell Transport • Entering and Leaving the Cell • A Cell Divides • How Does a Broken Bone Heal? • The Cell Cycle • The Human Body Systems • Interacting Systems • Advances in Medical Technology • Balancing Act • Communication and Homeostasis • Joints • A Variety of Symptoms

📱 VIRTUAL LAB

☑ ASSESSMENT

📖 eTEXT

📱 APP

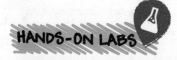

HANDS-ON LABS

uConnect What Can You See?

uInvestigate
• Observing Cells
• Comparing Cells
• Egg-speriment with a Cell
• Modeling Mitosis
• Observing Cells and Tissues
• Parts Working Together

uDemonstrate
Design and Build a Microscope

Elevate your thinking!

Elevate Science for Florida takes science to a whole new level and lets you take ownership of your learning. Explore science in the world around you. Investigate how things work. Think critically and solve problems! *Elevate Science* helps you think like a scientist, preparing you for a world of discoveries.

Explore Your World

Explore real-life scenarios with engaging Quests that dig into science topics in Florida and around the world. You can:

- Solve real-world problems
- Apply skills and knowledge
- Communicate solutions

Make Connections

Elevate Science connects science to other subjects and shows you how to better understand the world through:

- Mathematics
- Reading and Writing
- Literacy

Quest KICKOFF

What do you think is causing Pleasant Pond to turn green?

In 2016, algal blooms turned bodies of water green and slimy in Florida, Utah, California, and 17 other states. These blooms put people and ecosystems in danger. Scientists, such as limnologists, are working to predict and prevent future algal blooms. In this problem-based Quest activity, you will investigate an algal bloom at a lake and determine its cause. In labs and digital activities, you will apply what you learn in each lesson to help you gather evidence to solve the mystery. With enough evidence, you will be able to identify what you believe is the cause of the algal bloom and present a solution in the Findings activity.

SC.7.L.17.3 Describe and investigate various limiting factors in the local ecosystem and their impact on native populations, including food, shelter, water, space, disease, parasitism, predation, and nesting sites. (Also SC.7.N.1.1 and SC.7.N.1.4)

Math Toolbox

Graphing Population Changes

Ohio's Deer Population

Changes in a population over time, such as white-tailed deer in Ohio, can be displayed in a graph.

Deer Population Trends, 2000–2010

Year	Population (estimated)	Year	Population (estimated)
2000	525,000	2006	770,000
2001	560,000	2007	725,000
2002	620,000	2008	745,000
2003	670,000	2009	750,000
2004	715,000	2010	710,000
2005	720,000		

Relationships Use the data

| 800,000 |
| 750 |

READING CHECK Determine Central Ideas
What adaptations might the giraffe have that help it survive in its environment?

Academic Vocabulary
Have you heard the term *role* in other contexts? List some examples.

Build Skills for the Future

- Master the Engineering Design Process

- Apply critical thinking and analytical skills

- Learn about STEM careers

Focus on Inquiry

Case studies put you in the shoes of a scientist to solve real-world mysteries using real data. You will be able to:

- Analyze data

- Test a hypothesis

- Solve the case

Enter the Lab Zone

Hands-on experiments and virtual labs help you test ideas and show what you know in performance-based assessments. Scaffolded labs include:

- STEM Labs

- Design Your Own

- Open-ended Labs

Explore the Next Generation Sunshine State Science Standards for:

- **Connecting** concepts to make connections

- **Nature of Science standards** to build **inquiry** skills

- **Big ideas, benchmarks, and standards** to master content

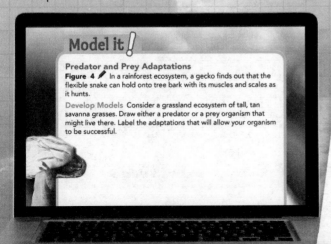

TOPIC
1

Energy

SC.6.P.11.1 Explore the Law of Conservation of Energy by differentiating between potential and kinetic energy. Identify situations where kinetic energy is transformed into potential energy and vice versa. (Also **SC.6.N.1.1** and **SC.6.N.3.4**)

HANDS-ON LAB

uConnect Explore how changes in energy can make a playing card jump.

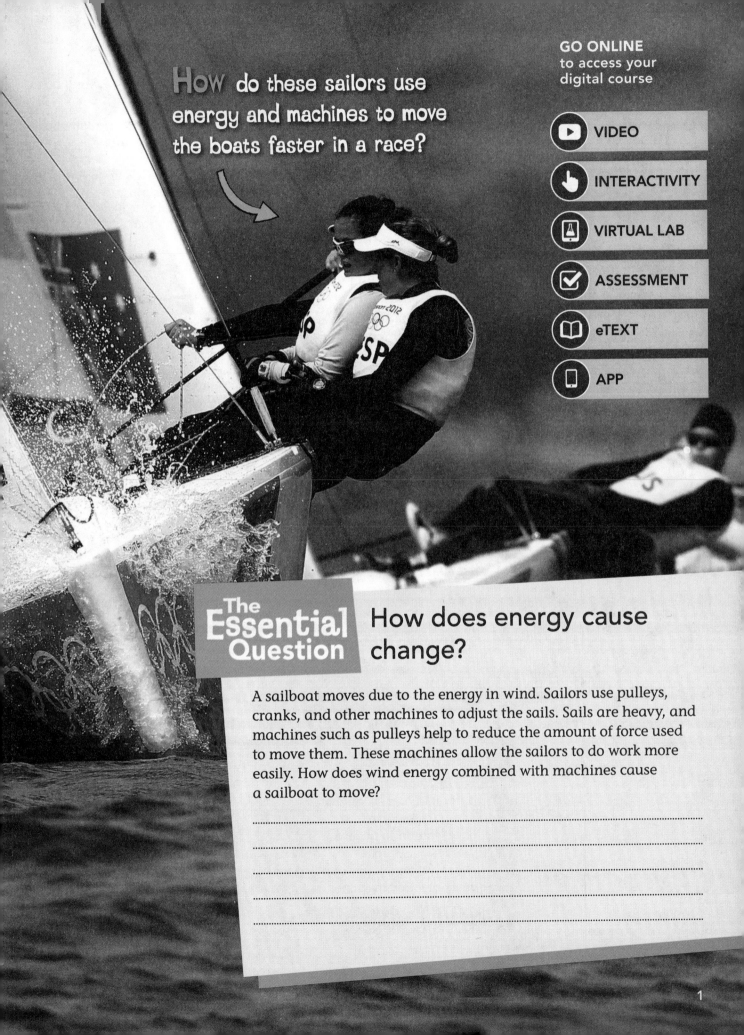

How do these sailors use energy and machines to move the boats faster in a race?

GO ONLINE
to access your digital course

- ▶ VIDEO
- 👆 INTERACTIVITY
- 📱 VIRTUAL LAB
- ☑ ASSESSMENT
- 📖 eTEXT
- 📱 APP

The Essential Question

How does energy cause change?

A sailboat moves due to the energy in wind. Sailors use pulleys, cranks, and other machines to adjust the sails. Sails are heavy, and machines such as pulleys help to reduce the amount of force used to move them. These machines allow the sailors to do work more easily. How does wind energy combined with machines cause a sailboat to move?

....
....
....
....
....

How can you build a complicated machine to do something simple?

STEM Rube Goldberg™ was a cartoonist and inventor. Goldberg is well-known for his cartoons, which include complex and wacky machines that perform simple tasks. Today, students who study machine design and engineering can participate in contests to build the best "Rube Goldberg Machine™." Building these machines helps students to understand energy transformations and hone their construction skills. In this Quest, you will design and build a Rube Goldberg Machine–an overly complicated machine with a simple end goal. You will use your understanding of energy transformations to construct the chain-reaction machine.

NBC LEARN ▶ VIDEO

After watching the Quest Kickoff video, answer the following questions.

What simple task might your machine perform?

....

....

....

....

What could be some of the components of the machine?

....

....

....

....

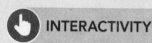

👆 **INTERACTIVITY**

Outrageous Energy Contraptions

SC.6.P.11.1 Explore the law of conservation of energy by differentiating between potential and kinetic energy. Identify situations where kinetic energy is transformed into potential energy and vice versa. (Also **SC.6.N.1.1**)

Quest CHECK-IN

IN LESSON 1

STEM How do machines exert force and transfer energy? Develop a design for a chain-reaction machine that can perform a simple task.

👆 **INTERACTIVITY**

Applying Energy

Quest CHECK-IN

IN LESSON 2

STEM What are the different types of kinetic energy? Use what you have learned to finalize the design, choose materials, and build your chain-reaction machine.

🧪 **HANDS-ON LAB**

Build a Chain-Reaction Machine

Quest CHECK-IN

IN LESSON 3

STEM What energy transformations take place in a chain-reaction machine? Test your chain-reaction machine prototype and evaluate its performance. Revise and retest it.

🧪 **HANDS-ON LAB**

Test and Evaluate a Chain-Reaction Machine

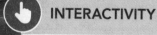

Many energy transformations occur in this complicated device. In the end, it simply turns on a light bulb!

Quest CHECK-IN

IN LESSON 4

STEM How can an additional energy transformation improve your design? Modify your chain-reaction machine to include at least one additional energy transformation. Then test, evaluate, and finalize it.

HANDS-ON LAB

Redesign and Retest a Chain-Reaction Machine

Quest FINDINGS

Complete the Quest!

Determine the best way to demonstrate your machine, and show how energy is used in the working of your machine from start to finish.

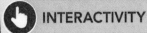

INTERACTIVITY

Reflect on Your Chain-Reaction Machine

Energy, Motion, Force, and Work

Guiding Questions

- How is energy related to motion and force?
- What are the relationships among energy, motion, force, and work?

Connections

Literacy Determine Central Ideas

Math Solve Linear Equations

SC.6.P.13 Forces and Changes in Motion
(Also **SC.6.N.3.4** and **SC.7.P.10**)

Vocabulary

energy
motion
force
work
power

Academic Vocabulary

maximum

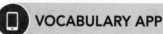 **VOCABULARY APP**

Practice vocabulary on a mobile device.

Quest CONNECTION

Think about how force and motion operate in machines you are familiar with. How do these factors allow machines to do work?

Connect It !

✏️ **Draw curved arrows on the photograph to represent the motion of the motorcycles.**

Apply Scientific Reasoning These motorcycles need energy to move. Where does the energy come from?

....

Write Explanatory Texts Describe how the rider exerts a force on the motorcycle.

....

....

Construct Explanations In what way do you think the motorcycles perform work?

....

Energy in Motion and Force

Energy is the ability to do work or cause change. You do work when you pick up your backpack. Motorcycles do work during a race, as in **Figure 1**. The energy to do this work comes from fuel. As the fuel burns, it changes into other substances and releases energy.

Energy comes in many forms. Light, sound, and electricity are all forms of energy. Energy can also be transferred from place to place. For example, chemical energy is transferred from the food you eat to your body. Energy from the sun is transferred to Earth in the form of electromagnetic radiation. Energy is not something you can see directly. You can, however, observe its effects. When you touch something hot, you don't see the energy, but you feel the heat. You can hear the sound of a bass drum, but you can't see the sound energy itself.

Energy and Motion
It takes energy for motion to occur. An object is in **motion** if its position changes relative to another object. A pitched ball would not speed toward home plate without energy supplied by the pitcher. Energy supplied by food enables a racehorse to run around a track. Energy stored in gasoline allows the motorcycles in **Figure 1** to move at high speeds. In each of these examples, the more energy that is used, the faster the object can move.

VIDEO

Watch this video to better understand energy.

Reflect Think about the different methods you used to travel from one place to another today. In your science notebook, describe two of these ways. For each, identify the energy source that caused the movement.

Racing Around the Track
Figure 1 Energy, motion, force, and work are all involved in a motorcycle race.

Energy and Force

The relationship between energy and motion also involves forces. A **force** is a push or pull. You can see many examples of this relationship on a construction site. Look at **Figure 2** and study the examples of how energy is used to apply a force that causes motion.

☑ **READING CHECK** **Explain** How would you describe a force?

....

....

Force

Figure 2 When energy is used to apply force, objects can move.

Apply Concepts ✏ Draw an arrow on each numbered picture to show the direction of the force being applied. Then label each arrow with "push" or "pull" to identify the type of force being applied.

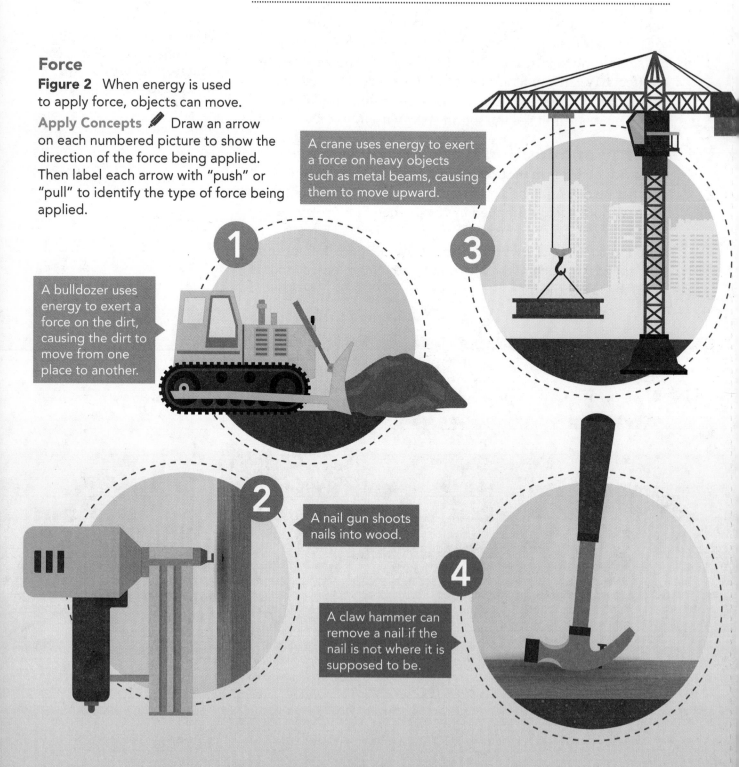

A crane uses energy to exert a force on heavy objects such as metal beams, causing them to move upward.

A bulldozer uses energy to exert a force on the dirt, causing the dirt to move from one place to another.

A nail gun shoots nails into wood.

A claw hammer can remove a nail if the nail is not where it is supposed to be.

Force and Work

You might think of "work" as a job, such as teaching, being a doctor, or bagging groceries at the local supermarket. But the scientific meaning of work is much broader than that. In scientific terms, you do **work** any time you exert a force on an object that causes the object to change its motion in the same direction in which you exert the force. All of the machines on the previous page show work being done because the forces are being applied in the same direction as the motion shown.

You probably carry your books from one class to another every school day. You know that you exert a force on the books as you carry them. However, you do very little work on them because of the direction of the force exerted. When you carry an object while walking at constant speed in a straight line, you exert an upward force on the object. Because the force is vertical and the motion is horizontal, you don't do any work on the object itself.

Figure 3 shows three different ways to move a tool bin. The weight of the bin is the same in each situation, but the amount of work varies. For a given force, the **maximum** amount of work is done when both the movement and the force are in the same direction.

INTERACTIVITY

Explore how levers work in this virtual activity.

Academic Vocabulary

Write a synonym for maximum.

....

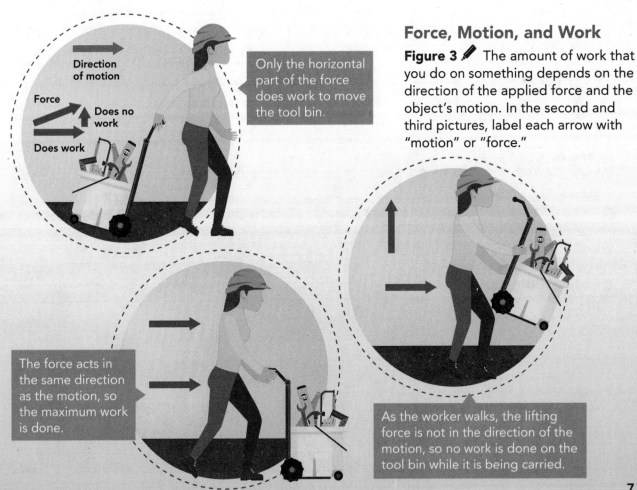

Direction of motion

Force

Does no work

Does work

Only the horizontal part of the force does work to move the tool bin.

The force acts in the same direction as the motion, so the maximum work is done.

As the worker walks, the lifting force is not in the direction of the motion, so no work is done on the tool bin while it is being carried.

Force, Motion, and Work

Figure 3 ✏ The amount of work that you do on something depends on the direction of the applied force and the object's motion. In the second and third pictures, label each arrow with "motion" or "force."

Work Done, or Not?

Figure 4 This girl struggles to open a jar, but the lid does not budge.

Apply Scientific Reasoning Is the girl doing work? Explain your reasoning.

....

....

....

....

....

👆 **INTERACTIVITY**

Explore how energy is needed to get an object to move, and discover how work on an object affects its motion.

Work Requires Motion Imagine that you are trying to open a jar, and the lid is stuck. You exert a lot of force on the lid, but it doesn't move. Are you doing work? No. No matter how much force you exert, you don't do any work if the lid does not move.

Calculating Work Suppose you bought a new painting for your room. You have to carry the painting up three porch steps to the first floor and then up another flight of 12 steps to the second floor. (See **Figure 5**.) Is it more work to lift the painting up 12 steps than three steps? As you might guess, moving an object a greater distance requires more work than moving the same object a shorter distance. The amount of work you do depends on both the amount of force you exert and the distance the object moves.

More or Less Work Done?

Figure 5 This person carries a painting up two sets of steps.

Predict ✏ Circle the image in which you think the person does more work.

The amount of work done on an object is calculated by multiplying force times distance. When force is measured in newtons and distance in meters, the SI unit of work is the newton-meter (N-m). This unit is also called a joule (J). One joule is the amount of work you do when you exert a force of 1 newton to move an object a distance of 1 meter.

✓ **READING CHECK** **Determine Central Ideas** What two factors affect how much work is done in any given action?

....

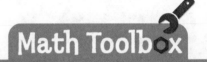

Math Toolbox

Calculating Work

A grandfather lifts a baby 1.5 m with an upward force of 80 N, as shown in the third photograph below. You can use the relationship among work, force, and distance to find out how much work is done:

Work = Force × Distance
Work = 80 N × 1.5 m
Work = 120 N-m

The amount of work done is 120 N-m, or 120 J.

Use the formula for finding work to answer questions 1–2. Show your calculations. Use joules as the unit for work.

1. **Solve Linear Equations** This woman lifts a plant 2 m with a force of 65 N. How much work does she do?

   ....

2. **Calculate** How much work is done when 300 N of force is used to lift the dog 1.5 m?

   ....

3. **Classify** Label the photos below with the words *least*, *medium*, and *most* to rank them from least work done to most work done.

Literacy Connection

Determine Central Ideas As you read, underline the main idea of each paragraph on this page.

Work Related to Energy and Power

Did you pull your shoes from the closet this morning? If so, then you did work on the shoes. As you have read, work is done when a force moves an object in the direction of the force. When an object moves, its position changes. What causes change? Recall that the ability to do work or cause change is called energy. Energy is measured in joules—the same units as work.

When you do work on an object, some of your energy is transferred to that object. Think about the plant shown in the Math Toolbox. When the gardener lifted the plant to the high shelf, she transferred energy to the plant.

If you carry a bag of groceries up a flight of stairs, the work you do is the same whether you walk or run. The time it takes to do the work does not affect the amount of work you do on an object. But something else—power—is affected. **Power** is the rate at which work is done, and it equals the amount of work done on an object in a unit of time. You can think of power in two main ways. An object that has more power than another object does more work in the same amount of time. It can also mean doing the same amount of work in less time. Look at **Figure 6** for other examples that compare power.

Work and Power

Figure 6 In each of these images, work is being done. For each image, give two examples of ways the people shown can increase the power being used.

These people load 10 items on the truck in 10 minutes. Ways power can be increased:

....

This person mows half of her backyard in one hour. Ways power can be increased:

....

Calculating Power

All you need to know to calculate power is how much and how quickly work is being done. Power is calculated by dividing the amount of work done by the amount of time it takes to do the work. This can be written as the following formula:

$$\text{Power} = \frac{\text{Work}}{\text{Time}}$$

Because work is equal to force times distance, you can rewrite the equation for power as follows:

$$\text{Power} = \frac{\text{Force} \times \text{Distance}}{\text{Time}}$$

When work is measured in joules and time in seconds, the SI unit of power is the watt (W). One watt equals one joule per second (1 W = 1 J/s). Examine **Figure 7** to learn more about calculating power.

INTERACTIVITY

Examine real-world examples of energy transformations and forces.

Power

Figure 7 Most climbers of the Himalayan Mountains would not make it to the peaks without the help of Sherpas. Sherpas are natives of Nepal, and they carry heavy loads of equipment up the mountains for the climbers. Suppose one Sherpa uses a force of 980 N to move a load of equipment to a height of 20 meters in 25 seconds. How much power is used?

Different Types of Power

Figure 8 Leaf blowers require gasoline for power, while rakes require power from your body.

Power and Energy

Recall that power is the rate at which work is done. Power is also the rate at which energy is transferred, or the amount of energy transferred in a unit of time.

$$\text{Power} = \frac{\text{Energy transferred}}{\text{Time}}$$

For example, a 60-watt lightbulb transfers 60 joules of energy per second. Different machines have different amounts of power. For instance, you can use either a rake or a leaf blower to remove leaves from your lawn (see **Figure 8**). Each tool transfers the same amount of energy to the leaves when it moves leaves the same distance. However, the leaf blower moves leaves faster than the rake. The leaf blower has more power because it transfers the same amount of energy to the leaves in less time.

☑ **READING CHECK** **Apply Concepts** What is the difference in power between a 60-watt lightbulb and a 100-watt lightbulb?

....

Model It !

Develop Models 🖊 In the concept map below, label each line to show how energy, motion, force, work, and power relate to each other. One line is labeled for you as an example.

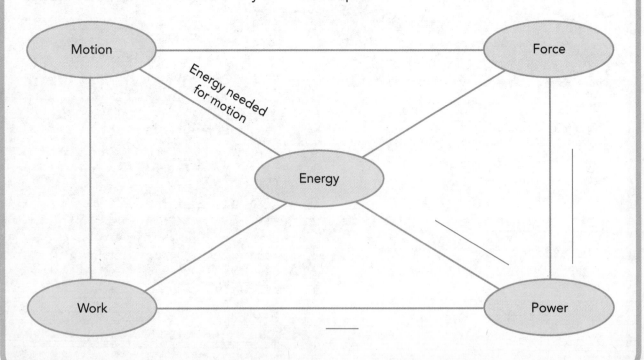

1. **Apply Concepts** Give an example, not from your textbook, in which energy produces a force that causes motion.

....

....

....

2. **Calculate** What force was applied to an object if 35 J of work was done and the object moved 7 m? Show your work.

....

....

....

3. **Evaluate Data** A student did 24 J of work on a chair. She applied a force of 12 N and moved the chair 2 m. What else do you need to know to determine the amount of power used?

....

4. **Identify Criteria** You need to carry six cans of paint from the basement of your house to the attic. Will you do more work if you take the cans two at a time or if you carry them all at once?

....

....

5. **Draw Conclusions** Is work done when you hold a heavy object for a long time? Explain.

....

....

....

6. **Distinguish Relationships** You carry a 50-N weight up a flight of stairs that is 3 m high in 10 s. Then you carry 40 N up two flights of stairs in 20 s. Finally, you carry 30 N up three flights in 45 s. Is the job that took the most power the same as the job that took the most energy? Explain.

....

....

....

....

Quest CHECK-IN

In this lesson, you learned about the basics of energy and how force and motion relate to it. You also learned about how these concepts relate to how work is done.

Identify How do the concepts of energy, force, and motion relate to the machine you will be designing? What factors will you need to consider in your design?

....

....

....

....

👆 INTERACTIVITY

Applying Energy

Go online to learn about how energy, force, and motion relate to machines. Then, develop the design for your machine.

Kinetic Energy and Potential Energy

Guiding Questions

- What determines an object's kinetic energy?
- What factors affect potential energy?
- What is the relationship between potential and kinetic energy?

Connections

Literacy Integrate With Visuals

Math Evaluate Expressions

 SC.6.P.11.1 Explore the Law of Conservation of Energy by differentiating between potential and kinetic energy. Identify situations where kinetic energy is transformed into potential energy and vice versa. (Also **SC.6.N.3.2**)

Vocabulary

kinetic energy
potential energy
gravitational
  potential
  energy
elastic potential
  energy

Academic Vocabulary

virtue

 VOCABULARY APP

Practice vocabulary on a mobile device.

Quest CONNECTION

Think about how your machine will use and rely on potential and kinetic energy.

Connect It!

✏ **Draw an arrow on the image to show the direction that you think the rocks and dirt are moving.**

Construct Explanations It takes a lot of energy to move this amount of dirt and rocks. What do you think is the source of this energy?

....

....

Apply Scientific Reasoning What is another example of something that starts moving suddenly?

....

....

Kinetic Energy

Study the landslide shown in **Figure 1**. In this image, dirt and rocks are moving rapidly down the side of the hill. As you read in Lesson 1, it takes energy to cause the motion you see in this photo. When objects are in motion, they are demonstrating a certain kind of energy—kinetic energy. **Kinetic energy** is the energy that an object possesses by **virtue** of being in motion.

Examples of kinetic energy are all around us. A car moving down a road exhibits kinetic energy. So does a runner participating in a race. As you sit at your desk in school, you exhibit kinetic energy every time you turn a page in a book or type on a keyboard.

Factors Affecting Kinetic Energy
The kinetic energy of an object depends on both its speed and its mass. The faster an object moves, the more kinetic energy it has. For example, if a tennis ball moves at great speed, it has more kinetic energy than if the ball had been softly lobbed over the net. Kinetic energy also increases as mass increases. A wheelbarrow full of dirt has more kinetic energy than an empty wheelbarrow has, due to its greater mass.

INTERACTIVITY

Interpret graphs to understand the relationships among a snowboarder's kinetic energy, mass, and speed.

Academic Vocabulary

The phrase *by virtue of* means "because of." In what other way have you heard the term virtue used?

....

....

....

Landslide!
Figure 1 A landslide is a sudden movement of rock and soil. Before the landslide, all the rocks and soil were in place and not moving.

HANDS-ON LAB

ʋInvestigate Use a skateboard to model changes in kinetic energy.

Calculating Kinetic Energy

Keeping in mind that the kinetic energy of an object depends on its mass and its speed, you can use the following equation to solve for the kinetic energy of an object:

$$\text{Kinetic energy} = \tfrac{1}{2} \times \text{Mass} \times \text{Speed}^2$$

The exponent "2" that follows "Speed" tells you that the speed is multiplied by itself first.

For example, suppose a girl with a mass of 50 kg is jogging at a speed of 2 meters per second (m/s). Note that $1\,kg \cdot m^2/s^2 = 1$ joule (J).

$$
\begin{aligned}
\text{Kinetic energy of girl} &= \tfrac{1}{2} \times 50\ kg \times (2\ m/s)^2 \\
&= \tfrac{1}{2} \times 50\ kg \times (2\ m/s \times 2\ m/s) \\
&= \tfrac{1}{2} \times 50\ kg \times 4\ m^2/s^2 \\
&= 100\ kg \cdot m^2/s^2 = 100\ J
\end{aligned}
$$

Do changes in speed and mass both have the same effect on kinetic energy? Use the Math Toolbox to answer this question.

✓ READING CHECK

Apply Concepts
Underline the unit of energy you get when you calculate kinetic energy.

Math Toolbox

Mass, Speed, and Kinetic Energy

A boy and his dog are running.
The dog has a mass of 20 kg.
The boy has a mass of 45 kg.

1. **Evaluate Expressions** Suppose both the dog and the boy run at a speed of 3 m/s. Evaluate the expression for kinetic energy to find both of their kinetic energies.
Kinetic energy of dog =

....

Kinetic energy of boy =

....

2. **Calculate** Suppose the dog speeds up and is now running at a speed of 6 m/s. Calculate the dog's new kinetic energy.
New kinetic energy of dog =

....

Use your answers from questions 1 and 2 to answer these questions.

3. **Distinguish Relationships** Which variables are proportional: kinetic energy and mass, or kinetic energy and speed?

....

....

4. **Apply Mathematical Concepts** If the speed of an object is doubled, what happens to the value of the object's kinetic energy?

....

....

Potential Energy

Kinetic energy is easy to observe because there is motion involved. But an object that is not moving may still have energy. Some objects have energy simply as a result of their shapes or positions. Energy that results from the position or shape of an object is called **potential energy**. This type of energy has the potential to transform into kinetic energy, or, in other words, to do work. Recall that work involves using force to move an object over a distance.

When you raise a bottle up to your mouth to take a drink of water, or when you stretch out a rubber band, you transfer energy to the object. The energy you transfer is stored, or held in readiness by the object. It may be used later if the bottle is dropped or the rubber band is released (see **Figure 2**).

Look back again at the photo of the landslide at the beginning of the lesson. You see the dirt and rocks moving, showing kinetic energy. At some point before the photo was taken, however, the dirt and rocks were not yet moving. At that stage, they held potential energy.

INTERACTIVITY

Investigate model racecars to see how mass affects kinetic energy.

Literacy Connection

Integrate With Visuals
In your notebook, draw an object with elastic potential energy.

Stored-Up Energy
Figure 2 This stretched rubber band is not moving, but it still contains energy—potential energy. Once the fingers that are stretching the rubber band release the band, what kind of energy will the rubber band have?

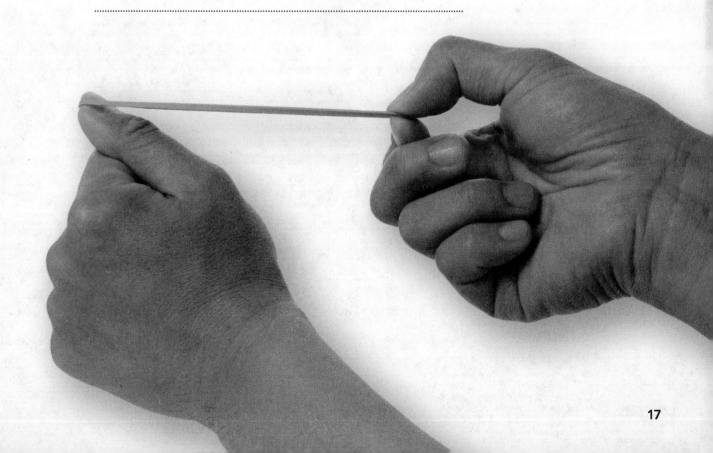

Investigate Develop a model with magnets to show how the arrangement of objects affects potential energy.

Gravitational Potential Energy

Figure 3 A cyclist sitting still at the top of a hill displays gravitational potential energy. What makes it possible for the cyclist to have this type of energy?

....

....

....

....

Gravitational Potential Energy There are two types of potential energy directly related to kinetic energy. One of these types is **gravitational potential energy**. This type of potential energy is related to an object's vertical position— how high it is above the ground. The potential energy is stored as a result of the gravitational pull of Earth on the object.

Gravitational potential energy can be measured by the amount of work needed to lift an object to a certain height. Remember that work is equal to force multiplied by distance. The force you use to lift the object is equal to its weight. Weight is the force that gravity exerts on an object. The distance you move the object is its height above ground level. You can calculate an object's gravitational potential energy using this equation:

$$\text{Gravitational potential energy} = \text{Weight} \times \text{Height above ground}$$

For example, suppose a cat has a weight of 40 newtons, which is about 9 pounds. The cat is lifted 2 meters off the ground. You can calculate its potential energy:

$$\text{Gravitational potential energy} = 40 \text{ N} \times 2 \text{ m}$$

$$= 80 \text{ N-m, or } 80 \text{ J}$$

The energy of the cyclist at the top of hill shown in **Figure 3** is another example of gravitational potential energy.

Elastic Potential Energy

Sometimes, an object has a different type of potential energy due to its shape. **Elastic potential energy** is the energy associated with objects that can be compressed or stretched. This type of potential energy can be stored in such items as rubber bands, bungee cords, springs, and an arrow drawn into a bow.

Trampolines also store elastic potential energy. Take a look at **Figure 4**. When the girl presses down on the trampoline, the trampoline changes shape. The trampoline now has elastic potential energy. When the girl jumps up off the trampoline, this stored energy is transferred from the trampoline to the girl, sending the girl upward. During this energy transfer, the elastic potential energy of the trampoline is transformed into different types of energy.

☑ **READING CHECK Integrate With Visuals** Explain your rankings of the trampoline's potential energy.

....

....

....

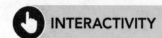

INTERACTIVITY

Explore the potential energy of roller coasters.

Elastic Potential Energy

Figure 4 The energy stored in a stretched object, such as a trampoline, is elastic potential energy. Rank the amount of elastic potential energy of the trampoline from greatest to least using the words *most*, *medium* and *least*. Write your answers in the boxes next to the images.

19

SC.6.P.11.1

1. **Calculate** A running deer has a mass of 100 kg and is running at a speed of 8 m/s. What is the deer's kinetic energy, in joules?

....

2. **Construct Explanations** Suppose you are using a bow to shoot an arrow at a target. At what point does the bow have the greatest elastic potential energy? At what point does the arrow have the greatest kinetic energy?

....
....
....
....
....

3. **Use Equations** Suppose that a bowling ball is lifted 1.5 m so that its gravitational potential energy is 90 J. How much does the bowling ball weigh?

....

4. **Determine Differences** What is the main difference between gravitational potential energy and elastic potential energy?

....
....

5. **Apply Scientific Reasoning** You have two identical tennis balls swinging on strings of the same length. At the lowest point in their paths, Ball A moves three times as fast as Ball B. Which ball will swing to a higher point, and how much higher will it go? Explain.

....
....
....
....
....
....
....
....

Quest CHECK-IN

In this lesson, you learned about potential and kinetic energy and the different roles they play with regard to forces and motion in everyday life.

Evaluate How might the concepts of potential and kinetic energy impact the design of your machine? What factors do you need to consider?

....
....
....
....

HANDS-ON LAB

Build a Chain-Reaction Machine

Go online to download the lab worksheet. Finalize the design for your machine, choose construction materials, and build it! Then, analyze the moving parts of your machine and identify the different types of energy that come into play.

SC.6.P.11.1, SC.6.N.2.3

Prosthetics on the Move

How might you design a prosthetic arm that meets the needs of a modern, on-the-go person? You engineer it!

The Challenge: To design a prosthetic arm based on research into current prosthetic technology.

Until very recently, prosthetics, or artificial limbs, were made of wood, rubber, or plastic. These older prosthetics were solid and heavy, and they often made movement difficult.

When you walk, your foot muscles and leg muscles provide the force to push off the ground. The potential energy stored in your body becomes the kinetic energy of motion. Using an artificial leg, however, takes practice and can be uncomfortable because other muscles strain to carry the artificial limb.

Prosthetic design has advanced thanks to new technologies. In the early 2000s, engineers developed a carbon prosthetic for track athletes. This flexible leg bends and provides elastic potential energy to help the athlete run. The lighter weight of the materials allows the runner to move more efficiently with less muscle strain. Today, advanced engineers are working on limbs that are controlled by the electrical impulses in the human brain, mimicking the way our brains signal our muscles to move!

INTERACTIVITY

Discover the properties of materials and changes in energy to guide your construction of a prosthetic limb.

This prosthetic leg has the shape, weight, and flexibility to allow this runner to sprint again!

DESIGN CHALLENGE

How can you design and build a new kind of prosthetic limb? Go to the Engineering Design Notebook to find out!

③ Other Forms of Energy

Guiding Questions

- How can different forms of energy be classified, quantified, and measured?
- How are these different forms of energy related to each other?

Connection

Literacy Cite Textual Evidence

🏴 **SC.6.P.11.1:** Explore the Law of Conservation of Energy by differentiating between potential and kinetic energy. Identify situations where kinetic energy is transformed into potential energy and vice versa. (Also **SC.6.N.3.1**)

Vocabulary

mechanical energy
nuclear energy
thermal energy
chemical energy
electrical energy
electromagnetic radiation

Academic Vocabulary

medium

 VOCABULARY APP

Practice vocabulary on a mobile device.

Quest CONNECTION

Think about how the machine you are designing might use different types of energy and how each type might impact the machine.

Connect It !

🖉 **Circle and label the parts of the drone that are similar to the parts of the hummingbird.**

Infer What kinds of energy provide power to the drone and to the hummingbird?

....

....

....

Determining Mechanical Energy

The term *mechanical* may make you think of images of metal machines or a mechanic tinkering under the hood of a car. In science, *mechanical* is an adjective that refers to things that are or can be in motion, which covers just about any object we can think of, from particles all the way up to Earth itself. **Mechanical energy** is the energy an object has due to its motion, shape, position, or a combination of these factors.

An object's mechanical energy equals the total of its kinetic and potential energy. For example, a train chugging uphill has energy, and much of that energy is energy of motion—kinetic energy. But a train that is sitting idle at the top of a hill also has energy—potential energy. By adding these two energy forms together, you can determine the train's mechanical energy:

Mechanical Energy = Potential Energy + Kinetic Energy

READING CHECK **Cite Textual Evidence** What are the three factors that determine an object's mechanical energy?

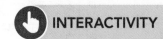 **INTERACTIVITY**

Discover several different types of energy.

Inspired by Nature

Figure 1 Engineers often look to nature for inspiration for their machines. This drone has features similar to those of the hummingbird, and they both need energy to function.

23

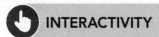

INTERACTIVITY

Investigate forms of energy involved with roller coasters and high divers.

VIDEO

Learn more about nuclear energy.

Literacy Connection

Cite Textual Evidence
As you read about different forms of energy, underline the types of evidence that can help you identify those different forms.

More Forms of Energy

Much of the energy that you observe is mechanical energy, but energy can take many other forms as well. Some other forms of energy are associated with tiny particles, such as atoms and molecules, that make up objects. These forms include nuclear energy, thermal energy, chemical energy, electric energy, and electromagnetic energy.

Nuclear Energy All matter is made of particles called atoms. The center of the atom is called the nucleus (plural: nuclei). **Nuclear energy** is a type of potential energy stored in the nucleus. It can be released through a nuclear reaction. In one type of nuclear reaction, called fission, a nucleus splits into smaller fragments. When it breaks apart, it releases energy (**Figure 2**). If fission reactions are controlled, the release of energy can be used to generate electricity. Nuclear power plants harness nuclear energy for this purpose.

Fusion is another type of nuclear reaction. In fusion, small nuclei combine to form larger nuclei. One place that fusion happens is inside the sun. Some of the energy released by this reaction makes its way to Earth as light. Fusion releases more energy than fission, but the extremely high temperatures that are required to start a fusion reaction make it more difficult to use and control.

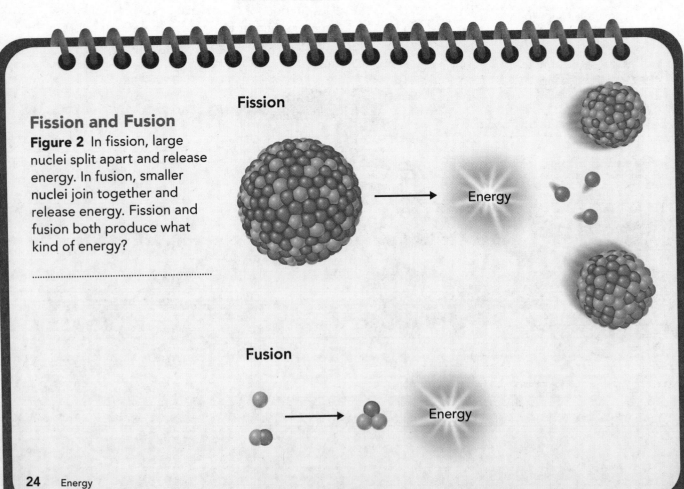

Fission and Fusion
Figure 2 In fission, large nuclei split apart and release energy. In fusion, smaller nuclei join together and release energy. Fission and fusion both produce what kind of energy?

Fission

Energy

Fusion

Energy

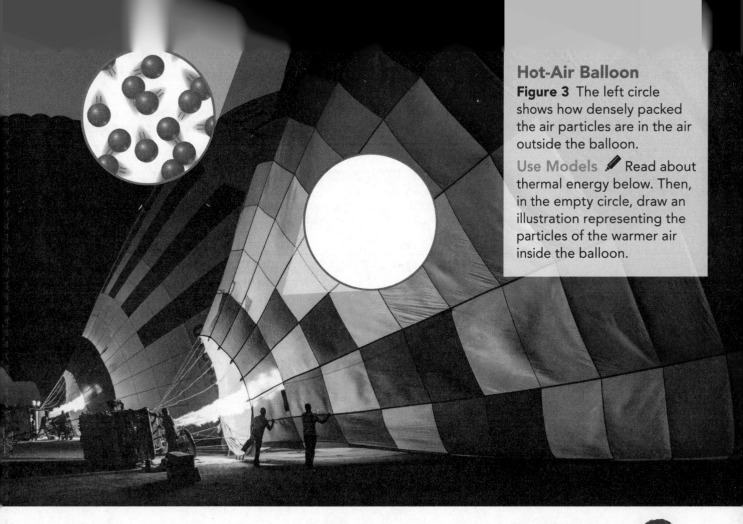

Hot-Air Balloon
Figure 3 The left circle shows how densely packed the air particles are in the air outside the balloon.

Use Models ✏ Read about thermal energy below. Then, in the empty circle, draw an illustration representing the particles of the warmer air inside the balloon.

Thermal Energy

Thermal Energy The total potential and kinetic energy of particles in an object is called **thermal energy**. Lots of particle movement means lots of kinetic energy, and that means a high temperature. Think of a pot of boiling water. The particles are moving very quickly, which results in a high temperature. This means the water has a lot of thermal energy. If the water is then put in the freezer, its kinetic energy will decrease. When its kinetic energy decreases, its thermal energy and temperature also decrease.

The transfer of energy into the thermal energy of an object is called heat. Heat flows from a hotter object to a cooler one through a combination of processes. These processes are called conduction, convection, and radiation. Most substances expand, or take up more space, when heated. When they lose heat, they contract and take up less space. The effect of heat allows a hot air balloon to rise. A flame heats the air inside the hot-air balloon, giving the particles more thermal energy (**Figure 3**). Since they have more thermal energy, they move faster and spread apart. The air in the balloon is then less dense than the air outside the balloon, so the balloon rises.

HANDS-ON LAB

🔍**Investigate** Observe the different types of energy at play when you use a flashlight.

Chemical Energy

What type of energy is in the food you eat, in the cells of your body, and in the substances that make a lightstick glow? It is called **chemical energy**. Chemical energy is a form of potential energy because it results from the relative positions of the particles within a material. The particles are held in those positions by chemical bonds. When these bonds are broken, energy is released.

Plants produce a form of stored chemical energy when they perform photosynthesis. In this process, plants take in energy from sunlight. They also take in water and carbon dioxide. Plant cells break the bonds of water and carbon dioxide to produce sugars. Those sugars store chemical energy. The plant later breaks the bonds of the sugar to release the chemical energy on which it lives. Similarly, your body breaks bonds of sugar from your food. Energy is released when your body breaks bonds that hold the sugar molecules together. Your body uses that energy to power your cells.

Petroleum, or oil, is another source of chemical energy. Oil is converted into gasoline and diesel fuel, which contain potential energy in the form of chemical bonds. When fuel is burned in engines, the energy in these fuels can be used to makes cars run.

Reflect What have you heard about the pros and cons of using oil for energy? In your science notebook, describe what you have heard, and write down your own conclusions about the burning of oil.

Question It!

1. **Draw Conclusions** Batteries allow us to store energy for when it's needed, such as starting a car engine or jump-starting another car whose battery has lost its charge. But batteries cannot operate without chemical reactions. What kind of energy do you think is stored in the substances within the battery?

....

2. **Apply Scientific Reasoning** When someone jump-starts a car, what do you think happens to the stored energy in the working battery?

....
....
....
....

Electrical Energy

Electrical energy is the form of energy most of us use to power devices such as lights, computers, and audio systems. **Electrical energy** is the energy of electric charges. Different materials, and even particles, can have different charges. These differences in charge can result in the movement of electrical charge—a type of kinetic energy called electricity. When charges are not moving but are near one another, they have electric potential energy. This energy can be converted to electricity.

Electromagnetic Radiation

Visible light is one type of electromagnetic radiation. **Electromagnetic radiation** is a form of kinetic energy that travels through space in waves. It does not need a **medium**, such as air or water, to travel through. This is why you can see the stars even though outer space does not contain a medium. Our world has a wide variety of electromagnetic energy, from X-rays that produce images of bones to microwaves that heat leftover food or transmit signals between mobile phones and towers. Other types of electromagnetic radiation include ultraviolet (UV) waves, infrared (or heat) waves, and radio waves. Like other forms of kinetic energy, all types of electromagnetic radiation can transform into thermal energy when heating something.

Academic Vocabulary

In your reading here, the word medium is used to indicate a substance through which a force acts. What are some other meanings of medium that you use or hear in everyday life?

....

....

....

....

✓ **READING CHECK** Classifying Forms of Energy ✏

Sort electromagnetic radiation, mechanical energy, electrical energy, thermal energy, chemical energy, and nuclear energy into one of the three categories in the diagram.

Potential Energy   Both   Kinetic Energy

Energy at the Cookout

Figure 4 Many objects in this scene contain more than one form of energy.

1. **Integrate Information** 🖊 Label this scene with as many forms of energy as you can find.

2. **Cite Evidence** 🖊 Draw a star next to an object that contains more than one form of energy and explain your reasoning below.

....

....

3. Construct Explanations The grill converts chemical energy from propane into thermal energy that heats food. What is another example of an energy change in this image?

....

....

....

....

....

☑LESSON 3 Check

SC.6.P.11.1

1. **Calculate** At a certain point, the kinetic energy of a falling basketball is 30.8 J, and its potential energy is 16.0 J. What is its total mechanical energy?

....

2. **Identify** What type(s) of energy do you acquire when you eat a bowl of hot vegetable soup? Explain.

....

....

....

....

3. **Cite Textual Evidence** Why is it true that particles in a rock lying on the ground have kinetic energy and potential energy?

....

....

....

....

....

4. **Relate Change** When you burn wood in a fireplace, you get light and heat. What kind of energy does the wood contain before it is burned, and where does that energy come from?

....

....

5. **Determine Differences** What is the difference between high temperature and low temperature? Use the concepts of thermal energy, kinetic energy, and particle movement to explain.

....

....

....

....

....

....

....

....

....

Quest CHECK-IN

In this lesson, you learned about other forms of energy, such as nuclear energy and electromagnetic radiation. You also started to think about how these forms of energy can change into other forms, and how to tell when such a change has occurred.

Evaluate Why do engineers need to keep track of potential and kinetic energy and energy transformations in prototypes of machines?

....

....

....

....

HANDS-ON LAB

Test and Evaluate a Chain-Reaction Machine

Go online to download the lab worksheet. Test your chain-reaction machine prototype and evaluate its performance. Then revise your machine's design and retest as needed. Think about energy transformations that are taking place and the roles of potential and kinetic energy.

CAREERS
Energy Engineer

Reinventing ENERGY SYSTEMS

We all use energy every moment of our lives. It lights our classrooms, runs our computers, and powers our industries. For much of the twentieth century, the United States depended largely on fossil fuels for energy. This has been changing in recent decades because the supply of fossil fuels is limited, and excessive use of these fuels has caused environmental damage on a vast scale. Today, people are turning more and more to renewable sources of fuel, such as solar and wind power. This is where the energy engineers play a role.

The purpose of an energy engineer's job is simple: to make the world more energy-efficient. Energy engineers carry out a wide range of work that involves research, design, and construction.

Some energy engineers explore new methods of obtaining energy, while others develop ways to integrate renewable energy sources into the existing power grid. Energy engineers also work with architects to incorporate clean energy sources in new construction. Additionally, some of these engineers help to develop more efficient machinery, such as cars that run on alternative fuels.

This type of work involves mathematics, physics, and chemistry. It offers creative challenges and a wide variety of tasks. If you enjoy these subjects and challenges, this career might be right for you!

▶ VIDEO

Learn about the work an energy engineer does.

MY CAREER

Speak with an energy engineer at a local laboratory or office to learn more about this career.

Energy engineers make important decisions in the design and construction of our energy systems.

Energy Change and Conservation

Guiding Questions

- In what ways can energy change from one form to another?
- How is energy transferred?
- How does the law of conservation of energy apply to transformations and transfers?

Connections

Literacy Cite Textual Evidence

Math Use Proportional Relationships

 SC.6.P.11.1 Explore the Law of Conservation of Energy by differentiating between potential and kinetic energy. Identify situations where kinetic energy is transformed into potential energy and vice versa. (Also **SC.6.N.1.5**)

Vocabulary

law of conservation of energy

Academic Vocabulary

pivot

📱 **VOCABULARY APP**

Practice vocabulary on a mobile device.

 Quest CONNECTION

Think about how your complex machine might use transfers of energy to complete a simple task. Also consider how much energy transforms into heat as the machine works.

Connect It!

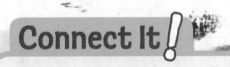

✏️ **Trace the movement of the snowboarder.**

Infer How is the snowboarder able to soar through the air?

....

....

....

Energy Changes Form

All forms of energy can be transformed into other forms of energy. Energy can transform once (which we call a single transformation) or multiple times. A toaster provides a good example of a single transformation. Electrical energy passes through metal wires and is transformed into thermal energy.

If you eat toast, the resulting process is an example of multiple transformations. Your body transforms chemical energy stored in cells into the kinetic energy that moves your mouth. Your digestive system uses mechanical and chemical energy to digest the bread. Some of the chemical energy in the bread is released as thermal energy that helps your body maintain its temperature. Some of the remaining chemical energy is delivered back to your body's cells. The cells then transform that chemical energy into mechanical energy that allows your body to function.

Multiple transformations also go into the making of the bread. Sunlight, which is a form of electromagnetic radiation, is harnessed by wheat plants to create chemical energy. Mechanical energy is used to grind the wheat into flour. The flour is combined with water and yeast to make dough—more chemical energy. As the dough is baked in the oven, electrical energy is used to increase the thermal energy of the oven. Heat is transferred from the oven to the dough, and the thermal energy of the dough increases as it bakes into bread. Many of the processes that we rely on daily involve multiple transformations.

Literacy Connection

Cite Textual Evidence
What evidence in the text supports the claim that energy changes form? List two examples.

....

....

....

....

....

....

Snowboard Jumping
Figure 1 The snowboarder thrusts up and forward by using her legs. But most of the energy that allows her to travel a great distance through the air is supplied by something else.

Kinetic and Potential Energy

One common energy transformation involves potential energy changing to kinetic energy. The snowboarder on the previous page had potential energy when she stood at the top of the hill. As she pushed herself off the top, gravity transformed the potential energy into kinetic energy. As she accelerated down the hill, the potential energy declined while the kinetic energy increased This is true of any falling object, such as the ball in **Figure 2**. Recall that the weight of an object and its height above the ground are proportionally related to its gravitational potential energy. And so, as the height of the ball decreases, it loses potential energy while gaining kinetic energy. The ball's kinetic energy is greatest right before it hits the ground.

A pendulum also demonstrates the relationship between kinetic and potential energy. A pendulum consists of something with mass suspended on an arm or pole that swings back and forth from a **pivot** point. A swinging boat ride at an amusement park is a kind of pendulum (**Figure 3**). At its highest point, the pendulum has no movement and therefore no kinetic energy. When it begins to swing down, potential energy declines as the kinetic energy increases. The kinetic energy and the speed of the pendulum are greatest at the bottom, or midpoint, of the swing. As the pendulum swings upward, it loses kinetic energy and gains potential energy until it is motionless again and ready to swing back to the other side.

Academic Vocabulary
The term pivot is often used in describing the action of basketball players when they keep one foot firmly in place while moving their other foot. What other things in everyday life might pivot?

....

....

....

Falling Objects
Figure 2 🖊 As an object falls, its potential energy decreases while its kinetic energy increases. Circle the location where the ball has the most kinetic energy.

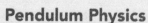

Pendulum Physics
Figure 3 This amusement park ride is basically a pendulum.

Use Models 🖊 Use the abbreviation *PE* for potential energy and *KE* for kinetic energy to label the positions where the boat has maximum PE, minimum PE, maximum KE, and minimum KE.

Energy Transformation and Transfer

Energy transformation and energy transfer sometimes occur in the same process at the same time, but they are not the same thing. Energy transformation occurs when one form of energy changes into another. The potential energy of a pendulum, such as the wrecking ball in **Figure 4**, transforms into kinetic energy as it falls due to the force of gravity. Energy transfer takes place when energy moves from one object to another. When the wrecking ball hits the wall, some of the kinetic energy of the ball transfers to the wall, causing the wall to fall over. As the wrecking ball swings, energy is also transferred from the ball to the air, due to the force of friction. In this case, energy transfers, but it is also transformed. Some of the mechanical energy of the moving wrecking ball is transferred and transformed into thermal energy of the surrounding air. Whenever a moving object experiences friction, some of its mechanical energy is transformed into thermal energy.

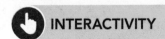

INTERACTIVITY

Explore different examples of energy transformations.

☑ READING CHECK **Cite Textual Evidence** Underline the sentences that explain the difference between energy transformation and energy transfer.

Model It !

Transformation and Transfer in Demolition

Figure 4 🖊 Draw pictures in the empty boxes to show what happens as the wrecking ball swings. Describe the energy transformations and transfers that are occurring.

Ball at top of swing	Ball at bottom of swing	Ball hitting the wall

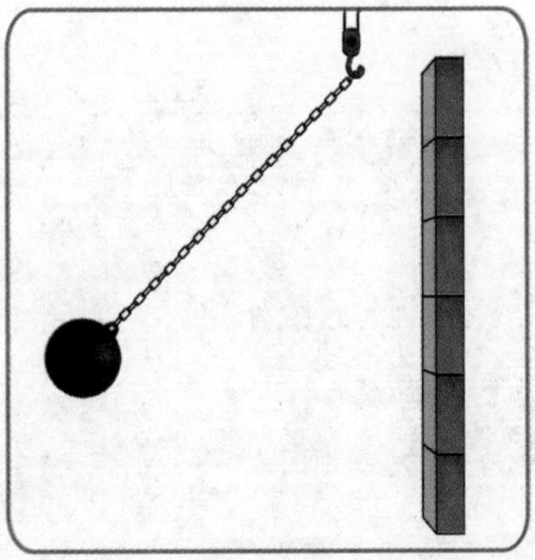

▶ **VIDEO**

Look into the future and learn about hydrogen fuel cell cars.

HANDS-ON LAB

☑**Investigate** Explore how the changing kinetic energy of a bouncing ball is related to conservation of energy.

Energy Is Conserved
Figure 5 After the ball is hit, it eventually slows down and falls. As it slows down, where does its kinetic energy go?

Energy Changes and the Law of Conservation

There is a certain amount of energy in the universe, and we cannot make more of it or destroy any that already exists. Another way to state this idea is to say that energy is conserved. When one object loses energy, other objects must gain it. This is known as the **law of conservation of energy**. This law is a factor in both energy transfers and energy transformations. Energy either moves from one place to another or changes forms, but no energy is created or destroyed.

When a baseball is hit by a bat, as in **Figure 5**, the ball flies through the air. The law of conservation of energy explains why it does not keep flying forever. The kinetic energy of the ball transfers to the air and transforms into thermal energy due to the force of friction. The more air particles there are, the more transfer there is. So more kinetic energy transfers to the air when the air is dense. That's why baseballs travel farther and faster at a baseball stadium in Denver, Colorado, where the air is thinner, than they do in low-altitude ballparks where the air is denser. You can learn more about this phenomenon in the Math Toolbox activity.

Conservation of Energy in Transfers Think back to the wrecking ball. Most of the kinetic energy in the moving ball is transferred directly to the wall. Any energy not transferred is transformed into thermal energy of the ball and air or the sound energy of the ball hitting the wall. Energy is conserved in this example, as it is in any example. No matter how energy is transformed or transferred, the total amount of energy in a system does not change.

Math Toolbox

Home Runs and Air Density

For more than 20 years, major league baseball games played in Denver, Colorado, have featured a high percentage of home runs. The high altitude of Denver means the air there is less dense than in lower-altitude locations, so balls flying through the air in Denver do not transfer as much energy to the air. They keep that kinetic energy and travel farther than they do in other ballparks. This table shows how many home runs the Colorado Rockies baseball team hit at home and away over 10 seasons.

Colorado Rockies' Home Runs at Home and Away										
	2007	**2008**	**2009**	**2010**	**2011**	**2012**	**2013**	**2014**	**2015**	**2016**
Home	103	92	98	108	94	100	88	119	102	116
Away	68	68	92	65	69	66	71	67	84	88

1. **Calculate** Over the 10-year span, how many more home runs did the Rockies score in their home ballpark in Denver than at other ballparks?

   ....

   ....

2. **Use Proportional Relationships** What is the ratio of home runs the team hit at home and home runs hit in away games over the 10-year period? Express the ratio in the smallest numbers possible.

   ....

   ....

   ....

3. **Summarize** Describe the high home-run numbers at the Rockies' home ball field in terms of kinetic energy and energy transformation.

   ....

   ....

   ....

   ....

   ....

   ....

   ....

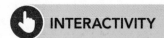
Conservation of Energy in Waves The vibrations that come from a wrecking ball smashing through a wall travel in sound waves. In a sound wave or any other type of wave, energy passes through matter without moving the matter to a new place. The matter vibrates, meaning it moves temporarily, but ends up back where it was. We can see this on the ocean surface with a floating object (**Figure 6**). An ocean wave passes under the object, lifts it, drops it, and the object ends up back where it was. That's why a surfer cannot catch a wave far out in the ocean. Once a wave breaks, matter is moved and energy is released. A surfer can ride the wave when it breaks (**Figure 7**). Energy is conserved as the breaking wave transfers its energy to the shore.

☑ **READING CHECK** **Connect to Engineering** Why would the energy industry be interested in developing technologies to transform the kinetic energy in ocean waves to electrical energy?

Waves and Matter

Figure 6 A wave's energy passes through matter. Whether the medium is air, water, or some other substance, the matter vibrates but does not end up in a new place. Similarly, a floating ball moves in a circular motion as the wave passes, and the ball ends up back where it started.

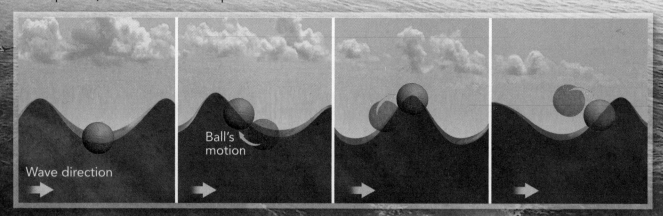

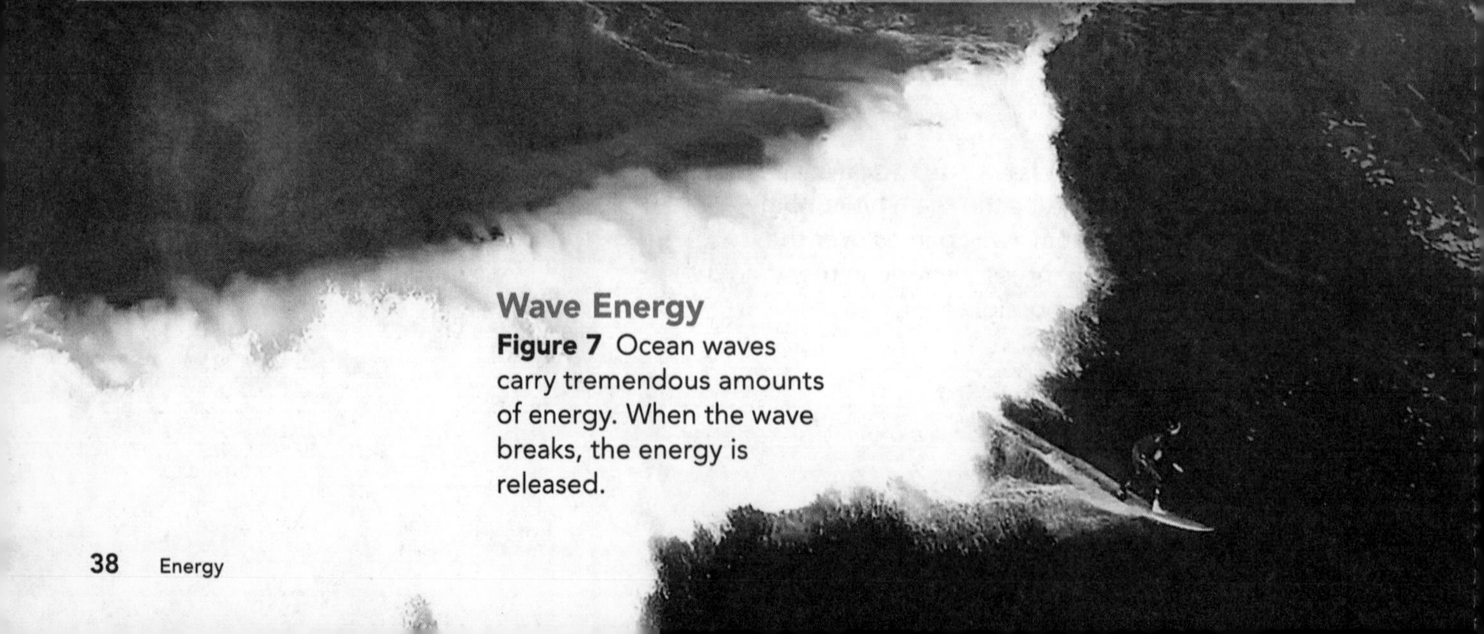

Wave direction

Ball's motion

Wave Energy

Figure 7 Ocean waves carry tremendous amounts of energy. When the wave breaks, the energy is released.

1. Distinguish Relationships What does it mean to say that energy is conserved in an energy transformation?

....

....

2. Integrate Information A train rumbles along the tracks at high speed. After it passes, the rail feels hot. What kind of energy transformation has taken place?

....

....

....

3. Connect to Society A generator that produces 40 kilowatts uses twice as much fuel in an hour as a generator that produces 20 kilowatts. Explain why, in terms of energy transformations.

....

....

....

....

....

4. Construct Explanations Explain the changes in kinetic energy (KE) and potential energy (PE) that occur when an apple falls off the table and hits the floor.

....

....

....

....

....

....

5. Cite Evidence After a tornado moved through a forest, what kinds of evidence would there be of energy transformations or transfers?

....

....

....

....

....

....

Quest CHECK-IN

In this lesson, you learned about energy transformations and energy transfers and how energy is conserved in both.

Evaluate Why is it important for engineers to understand and quantify how energy changes as it moves through a machine, or from one object to another?

....

....

....

....

HANDS-ON LAB

Redesign and Retest a Chain-Reaction Machine

Go online to download the lab worksheet. Modify your chain-reaction machine prototype to include at least one additional energy transformation. Then test, evaluate, and finalize the design, and present it to the class.

U.S. ENERGY CONSUMPTION

As we know from the law of conservation of energy, new energy cannot simply be created. Therefore, many people feel that it's important for countries to study how they are using their energy resources. The pie chart shows the sources of energy used in the United States.

Renewable Energy

Light and heat from the sun, energy from wind and water, and heat from wood fires were the major sources of energy until the eighteenth century, when fossil fuels began to dominate. More recently, nations of the world have begun to return to renewable energy sources. These sources exist in an unlimited supply, and they are cleaner and safer for the environment. One disadvantage to renewable energy is the high initial cost involved in switching from fossil fuel systems to renewable energy systems.

Coal

Coal comes from the Earth, and it is easily transported. However, this fossil fuel must be mined from underground. The process damages the environment, and coal miners face some of the most dangerous work there is. Burning coal also releases pollutants into the atmosphere.

Petroleum

The main advantage to petroleum, also called crude oil, is that it is a powerful fuel. However, crude oil exists only in a limited supply. Petroleum also requires drilling to access it. The process is expensive and it damages the environment. Finally, the burning and accidental spilling of petroleum results in air pollution, land pollution, and water pollution on a vast scale.

Natural Gas

Natural gas is cheap and abundant. However, it must be transported through pipelines that often leak. Like petroleum, it requires drilling, which harms the environment. And burning natural gas releases carbon dioxide, which contributes to global warming.

Nuclear Energy

Nuclear energy is the most recently discovered source of power. It is a cleaner form of energy because it does not involve the burning of fossil fuels. The United States can generate its own nuclear power, so there are economic advantages as well. The major drawbacks to nuclear power are its expensive cost, the potential for accidents, and the need to dispose of radioactive wastes that will remain dangerous for thousands of years.

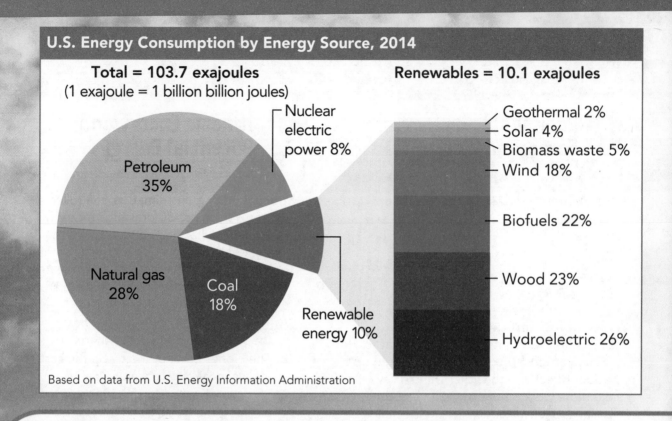

U.S. Energy Consumption by Energy Source, 2014

Total = 103.7 exajoules
(1 exajoule = 1 billion billion joules)

Renewables = 10.1 exajoules

Petroleum 35%

Nuclear electric power 8%

Natural gas 28%

Coal 18%

Renewable energy 10%

Geothermal 2%
Solar 4%
Biomass waste 5%
Wind 18%
Biofuels 22%
Wood 23%
Hydroelectric 26%

Based on data from U.S. Energy Information Administration

1. **Obtain information** According to the pie chart, which source of energy is used the most in the United States? Which of the five main sources is used the least?

....

....

2. **Predict** How do you think the same pie chart might look ten years from now? Why do you think so?

....

....

....

3. **Construct Explanations** Explain why the nations of the world are turning more and more to renewable energy sources.

....

....

....

4. **Solve Problems** Suppose you are in charge of energy policy for the United States. Choose any two sources of fuel in the pie chart and construct an argument for or against the United States expanding its dependence on each.

....

....

....

....

1 Energy, Motion, Force, and Work

SC.6.P.13

1. Which of the following is not a form of energy?

A. light

B. sound

C. air

D. electricity

2. Identify Criteria A girl carried a box of books up two flights of stairs to her attic. Her father carried a box of the same weight up a ladder directly to the attic. The girl says she did more work on the box than her father because she walked farther up the stairs. Is she correct?

....

....

....

....

....

....

3. Cause and Effect Nick and Bart climbed a 2000-m mountain. Nick took a 3-km trail, and Bart took a 6-km trail. If Nick and Bart weigh the same, their packs weigh the same, and they walked at the same speed, why did Nick have a harder climb?

....

....

....

....

....

2 Kinetic Energy and Potential Energy

SC.6.P.11.1

4. You are editing an animation of a roller coaster, which has 30 drawings for each second. On what part of the track is the cart in most of the drawings? Remember that an object moving quickly will travel a greater distance in a given time interval than an object moving more slowly.

A. The lower parts of the track; the cart has the least potential energy there.

B. The higher parts of the track; the cart moves more slowly there.

C. There will be a uniform number of drawings all along the track, since there are 30 each second.

D. The lower parts of the track; the cart has the greatest kinetic energy there.

5. ✏ Draw a circle where the sled rider has the most potential energy. Draw a square where the rider has the most kinetic energy.

6. Cause and Effect What has a greater effect on an object's kinetic energy—increasing its speed by 50 percent or increasing its mass by 75 percent? Explain.

....

....

....

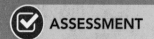
3 Other Forms of Energy
SC.6.P.11.1

7. During the summer pavement gets hot when the sun shines on it. How can you describe the process?

A. Energy transformed by radiation transfers to thermal energy.

B. Thermal energy transforms by conduction.

C. Electromagnetic radiation transforms to thermal energy.

D. Energy transferred by conduction is transformed to radiation.

8. Corn can be made into alcohol fuel that is burned in an automobile's engine to make it move. Put the following forms of energy into the order they occur in the process: chemical energy, kinetic energy, solar radiation, thermal energy

A. kinetic energy, chemical energy, solar radiation, thermal energy

B. solar radiation, chemical energy, thermal energy, kinetic energy

C. solar radiation, thermal energy, kinetic energy, chemical energy

D. solar radiation, chemical energy, kinetic energy, thermal energy

9. Apply Concepts When an atom splits apart through fission, the pieces of the nucleus both have large positive charges that push them apart. What force pushes them apart, and what kind of energy does that force produce?

....

10. Determine Differences What is the difference between thermal energy and temperature of a substance?

....

....

....

....

4 Energy Change and Conservation
SC.6.P.11.1

11. Which of the following describes the law of conservation of energy?

A. Energy cannot be created or destroyed.

B. Energy can only be released through transformation.

C. When energy is conserved, it always changes form.

D. Energy increases when it is transferred from one object to another.

12. Apply Scientific Reasoning In nuclear fusion, hydrogen nuclei join together to make helium and other elements. The hydrogen nuclei all have a positive charge, which means they push one another apart very strongly. Using what you know about thermal energy, draw a series of diagrams to illustrate how a cloud of gas could contract to start a fusion reaction.

13. Construct Explanations Flora is a pilot. She knows that it is very dangerous to put an airplane into a dive that is too steep. Explain what the danger is, in terms of potential and kinetic energy.

....

....

....

....

....

Circle the letter of the best answer.
Emily brings home a painting. **Use the diagram to answer questions 1, 2, and 3.**

1 Emily exerts a force of 30 N on the painting in the direction she travels as she first carries it 15 m on a level sidewalk and then climbs 1.5 m up the stairs. Her walk takes 15 s. How much work does Emily do on the painting in all?

A 2 W
B 45 J
C 33 W
D 85 J

2 Emily's friend Sophia tells her that if the paining is hung on her wall, it will have greater kinetic energy. Is Sophia correct?

F No, the energy will not change if it is hung up.
G Yes, Sophia is correct.
H No, hanging the painting increases its potential energy.
I No, the painting cannot have kinetic energy.

3 As Emily is hanging the painting on her wall, she accidentally drops it. Which statement describes how the energy of the painting transforms as it falls to the floor?

A Energy is created as potential energy transforms into kinetic energy.
B Energy is destroyed as potential energy transforms into kinetic energy.
C Energy is conserved as potential energy transforms into kinetic energy.
D Energy is conserved as kinetic energy transforms into potential energy.

The table shows the kinetic and potential energy of a roller coaster cart at four different locations along a track. **Use the table to answer questions 4 and 5.**

Location	Kinetic Energy (kJ)	Potential Energy (kJ)
1	0	400
2	200	200
3	400	0
4	100	300

4 At which location is the roller coaster cart at the greatest height?

F 1
G 2
H 3
I 4

5 At which location does the roller coaster cart have twice the speed it has at location 4?

A 1
B 2
C 3
D 4

6 A car's brakes use friction to stop the car. When it stops, what happens to the car's kinetic energy?

F It is destroyed.

G It is transformed to electrical energy.

H It is transformed to thermal energy.

I It is transformed to elastic potential energy.

7 A person eats a sandwich, and much of the chemical energy from the food transforms into mechanical energy in the body. Which of the following statements is true about the process?

A Energy is lost during the process.

B Energy is gained during the process.

C No energy is lost or gained during the process.

D The loss or gain depends on the size of the person.

8 You want to make an animation of a roller coaster. You will need to make 30 drawings for each second. In which part of the track will most of your drawings show the cart? Remember that an object moving quickly will move a greater distance in a given time interval than an object moving slowly.

F Most of the drawings will show the cart in the lower parts of the track, since the cart has the least potential energy there.

G Each area of the track will have a similar number of drawings since there are 30 drawings for each second.

H Most of the drawings will show the cart in the lower parts of the track, since the cart has the greatest kinetic energy there.

I Most of the drawings will show the cart in the higher parts of the track, since the cart moves more slowly there.

Complete the Quest!

Determine the best way to demonstrate your chain-reaction machine and show how energy is transformed and transferred from start to finish.

Evaluate Change How did energy change form as it made its way through your chain-reaction machine to perform a task?

....

....

....

....

....

....

....

....

....

👆 **INTERACTIVITY**

Reflect on Your Chain-Reaction Machine

SC.6.P.11.1, SC.6.N.1.1, SC.6.N.3.4

3, 2, 1... Liftoff!

> How can you **design** and build a **model** that explains the relationship between **potential and kinetic energy** in a rocket system?

Background

NASA is building a new website devoted to explaining the physics involved in launching rockets. They have asked you to help with a section of the website that deals with energy transfers and transformations. Your task is to design and build a model that explains the relationship between potential and kinetic energy in a rocket system.

Materials

(per group)

- scissors
- rubber bands
- meter stick
- marker
- metric ruler
- stapler
- cardboard tubes of varying diameters (from paper towels or wrapping paper)
- tape
- construction paper

Safety

Be sure to follow all safety guidelines provided by your teacher.

HANDS-ON LAB

▢Demonstrate Go online for a downloadable worksheet of this lab.

Design a Model

☐ **1.** Work with your group to develop a model of a rocket and launcher using the rubber bands, cardboard tubes, stapler, and other materials listed. Keep the following criteria in mind:

    A. Your rocket must be able to launch vertically into the air. As you work with your group, think about what each of the materials in your model will represent and how the model will operate.

    B. You will need to take at least three different measurements of how far the rubber band stretches and how far your rocket travels.

Plan Your Investigation

☐ **2.** As a group, design an investigation to show that the amount of elastic potential energy in the rocket launcher system affects the kinetic energy of the rocket.

As you plan your investigation, consider these questions. Write your ideas in the space below.

- How can you use the meter stick and the ruler in your investigation?

- What tests will you perform?

- How many trials of each test will you perform?

- What variables will you measure?

- What are the dependent and independent variables?

....

....

....

....

....

....

....

....

....

....

☐ **3.** After getting approval from your teacher for your model design and procedure, conduct your experiment. Record the data in your table. See if you can discover a relationship between how far the rubber band stretches and how far the rocket travels.

Sketch of Rocket Launcher Model

Procedure

....
....
....
....
....
....
....
....
....
....
....

Data Table

Distance Traveled by Rocket (cm)				
Rubber band stretch (cm)	Trial 1	Trial 2	Trial 3	Average

Analyze and Interpret Data

1. **Analyze Structures**   Describe how your rocket launcher works. What might you do to improve it if you could do this experiment again?

   ....

   ....

   ....

   ....

2. **Make Observations**   What is the relationship between the amount of potential energy in the rocket launcher system and the kinetic energy of the rocket? Explain.

   ....

   ....

   ....

   ....

3. **Analyze Systems**   What transfers of energy did you observe in the rocket launcher system? What transformation of energy did you observe? Remember to consider gravity in your answer.

   ....

   ....

   ....

   ....

4. **Construct Arguments**   Use evidence from your investigation to support the argument that energy is being transferred and transformed throughout the rocket's travel. Draw a diagram that shows the rocket traveling upward, with different stages (on the ground, midway up, at its peak, and on its way down). Use labels to describe what is happening to the potential and kinetic energy at each stage. Label the position of maximum kinetic energy and the position of maximum potential energy.

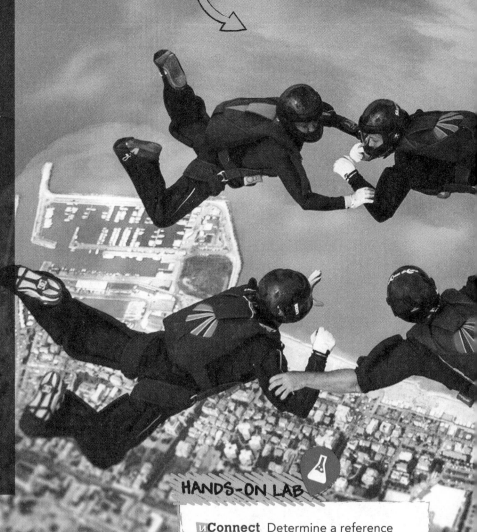

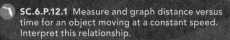
SC.6.P.12.1 Measure and graph distance versus time for an object moving at a constant speed. Interpret this relationship.

SC.6.P.13.1 Investigate and describe types of forces including contact forces and forces acting at a distance, such as electrical, magnetic, and gravitational.

SC.6.P.13.2 Explore the Law of Gravity by recognizing that every object exerts gravitational force on every other object and that the force depends on how much mass the objects have and how far apart they are.

SC.6.P.13.3 Investigate and describe that an unbalanced force acting on an object changes its speed, or direction of motion, or both. (Also **SC.6.N.1.1** and **SC.6.N.1.4**)

What forces act on these skydivers?

HANDS-ON LAB

uConnect Determine a reference point for two different observers.

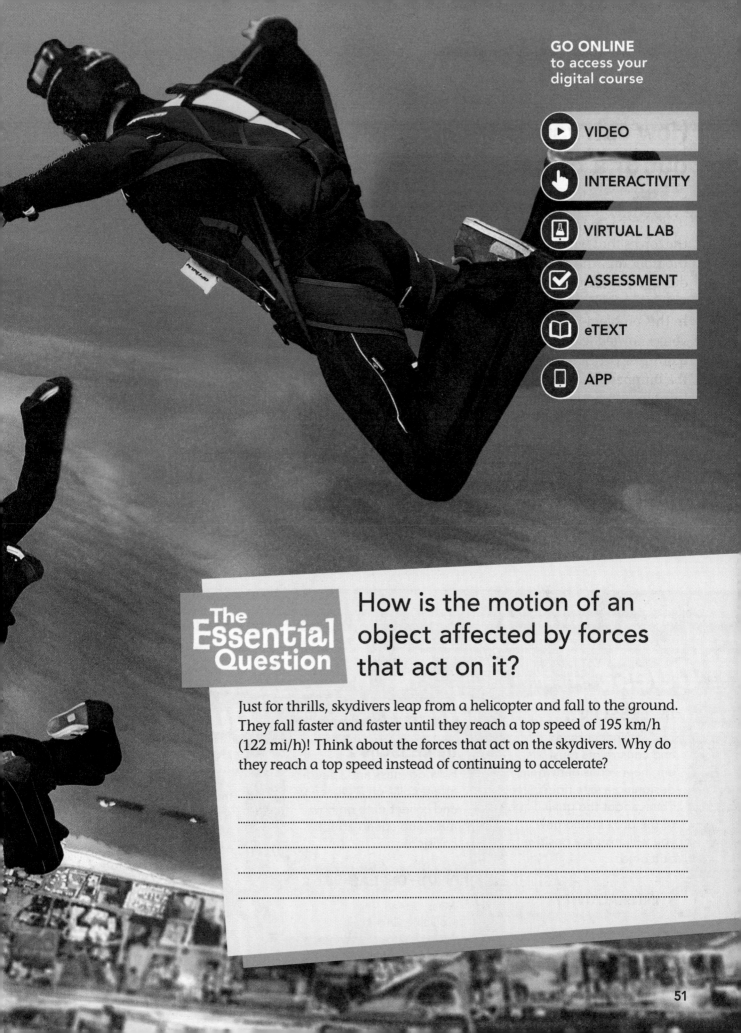

GO ONLINE
to access your
digital course

▶ VIDEO

👆 INTERACTIVITY

🧪 VIRTUAL LAB

☑ ASSESSMENT

📖 eTEXT

📱 APP

The Essential Question

How is the motion of an object affected by forces that act on it?

Just for thrills, skydivers leap from a helicopter and fall to the ground. They fall faster and faster until they reach a top speed of 195 km/h (122 mi/h)! Think about the forces that act on the skydivers. Why do they reach a top speed instead of continuing to accelerate?

....

....

....

....

Quest KICKOFF

How can you take the crash out of a collision?

STEM When engineers design amusement park rides, they have to consider all of the forces that will be acting on riders and make sure the rides are safe. Engineers test their designs with dummies to ensure that riders will not fall out of their seats and collisions will not be harmful to them. In this problem-based Quest activity, you will use your knowledge of Newton's laws of motion to design a bumper car ride that is safe—for both the rider and the bumper car. You will explore forces and Newton's third law of motion as you design, build, test, and refine a model bumper car.

NBC LEARN ▶ VIDEO

After watching the Quest Kickoff video, which examines forces and the laws of motion, think about amusement park rides. Complete the 3-2-1 activity.

3 things riders want to experience

....

....

....

2 ways that rides keep riders safe

....

....

1 way in which riders sometimes get injured

....

....

👆 **INTERACTIVITY**

Build a Better Bumper Car

SC.6.P.13.1 Investigate and describe types of forces including contact forces and forces acting at a distance, such as electrical, magnetic, and gravitational.
SC.6.P.13.3 Investigate and describe that an unbalanced force acting on an object changes its speed, or direction of motion, or both. (Also **SC.6.N.1.1** and **SC.6.N.1.5**)

Quest CHECK-IN

IN LESSON 1

STEM What criteria and constraints must engineers consider when designing a safe ride? Think about the goals of the project and how you will ensure a positive outcome.

👆 **INTERACTIVITY**

Define Criteria and Constraints

Quest CHECK-IN

IN LESSON 2

How do mass and speed affect collisions? Observe and collect data on how mass and speed affect collisions.

HANDS-ON LAB

Mass, Speed, and Colliding Cars

Quest CHECK-IN

IN LESSON 3

STEM How do varying masses and rates of speed affect bumper cars and their riders? Develop and evaluate a design for a safe and fun bumper car.

👆 **INTERACTIVITY**

Apply Newton's Laws of Motion

Every time a bumper car moves forward and hits another car, there is an equal push in the opposite direction. That is part of what makes riding bumper cars fun.

Quest CHECK-IN

IN LESSON 4

STEM How do the action-reaction forces affect bumper cars and their riders? Build, test, evaluate, and improve your bumper car model.

HANDS-ON LAB

Bumping Cars, Bumper Solutions

Quest FINDINGS

Complete the Quest!

Present your final design and explain how you applied Newton's third law of motion as you developed your design.

INTERACTIVITY

Reflect on Your Bumper Car Solution

Guiding Questions

- When is an object in motion?
- How do different types of forces affect motion?

Connections

Literacy Draw Evidence

Math Write an Inequality

 SC.6.P.13.1 Investigate and describe types of forces including contact forces and forces acting at a distance, such as electrical, magnetic, and gravitational. **SC.6.P.13.3** Investigate and describe that an unbalanced force acting on an object changes its speed, or direction of motion, or both. (Also **SC.6.N.3.2** and **SC.6.N.3.3**)

Vocabulary

motion
reference point
force
newton
friction
gravity
net force

Academic Vocabulary

relative

📱 **VOCABULARY APP**

Practice vocabulary on a mobile device.

 CONNECTION

Think about how forces acting on amusement park rides might affect their motion.

Connect It !

🖉 **What part of the image indicates that there is motion? Label it with the word "motion."**

Constructing Explanations Why did you label that part of the image?

....

....

Apply Scientific Reasoning This image shows a car traveling down a road. Why do you think the dog in the car does not appear to be moving?

....

....

....

An Object in Motion

How do you decide whether something is moving? For example, if you were the photographer riding in the car in **Figure 1**, would you say the dog is moving? Parts of it would seem to be. Its eyes blink, and its ears flap in the wind. But to you, the dog would appear to be staying in one position. You know, however, that the dog is in a car that is speeding down the road, so it must be moving. What determines whether the dog is moving or not?

Reference Points An object is in **motion** if its position changes when compared to another object. To decide whether the dog is moving, you might use yourself as a reference point. A **reference point** is a place or object used for comparison to determine whether something is in motion. Objects that are fixed to Earth—such as a tree, a stop sign, or a building—make good reference points. Suppose a tree along the road in **Figure 1** is used as a reference point. The car moves past the tree, as does the dog inside the car. In relation to the tree, the dog changes position, and therefore is in motion. However, if you are the photographer in **Figure 1**, and you are the reference point, your position relative to the dog does not change. You could say that, compared to you, the dog is not in motion.

✓ READING CHECK **Determine Conclusions** Suppose that you are in the car with the dog. What might be your reference point, other than yourself, if you determine that the dog is not moving?

....

....

👆 **INTERACTIVITY**

Discover how to use reference points.

Movin' Along
Figure 1 The dog is moving in relation to the landscape, but it is not moving in relation to the car.

☑**Investigate** Explore how to tell whether an object you are observing is in motion.

Academic Vocabulary

In this lesson, *relative* means "not fixed, not absolute." What does *relative* mean when you use it as a noun?

....

....

....

....

Relative Motion Because motion is determined by a reference point that can change, motion is **relative**. Suppose you are relaxing on a beach. If you use your beach towel as your reference point, you are not moving. You and the beach towel are not changing positions relative to each other. Suppose you use the sun as a reference point instead of your beach towel. If you compare your position to the sun, you are moving quite rapidly, because you are on Earth and Earth revolves around the sun. Relative to the sun, you are moving, but relative to Earth, you are sitting still, so you don't feel as if you are in motion. See **Figure 2** for another example of relative motion.

☑READING CHECK **Draw Evidence** What sources of information might you use to determine the relative motion of Earth compared to other planets in the solar system?

....

....

Relative Motion

Figure 2 🖊 Circle the person on the right side of the front car. In the table, list three reference points that could be used to show that the person is in motion. List three reference points that could be used to show that the person is stationary.

In motion relative to...	Stationary relative to...

How Forces Affect Motion

While objects move relative to one another, they can also speed up, slow down, and change direction. The motion of an object can change when one or more forces act on the object. A **force** is a push or a pull. When one object pushes or pulls another object, the first object exerts a force on the second object. You exert a force on a book when you push it into your book bag. You exert a force on the sleeve of your jacket when you pull it off your arm.

Describing Force A force is described by its strength and by the direction in which it acts. The force needed to lift a dinner plate requires less strength than the force needed to push a refrigerator. Pushing a faucet handle to the left is a different force from pushing it to the right. In an image, the direction and strength of a force acting on an object can be represented by an arrow. The arrow points in the direction of the force, as shown in **Figure 3**. The length of the arrow indicates the strength of the force—the longer the arrow, the greater the force. In the International System of Units (SI), the unit for the strength of a force is called a **newton** (N), after the scientist Sir Isaac Newton.

A bird sits on top of an elephant.

A horse starts pulling a man in a buggy.

A cat pushes a dog.

Representing Forces

Figure 3 🖊 In the first image, a short arrow in a downward direction shows that the bird is exerting a small downward force on the elephant. Draw arrows on the other images to represent the size and direction of the forces applied by the animals in action.

Infer Which image shows a force that causes a change in motion? Why does this force cause a change in motion, but the forces in the other images do not?

....

....

....

VIDEO

Learn about contact and noncontact forces.

Literacy Connection

Draw Evidence Use an additional source to find out what a "normal" force is. Is a normal force a contact force or a noncontact force? What is the normal force on a single book on a shelf?

....

....

....

....

....

....

....

....

....

Types of Forces

Forces can be classified as either contact forces or noncontact forces. Contact forces are those applied only when one object actually touches another. When you push a box across the floor, your push is a contact force because the force only exists while you touch the box. The box may be difficult to push because there is another contact force acting on the box in the opposite direction of your push. It is the force of friction between the box and the floor. **Friction** is a contact force that two surfaces exert on each other when they rub against each other. Friction between your feet and the sidewalk prevents you from slipping as you walk. Ice on the sidewalk greatly reduces that friction.

A noncontact force is a force applied to an object whether it touches the object or not. One noncontact force that you experience every day is **gravity**—a force that pulls objects toward each other as a result of their masses. The force of gravity pulls your body toward Earth. Magnetism and electrical forces are also noncontact forces. **Figure 4** shows examples of contact forces and noncontact forces.

✓ **READING CHECK** **Identify** What are three examples of noncontact forces?

....

....

Contact and Noncontact Forces

Figure 4 You use contact and noncontact forces daily. Complete the sentence in each caption by underlining either "contact" or "noncontact."

This girl exerts a force on the pedals of this bicycle, and friction between the tires and the road help to keep the bike from slipping. Both the force on the pedals and friction are (contact/noncontact) forces.

Even when your feet don't touch the ground, gravity pulls you toward Earth's surface. Gravity is a (contact/noncontact) force.

Balanced and Unbalanced Forces

More than one force can act on an object. If two forces acting on an object are equal in strength and opposite in direction, they are balanced forces. A single book resting on a shelf has two forces acting on it. The downward force of gravity is equal in strength and opposite in direction to the upward force of the shelf on the book. The forces are balanced.

What happens when someone pulls the book off the shelf? The pull of the person removing the book and the friction between the shelf and the book also act in opposite directions. These two forces, however are not equal in strength. The pull is stronger than the friction. These forces are unbalanced.

When the forces on an object are unbalanced, there is a nonzero net force acting on the object. The **net force** on an object is the combination of all the forces acting on that object. If the forces act in the same direction, the net force is the sum of the forces. If the forces act in opposite directions, the net force is the difference in the strengths of those forces. If the net force turns out to be zero, the forces are balanced. Otherwise, the forces are unbalanced. A nonzero net force acting on an object causes a change in the object's motion.

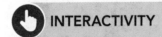

INTERACTIVITY

Explore balanced and unbalanced forces in action.

Write About It! In your science notebook, describe two examples of how unbalanced forces help you in your everyday life.

Model It!

Forces in Tug-of-War

Figure 5 A tug-of-war competition demonstrates the effects of balanced and unbalanced forces on motion. The people on the left side of the rope are experiencing a force from the rope pulling them to the right. They are also experiencing friction from the ground pushing them to the left. The winning team is the team that experiences the greater force of friction.

Develop Models ✏ Draw more people on the left side of the rope to increase the force of friction experienced by this team. Add arrows to the model to represent the force from the rope and the force of friction on the people.

Math Toolbox

Effects of Net Force

In each diagram, two animals push on an apple. The forces of gravity and friction acting on the apple in each scenario does not change, so the forces that may cause a change will come from the animals.

Two chipmunks push on the apple in opposite directions with forces of equal strength. The forces on the apple are balanced. The motion and position of the apple do not change.

A chipmunk and a squirrel push on the apple in opposite directions with forces of different strengths. The forces on the apple are unbalanced. In this case, the strength of the net force on the apple is found by subtracting the strength of the smaller force from the strength of the larger force. The net force is in the same direction as the larger force.

A chipmunk and a squirrel push on the apple in the same direction. The forces on the apple are unbalanced. The net force on the apple is the sum of these forces. The apple will start moving to the right.

2N ➡ ⬅ 2N

2N ➡ ⬅ 6N

6N ➡
2N ➡

Net Force:

Net Force:

Net Force:

1. **Write an Inequality** For each set of forces, write one of these signs to compare the forces: =, >, <.

   2 N .... 2 N

   2 N .... 6 N

   8 N .... 0 N

2. **Apply Mathematical Concepts** 🖊 Label each diagram with the strength of the net force in newtons (N).

3. **Reason Quantitatively** In the center diagram, which direction will the apple start moving?

   ....

INTERACTIVITY

Check your understanding of net force in this interactivity.

✓ READING CHECK **Infer** A girl picks up a bag of apples that are at rest on the floor. How does the force the girl applies compare to the force of gravity acting on the apples?

....

....

....

☑ LESSON 1 Check

1. **Determine Differences** What is the difference between a contact force and a noncontact force?

....

....

....

....

....

2. **Apply Concepts** Two teams of girls are having a tug-of-war, and neither side is winning. Each of the four girls on the west team is pulling with a force of 250 N. Three of the four girls on the east team are pulling with a force of 260 N each. With what force is the fourth girl on the east pulling?

....

....

....

....

....

....

....

3. **Synthesize Information** Nancy is sailing her boat toward Sam's boat at 5 km/h. Nora, who is just a few meters behind Nancy, is not moving in relation to Nora. From Sam's point of view, how is Nora's boat moving?

....

....

....

....

4. **Apply Scientific Reasoning** Four boys push on the front, back, and sides of a shopping cart. The boys in the front and on the two sides push with a force of 60 N. The boy in back pushes with a force of 50 N. Which way does the cart move?

....

....

....

....

....

....

Quest CHECK-IN

In this lesson, you learned about the motion of objects. You also learned about different types of forces and how these forces affect the movement of objects.

Identify   What are the forces that act upon amusement park rides? Why is it important for engineers to understand how motion and forces affect the rides they design?

....

....

....

....

....

👆 INTERACTIVITY

Define Criteria and Constraints

Go online to identify the problem, consider criteria and constraints, and develop a design for your prototype.

② Speed, Velocity, and Acceleration

Guiding Questions

- How do you determine speed from calculations and distance-versus-time graphs?
- How is velocity related to speed and acceleration?
- How can you interpret graphs to determine acceleration?

Connections

| Literacy | Determine Conclusions |

| Math | Solve Linear Equations |

 SC.6.P.12.1 Measure and graph distance versus time for an object moving at a constant speed. Interpret this relationship. (Also **SC.6.N.3.3** and **SC.6.N.3.4**)

Vocabulary

speed
slope
velocity
acceleration

Academic Vocabulary

average
variable

📱 VOCABULARY APP

Practice vocabulary on a mobile device.

Quest CONNECTION

Think about what might cause bumper cars to speed up, slow down, or change direction.

Connect It

✏️ **Draw an arrow to show the strength and direction of the force applied to the sled by the people pushing the sled.**

Construct Explanations How does the snow help the sled move down the hill?

....

....

....

Describe How would you describe the difference in the motion of the sled from when the people first start pushing to when the sled is halfway down the hill?

....

....

Calculating Speed

You might describe the motion of the sled in **Figure 1** as slow when it starts moving and fast when it reaches the bottom of the hill. By using these words, you are describing the sled's speed. The **speed** of an object is the distance the object moves per unit of time. Speed is a type of rate. A rate tells you the amount of something that occurs or changes in one unit of time.

Distance Over Time To calculate the speed of an object, divide the distance the object travels by the amount of time it takes to travel that distance. This relationship can be written as an equation:

$$\text{Speed} = \frac{\text{Distance}}{\text{Time}}$$

Any unit that expresses distance over time is a unit of speed. Some examples of units of speed include kilometers per hour, miles per hour, and feet per minute. The SI unit for speed is meters per second, or m/s. For example, the sled might travel at a speed of 5 m/s near its starting point. This means that the sled travels a distance of 5 meters in 1 second. As it nears the bottom of the hill, the sled might be moving at a speed of about 15 m/s. This means that the sled travels a distance of 15 meters in 1 second. The greater the number of meters per second, the faster the speed at which the object is traveling.

INTERACTIVITY

Imagine what it would feel like to ride on a very fast amusement park ride.

Picking up Speed
Figure 1 Family members push each other on a sled from a stopped position at the top of the hill. As the sled glides down the hill, it moves faster and faster. This fast speed makes for a fun ride!

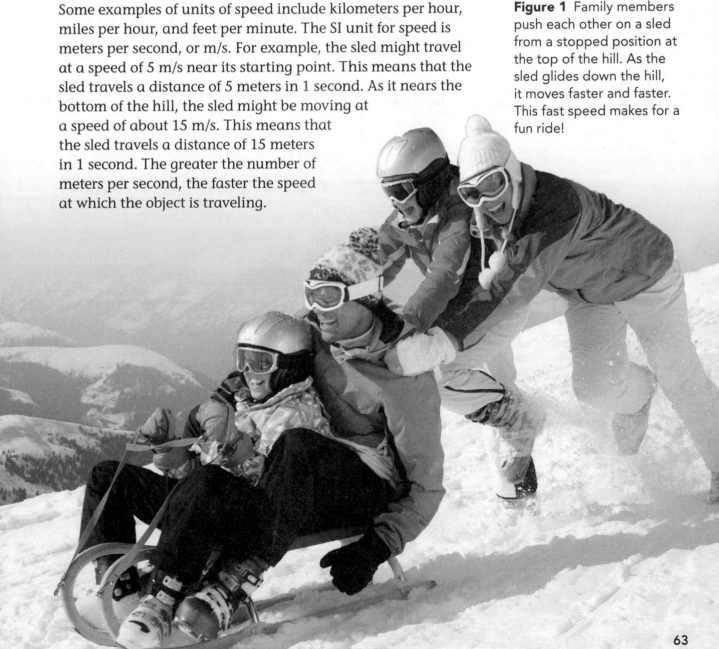

HANDS-ON LAB

Investigate Experiment to find out how you can calculate your speed as you walk to your locker.

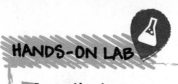

Academic Vocabulary

In math, you find an average by dividing the sum of values by the number of values given. How might you use the word *average* in a situation that does not involve math?

Instantaneous and Average Speeds

Think about the last time you rode in a car. Depending on road conditions and traffic, the speed of the vehicle varied. If you had looked at the speedometer for a moment in a traffic jam, it might have read 5 kilometers per hour. On the highway, at a particular instant, it might have read 88 kilometers per hour. The speed at a particular instant in time is called instantaneous speed.

Although you did not travel at the same speed for the whole trip, you did have an **average** speed throughout the trip. To calculate average speed, divide the total distance traveled by the total time. For example, suppose you drove a distance of 3 kilometers in 1 hour while in heavy traffic. Then, it took you 1 hour to drive 50 kilometers from one side of a city to the other. Finally, you traveled 211 kilometers on an interstate highway in 2 hours. The average speed of the car is the total distance traveled divided by the total time. In the equation below, you can see that your average speed on the road trip was 66 kilometers per hour.

$$\text{Total distance} = 3\text{ km} + 50\text{ km} + 211\text{ km} = 264\text{ km}$$

$$\text{Total time} = 1\text{ h} + 1\text{ h} + 2\text{ h} = 4\text{ h}$$

$$\text{Average speed} = \frac{264\text{ km}}{4\text{ h}} = 66\text{ km/h}$$

READING CHECK **Explain** How does instantaneous speed differ from average speed?

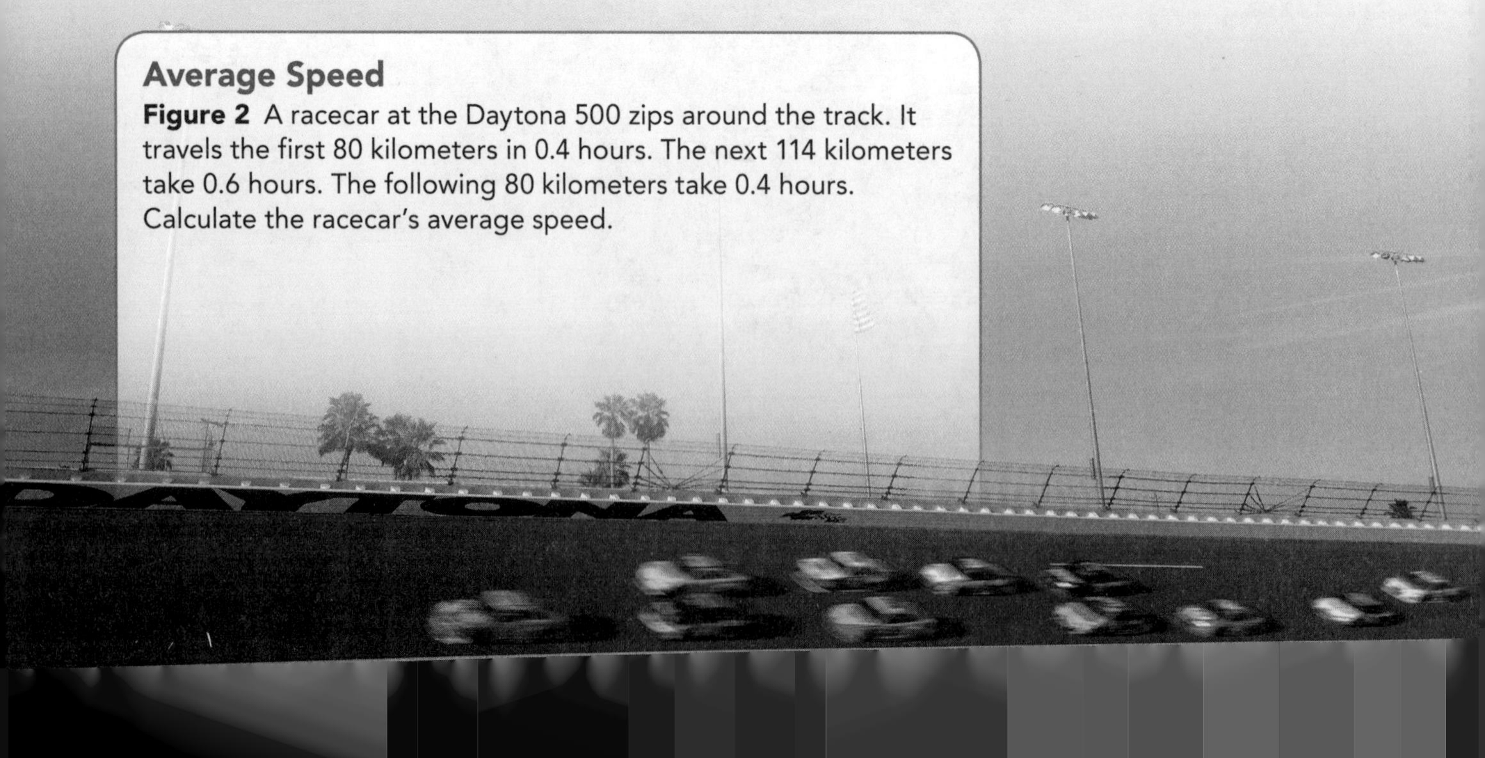

Average Speed

Figure 2 A racecar at the Daytona 500 zips around the track. It travels the first 80 kilometers in 0.4 hours. The next 114 kilometers take 0.6 hours. The following 80 kilometers take 0.4 hours. Calculate the racecar's average speed.

Calculating Speed From a Graph

The graph you see on this page is a distance-versus-time graph. Time is shown on the horizontal axis, or *x*-axis. Distance is shown on the vertical axis, or *y*-axis. A point on the line represents the distance an object has traveled during a given time period. The *x* value of the point is time, and the *y* value is distance. The angle of a line on a graph is called **slope**. The slope tells you how one **variable** changes in relation to the other variable in the graph. In other words, slope tells you the rate of change. You can calculate the slope of a line by dividing the rise by the run. The rise is the vertical difference between any two points on the line. The run is the horizontal difference between the same two points.

$$\text{Slope} = \frac{\text{Rise}}{\text{Run}}$$

The points in the graph below show a rise of 50 meters and a run of 2 seconds. To find the slope, divide 50 meters by 2 seconds. The slope is 25 meters per second. What do you notice about the units of slope? On a distance-versus-time graph, the units of the slope of the line are the same as the units for speed. Because speed is the rate that distance changes in relation to time, the slope of a distance-versus-time graph represents speed. The steeper the slope is, the greater the speed. A constant slope represents motion at constant speed.

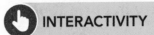

INTERACTIVITY

Explore the speed of a space probe using a distance-versus-time graph.

Academic Vocabulary

A variable is a letter or symbol that represents a number that can change. Use *variable* as an adjective in a sentence. Explain what it means.

....

....

....

....

....

Math Toolbox

Using a Distance-Versus-Time Graph

The cheetah in this photograph is running at a constant speed. The graph shows the distance the cheetah moves and the time it takes the cheetah to move that distance.

Cheetah's Motion

Distance (m) vs. Time (s)

B (2,50)
A (0,0)

1. **Calculate** 🖋 Mark two new points on the line. Use these points to calculate the slope.

   ....

   ....

2. **Draw Conclusions** What is the average speed of the cheetah?

   ....

3. **Solve Linear Equations** The graph of a straight line that goes through the origin can be represented by the equation, $y = mx$. This equation describes the relationship between the two variables *x* and *y*. In this equation, *m* represents the constant slope of the line. Use this equation to determine the distance the cheetah traveled in 4 seconds.

   ....

65

Velocity in Formations

Figure 3 Each member in this marching band must move at a specific velocity to be in the correct place in the formation. What part of velocity that is important for this formation is not shown by a distance-versus-time graph?

....

Apply Scientific Reasoning Do all of the members of the band have to move at the same velocity at all times? Explain your reasoning.

....
....
....
....
....
....
....
....

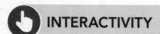

INTERACTIVITY

Investigate the speed, velocity, and acceleration of a skydiver.

Describing Velocity

To describe an object's motion, you also need to know its direction. For example, suppose you hear that a thunderstorm is traveling at a speed of 25 km/h. Should you prepare for the storm? That depends on the direction in which the storm is moving. If it is traveling toward you, you might want to take cover. The speed at which an object travels in a given direction is called **velocity**. You know the velocity of a storm when you know that it is moving 25 km/h eastward.

In certain situations, describing the velocity of moving objects is important. For example, air traffic controllers must keep close track of the velocities of aircrafts. These velocities change as airplanes move overhead and on the runways. An error in determining a velocity, either in speed or in direction, could lead to a collision.

READING CHECK **Determine Conclusions** How can understanding velocity help to prevent a mid-air collision?

....
....
....
....

Determining Acceleration

Speed and velocity are not the only ways to describe motion. Suppose you are a passenger in a car stopped at a red light. When the light changes to green, the driver steps on the gas pedal. As a result, the car speeds up, or accelerates. But acceleration means more than just speeding up. Scientists define **acceleration** as the rate at which velocity changes. A change in velocity can involve a change in speed, direction, or both. In science, when an object accelerates, it increases speed, decreases speed, or changes direction.

Change in Speed or Direction

When the term *acceleration* is used, it means one of two things—any change in speed or any change in direction. A dog that starts running to chase a squirrel is accelerating. You accelerate when you start walking faster to get to class on time. When objects slow down, they are also accelerating. A car accelerates as it comes to a stop at a red light. A water skier accelerates as the boat slows down. A decrease in speed is sometimes called deceleration.

Even an object that is traveling at a constant speed is accelerating when it changes direction. Therefore, a car accelerates as it follows a gentle curve in the road or changes lanes. Runners accelerate as they round the curve in a track.

VIDEO

Compare the speed and acceleration of different animals.

Model It!

Acceleration

Figure 4 This image shows a basketball player shooting a ball.

1. **Develop Models** ✏️
   Label the two sections of the path to identify where the ball increases speed and decreases speed.

2. **Use Models** Besides the labels for changing speed, what is another way that you can tell from this model that the ball is accelerating?

....

....

....

Acceleration in Racing

Figure 5 The pictures show different ways acceleration occurs in a race. Label each image as either increasing speed, decreasing speed, or changing direction.

Starting Line

Curve

Finish Line

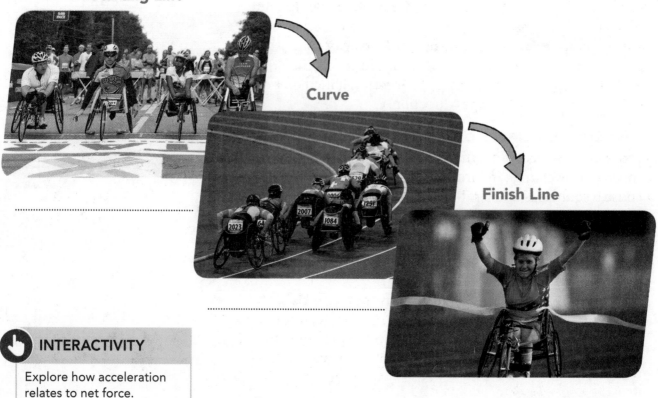

....

....

....

INTERACTIVITY

Explore how acceleration relates to net force.

Acceleration of a Plane

Figure 6 A plane speeds up and decelerates throughout its flight.

1. Identify As the plane travels down the runway for takeoff, is the plane speeding up or decelerating?

....

0.0 s   1.0 s   2.0 s   3.0 s

0 m/s   8 m/s   16 m/s   24 m/s

Calculating Acceleration

If an object is not changing direction, you can describe its acceleration as the rate at which its speed changes. To determine the acceleration of an object moving in a straight line, you calculate the change in speed per unit of time. This is summarized by the following equation:

$$\text{Acceleration} = \frac{\text{Final speed} - \text{Initial speed}}{\text{Time}}$$

Since speed is measured in meters per second (m/s) and time is measured in seconds, acceleration is meters per second per second, or m/s^2. This unit is the SI unit for acceleration.

To understand acceleration, imagine a small airplane moving down a runway, preparing for takeoff. **Figure 6** shows the airplane's speed after each second of its acceleration. To calculate the acceleration of the airplane during takeoff, you must first subtract the initial speed of 0 m/s from its final speed of 24 m/s. Then divide the change in speed by the time, 3 seconds.

$$\text{Acceleration} = \frac{24 \text{ m/s} - 0 \text{ m/s}}{3 \text{ s}}$$

$$\text{Acceleration} = 8 \text{ m/s}^2$$

The airplane accelerates at a rate of 8 m/s^2. This means that the airplane's speed increases by 8 m/s every second. Notice in **Figure 6** that after each second of travel during takeoff, the airplane's speed is 8 m/s greater than its speed in the previous second.

Literacy Connection

Determine Conclusions
As you study the examples on this page, describe an example of your own that shows the three ways an object can accelerate.

....

....

....

....

....

....

2. **Calculate** On landing, the plane touches the runway with a speed of 65 m/s. The figure shows the speed of the plane after 1 second. Calculate the acceleration of the plane during its landing.

....

....

3. **Translate Information** What does a negative value for acceleration mean here?

....

....

65 m/s

60 m/s

Graphing Acceleration Suppose you bike down a long, steep hill. At the top of the hill, your speed is 0 m/s. As you start down the hill, your speed increases. Each second, you move at a greater speed and travel a greater distance than the second before. During the five seconds it takes you to reach the bottom of the hill, you are accelerating. Use the data provided in **Figure 7** to graph and analyze your motion on the accelerating bike.

☑ READING CHECK **Summarize** How are the speed, velocity, and acceleration of a moving object related?

....

....

....

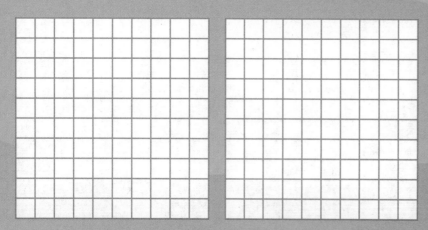

0s
1s
2s
3s
4s
5s

Graphing Acceleration

Figure 7 This table lists the distance the bike travels from the top of the hill and the speed of the bike at each second as it accelerates down the hill.

Time (s)	Distance (m)	Speed (m/s)
0	0	0
1	1	2
2	4	4
3	9	6
4	16	8
5	25	10

1. **Create a Graph** ✏ Use the data in the table to create a distance-versus-time graph on the first grid. Plot distance on the vertical axis and time on the horizontal axis.

2. **Create a Graph** ✏ On the second grid, create a speed-versus-time graph. Plot speed on the vertical axis and time on the horizontal axis.

3. **Apply Concepts** Compare the distance-versus-time graph in this figure to the distance-versus-time graph in the Math Toolbox in this lesson. Why does one graph have a straight line, while the other graph has a curved line?

....

....

....

....

1. **Relate Change** What three changes in motion show that an object is accelerating?

....

....

2. **Calculate** The three stages of a train's route took 1 hour, 2 hours, and 4 hours. The first two stages were 80 km and 200 km. If the train's average speed over the course of the trip was 100 km/h, how many kilometers long was the third stage?

....

....

....

3. **Evaluate Your Claim** A ball is pushed from a stop and rolls 6 m in 2 s. Student A says the average speed of the ball is 3 m/s. Student B says the average speed of the ball is 1.5 m/s². Which student is correct? Explain your answer.

....

....

....

4. **Interpret Data** A student graphed distance versus time for an object that moves 14 m every 2 s. What is the slope of the line on the graph? Explain.

....

....

....

....

5. **Apply Scientific Reasoning** Suppose the line on a distance-versus-time graph and the line on a speed-versus-time graph are both slanted straight lines going through the origin. Can the two graphs be displaying the motion of the same object? Explain.

....

....

....

....

....

Quest CHECK-IN

In this lesson, you learned how motion can be described by speed, velocity, and acceleration. You also learned how to use mathematical formulas to calculate and graph average speed and acceleration.

Use Models How might you use a model of a bumper car to determine how speed and acceleration affect the motion of the car? What materials might you use?

....

....

....

....

....

HANDS-ON LAB

Mass, Speed, and Colliding Cars

Go online to download the lab worksheet. Learn about the features of bumper cars that affect acceleration, including positive acceleration, deceleration, and changes in direction. Brainstorm additional features that might affect speed in bumper cars.

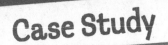

FINDING YOUR WAY WITH GPS

Before the advent of the global positioning system (GPS), people had two choices if they were traveling in an unfamiliar area. They could either use a map or find someone to ask for directions.

Today, almost everyone relies on GPS, whether in car navigation systems or on smartphones and tablets. But what exactly is GPS, and how does it provide data about a moving object's location and speed?

The heart of this system is a network of more than 24 satellites orbiting Earth. These satellites form a "cloud" around the planet so that at least four of them are in the sky at any given place and time. System engineers monitor each satellite to keep careful track of its position.

How GPS Works

Nearby satellites send radio signals to the GPS device, and the device calculates its position based on its distance from those satellites. Four satellites are needed for a GPS to calculate its latitude, longitude, and altitude with accuracy. If fewer satellites are used, only a relative position of the GPS device can be determined, not an exact location.

How GPS WORKS

Satellite

1 Each satellite transmits a radio signal in the form of electromagnetic waves. The signal contains data about the satellite's precise location and the time the signal was sent.

2 The radio signal travels toward Earth at the speed of light.

3 A GPS device receives the signals from the satellites overhead. The device uses the speed of light and the time it takes for the signal to reach the receiver to calculate its distance from each satellite. Using these distances, the device calculates its exact position.

DISTANCE

GPS Receiver

Use the text and the diagram to answer the following questions.

1. Use Models How does the GPS determine its distance from each satellite?

2. Calculate A radio signal from a GPS satellite takes only about 0.067 seconds to reach a GPS receiver. If the speed of light is about 300,000 km/s, then approximately how far away is the receiver from the satellite? Show your calculations.

3. Apply Scientific Reasoning Why is it necessary for engineers to know the precise location of each GPS satellite in the system?

4. Construct Explanations Explain how a GPS device can determine the speed at which it is moving. Provide a real-world example to support your response.

LESSON

3 Newton's Laws of Motion

Guiding Questions

- How do Newton's laws of motion describe when and how objects move?
- How do an object's mass and the forces acting upon an object affect its motion?
- What are action and reaction forces, and how do they impact an object's motion?

Connections

Literacy Use Information

Math Evaluate Expressions

SC.6.P.13.3 Investigate and describe that an unbalanced force acting on an object changes its speed, or direction of motion, or both. (Also **SC.6.N.3.2** and **SC.6.N.3.3**)

Vocabulary

inertia

Academic Vocabulary

derived

 VOCABULARY APP

Practice vocabulary on a mobile device.

Quest CONNECTION

Think about how the size of the bumper cars and the riders in the cars, along with the speed of the cars, might impact the safety of this ride.

Connect It!

✏ **A hockey player hits a puck that was at rest on the ice. Mark an X on the point in the image where the hockey player first applied a net force to the puck.**

Cause and Effect How did the motion of the puck change as a result of being hit?

....

....

Infer After being hit, the puck travels along the ice at a constant speed. What might cause its motion to change?

....

....

Newton's First Law of Motion

If you were watching an ice-hockey game, you would be surprised if a puck that was sitting still suddenly started moving without being hit. You would also be surprised if a moving puck suddenly stopped in the middle of the ice. Your surprise would be the result of knowing that a net force must act upon an object to cause a change in motion. This natural phenomenon that you observe in the world demonstrates Newton's first law of motion.

Newton's first law of motion states that an object at rest will remain at rest unless acted upon by a nonzero net force. Therefore, a hockey puck that is sitting still will remain at rest unless a player hits it, applying a net force. This law also states that an object moving at a constant velocity will continue moving at a constant velocity unless acted upon by a nonzero net force. You can see this law in action when a hockey puck slides in a straight line across the ice. The motion remains constant until it hits something like the net of the goal or another hockey stick.

A simple statement of Newton's first law of motion is that if an object is not moving, it will not start moving until a net force acts on it. If an object is moving, it will continue at a constant velocity until a net force acts to change its speed or its direction. If there is a net force acting on an object, it will accelerate.

Literacy Connection

Use Information As you read these pages, underline information you can use to define Newton's first law.

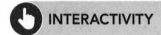

INTERACTIVITY

Explore what causes a ball to stop rolling.

Speeding Up

Figure 1 Just a moment ago, the puck was at rest on the ice. The net force that the player applied to the puck caused the puck to accelerate.

Mass and Inertia

Figure 2 Suppose each of these women wants to move the dog off of her lap.

Which dog has less inertia? ....

Which dog is harder to move?

....

Inertia Resistance to change in motion is called **inertia**. So Newton's first law is also called the law of inertia. Inertia explains many common events, including why seat belts and air bags are used in vehicles. If you are riding in a moving car, you are moving at the same speed the car is moving. When brakes apply a force to the car, the car decelerates. The brakes did not apply a force to you, however, so inertia keeps you moving forward at the same speed and direction you were going before the car decelerated. A force, such as the pull of a seat belt, is needed to pull you back.

Inertia and Mass Which object—you or the car—is harder to stop? Based on your own experience, you can probably figure out that the car is harder to stop. That is because it has more mass. The more massive object has a greater inertia, as in **Figure 2**.

Once Newton had described the connection between inertia and mass, he next figured out how to find the acceleration of an object when a force acted on it.

☑ READING CHECK **Summarize** How does mass relate to inertia?

....

....

Newton's Second Law of Motion

Newton's first law stated that inertia exists for an object. Newton then explained that an object's mass directly affects how much force is needed to accelerate the object.

Changes in Acceleration and Mass Suppose that you apply a constant net force on an object. How does changing the mass of the object affect its acceleration? You can see this with a horse-drawn sleigh, shown in **Figure 3**. The horses provide a steady force. If the sleigh is empty, it will accelerate quickly when the horses pull on it. If the sleigh is full of people, it has a greater inertia and will accelerate slowly. The acceleration of the sleigh will change depending on the mass of the load it carries. Newton understood these relationships and found a way to represent them mathematically.

Calculating Force Newton's second law of motion states that the size and direction of a net force equals the mass times the acceleration. The net force will have the same direction as the acceleration. This relationship can be written as follows:

$$\text{Net force} = \text{Mass} \times \text{Acceleration}$$

If the net force and mass are known, the resulting acceleration can be **derived** by using this equation:

$$\text{Acceleration} = \frac{\text{Net force}}{\text{Mass}}$$

Academic Vocabulary

Read the sentence in which the word *derived* is used, and infer its meaning.

....

....

....

....

Newton's Second Law
Figure 3 The force applied by these two horses pulls the sleigh and the people it contains. This sleigh can contain up to 12 people.

1. **Reason Quantitatively** How might you change the number of people to increase the sleigh's acceleration?

....

....

....

2. **Apply Scientific Reasoning** How might you change the number of people to decrease the sleigh's acceleration?

....

....

....

Calculations with Newton's Second Law

As you have already seen, the formula for Newton's second law can be written to solve for force or acceleration. Newton's second law can also be written to solve for mass.

You already know that acceleration is measured in meters per second squared (m/s^2), and that mass is measured in kilograms (kg). When you multiply mass and acceleration according to Newton's second law, you find that force is measured in kilograms times meters per second squared ($kg\text{-}m/s^2$). This unit is also called a newton (N), which is the SI unit of force. One newton is the force required to give a 1-kg mass an acceleration of 1 m/s^2.

☑ READING CHECK **Apply Concepts** Based on what you've learned, derive another equation for Newton's second law that is written to solve for mass.

Math Toolbox

Using Newton's Second Law

Use the equations for Newton's second law to understand how mass and force affect the motion of a volleyball.

Evaluate Expressions Show your calculations for each problem.

a. A volleyball is hit and experiences a net force of 2 N, which causes it to accelerate at 8 m/s^2. What is the mass of the volleyball?

b. The same ball is hit again and experiences a net force of 3.5 N instead. What is the acceleration of the volleyball?

c. The same ball rolls horizontally along the sand and decelerates at a rate of 6 m/s^2. Calculate the force of friction that caused this deceleration.

Newton's Third Law of Motion

A library is full of shelves of books. Gravity pulls each book down. If the shelf did not push upward on each book with equal force, the books would fall through the shelf. The force exerted by the shelf is equal in strength and opposite in direction to the force the books exert on the shelf. Newton's third law of motion states that if one object exerts a force on another object, then the second object exerts a force of equal strength in the opposite direction on the first object. Another way to state Newton's third law is that for every action there is an equal (in strength) but opposite (in direction) reaction.

HANDS-ON LAB

☑**Investigate** Use Newton's third law to design a vehicle that moves forward by pushing backward.

▶ **VIDEO**

Examine how action-reaction pairs cause motion in real-world scenarios.

Action-Reaction Pairs

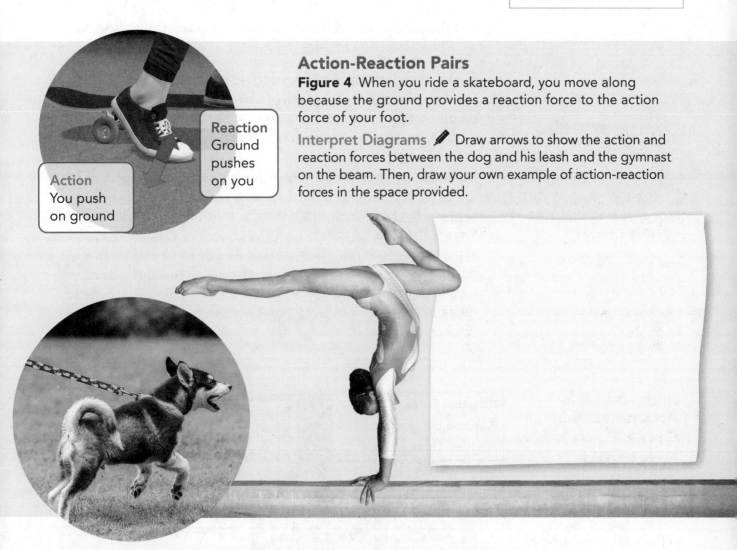

Figure 4 When you ride a skateboard, you move along because the ground provides a reaction force to the action force of your foot.

Reaction Ground pushes on you

Action You push on ground

Interpret Diagrams ✎ Draw arrows to show the action and reaction forces between the dog and his leash and the gymnast on the beam. Then, draw your own example of action-reaction forces in the space provided.

Action-Reaction Pairs An action force is always paired with a reaction force. Pairs of action and reaction forces are all around you. When you walk, you push backward on the ground with your feet. Think of this as an action force. The ground pushes forward on your feet with an equal and opposite force. This is the reaction force. You can walk only because the ground pushes you forward!

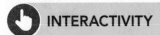

INTERACTIVITY

Use Newton's laws to discover how a baseball player can hit more home runs.

VIDEO

Discover how a mechanical engineer uses science to solve engineering problems.

READING CHECK

Use Information A dog walks along the ground. If the dog applies an action force on the ground, what is the reaction force?

....

....

....

Detecting Forces and Motion

Some results of action-reaction forces are easily observed. If you were the skateboarder in **Figure 4**, you could feel the force of the ground on your foot. You could see and feel the skateboard accelerate. If you drop your pen, gravity pulls the pen downward and you can see it fall.

But some changes caused by action-reaction forces are not as easily detected. When you drop your pen, the pen pulls Earth upward with an equal and opposite reaction force, according to Newton's third law. You see the pen fall, but you don't see Earth accelerate toward the pen. Remember Newton's second law. If mass increases and force stays the same, acceleration decreases. The same force acts on both Earth and your pen. Because Earth has such a large mass, its acceleration is so small that you don't notice it.

Balanced and Action-Reaction Forces

You have learned that two equal forces acting in opposite directions on an object balance each other and produce no change in motion. So why aren't the action-reaction forces in Newton's third law of motion balanced as well? In order for forces to balance, they must act on the same object. Action-reaction forces are not balanced because they act on different objects. When a hockey player hits a puck with his stick, the action force is the force of the stick on the puck. The reaction force is the force of the puck on the stick. So one force acts on the puck, while the other acts on the stick. The puck has a much smaller mass than the player and his stick, so you see the puck accelerate. See how other action-reaction forces act on different objects in **Figure 5**.

Understanding Action-Reaction

Figure 5 ✏ Action-reaction forces are applied to different objects. The action and reaction forces acting on a soccer player, a soccer ball, and the ground are shown with arrows. Finish labeling the forces to describe how they are being applied.

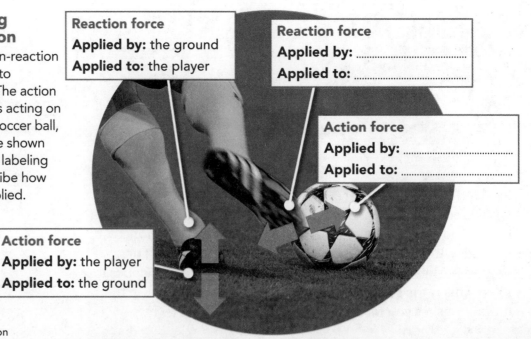

Reaction force
Applied by: the ground
Applied to: the player

Reaction force
Applied by: ....
Applied to: ....

Action force
Applied by: ....
Applied to: ....

Action force
Applied by: the player
Applied to: the ground

Question It !

Applying Newton's Laws

Kirsten has a parakeet that likes to sit on a swing. Sometimes the bird makes the swing move back and forth.

Ask Questions You want to investigate the bird and his swing and how they relate to Newton's laws of motion. List at least two questions you might ask.

....

....

Newton's Laws Together When you have a situation involving force, acceleration, and mass, it usually involves two or even all three of Newton's laws! Look at **Figure 6** to see how Newton's laws apply to an amusement park ride.

Reflect Describe how Newton's laws of motion are involved in an activity in your daily life.

Newton's First Law:	Newton's Second Law:	Newton's Third Law:

Newton's Laws

Figure 6 In each space provided, give an example of a way that one of Newton's laws is shown in this amusement park ride.

SC.6.P.13.3

1. Synthesize Information You push your younger sister on a swing in a park. Then you give her a harder push. Explain what happens in each case, in terms of the second and third laws of motion.

....

....

....

....

....

2. Apply Concepts When a batter hits a baseball, the ball often goes much faster than the bat. It may travel as fast as 45 m/s! Explain how that can happen. Does hitting a ball violate the conservation of energy?

....

....

....

....

....

....

....

3. Apply Concepts What is inertia? Give an example that is not from your text.

....

....

....

....

....

4. Explain Phenomena You push on a door, and it opens. Explain what happens in terms of action-reaction forces.

....

....

....

....

....

5. Calculate A 12-N net force acts on a 4-kg jug of water. What is the resulting acceleration of the jug? Show your calculations.

....

....

....

Quest CHECK-IN

In this lesson, you learned how Newton's laws explain the motions of moving objects and how mass affects acceleration. You also learned that every action has an equal and opposite reaction.

Apply Concepts How would Newton's laws of motion relate to the movement of bumper cars? How might the mass of the riders and the speed of the cars affect this movement?

....

....

....

....

....

👆 INTERACTIVITY

Apply Newton's Laws of Motion

Go online to learn about how action-reaction forces affect the movement of vehicles in collisions. Then brainstorm how these forces would affect bumper cars.

SC.6.P.13.3, SC.6.N.2.3

GENERATING ENERGY
from Potholes

INTERACTIVITY

Explore how Newton's laws can be used to design more fuel-efficient vehicles.

Traveling in a car over uneven road surfaces and potholes can make for a bouncy ride. How can you capture the energy generated by that bouncing motion? You engineer it!

The Challenge: To convert the motion of a car into electrical energy.

When a car travels down the road, the car exerts an action force on the road, and the road exerts a reaction force on the wheels of the car. A bumpy road occasionally exerts a stronger force than a smooth road, which means an uncomfortable ride for passengers. That's where shock absorbers come in. Shock absorbers are part of a car's suspension system, and they cause the body of the car to react slowly to bumps. This decreases the force exerted on a car by the road.

With traditional shock absorbers, the energy that is absorbed is then released as heat. Auto engineers have now found a way to use their understanding of the Law of Conservation of Energy to harness this energy. They have developed electromechanical shock absorbers that use a lever arm to capture the up-and-down motion of the wheels. A device called an alternator transforms this kinetic energy into electricity. The engineers hope that this electrical energy can be used to increase the fuel efficiency of cars.

With electromechanical shock absorbers, the energy generated by bumps and potholes can be transformed into electrical energy.

DESIGN CHALLENGE Can you build a shock absorber? Go to the Engineering Design Notebook to find out!

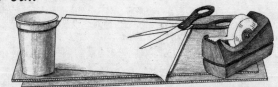

Friction and Gravitational Interactions

Guiding Questions

- What factors affect the different types of friction?
- What factors affect gravity?
- How are gravity and friction related to motion and energy?

Connections

Literacy Write Arguments

Math Analyze Relationships

 SC.6.P.13.1 Investigate and describe types of forces including contact forces and forces acting at a distance, such as electrical, magnetic, and gravitational.
SC.6.P.13.2 Explore the Law of Gravity by recognizing that every object exerts gravitational force on every other object and that the force depends on how much mass the objects have and how far apart they are.
(Also **SC.6.N.3.3** and **SC.6.N.3.4**)

Vocabulary

weight

Academic Vocabulary

associate

 VOCABULARY APP

Practice vocabulary on a mobile device.

Quest CONNECTION

Think about how different road conditions affect the movement of a car. How might the surface upon which bumper cars move affect their motion?

Connect It!

✏ **Circle two areas that show what causes the bike to slow down.**

Identify What force is responsible for stopping the bike?

....

Classify Is this force a contact or noncontact force? Explain.

....

....

....

Factors That Affect Friction

Recall that the force two surfaces exert on each other when they rub against each other is the contact force called friction. For example, if you slide a book across a table, the surface of the book rubs against the surface of the table. The resulting force is friction. This force acts in a direction opposite to the motion of the book and eventually stops the book.

Two Factors Both the types of surfaces involved and how hard the surfaces are pushed together affect the friction between two surfaces. The bicyclist in **Figure 1** is using friction to slow his bicycle. One place where friction occurs on the bicycle is between the tires and the ground. Have you ever examined the surface of a tire? The tread on the tire results in more friction between the tire and the ground. A tire on a mountain bike has more tread on it than a regular bike tire, so a lot of friction is produced between a mountain bike tire and the ground. In general, smoother surfaces produce less friction than rougher surfaces.

In this instance, friction also occurs between the brake pads and the wheels. This friction prevents the tire from turning. The harder the bicyclist applies the brakes, the more quickly the bike will come to a stop. Friction increases as surfaces push harder against each other.

Friction acts in a direction opposite to the direction of the object's motion. Without friction or some other force acting in the opposite direction, a moving object will not stop until it strikes another object.

INTERACTIVITY

Describe your experiences riding a bicycle on different surfaces.

Skidding to a Stop
Figure 1 This mountain biker applies his brakes and skids to slow down.

Types of Friction

Use **Figure 2** to find out more about four different types of friction.

> ☑ READING CHECK **Write Arguments** How can you be sure that the skater leaping through the air is moving faster than the one speeding along the ground?
>
> ....
>
> ....

Friction in a Skatepark

Figure 2 ✎ Add labels to three other skaters in the figure to identify the type of friction that is opposing their motion. Then, for each type of friction described, identify another example of that type of friction.

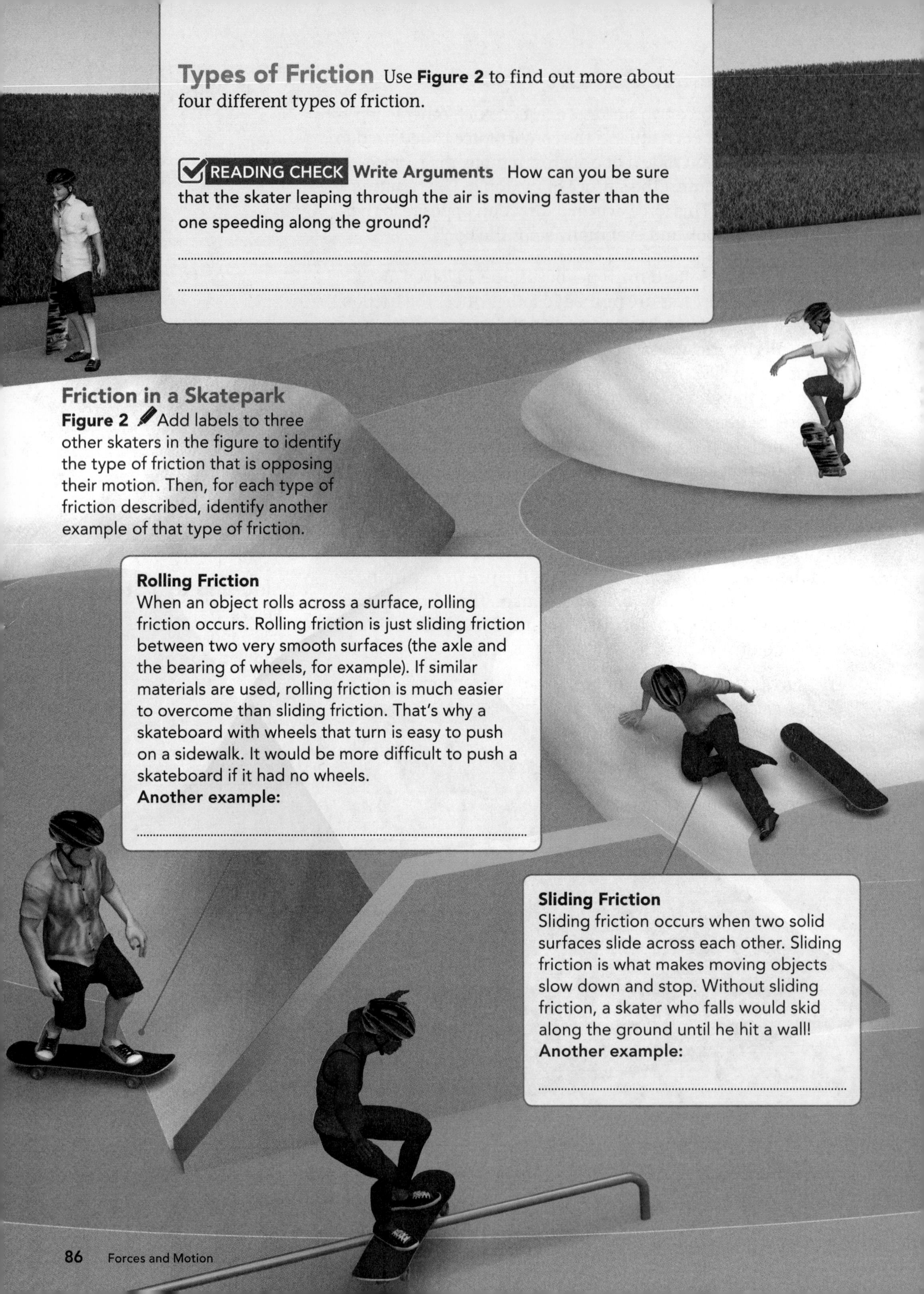

Rolling Friction

When an object rolls across a surface, rolling friction occurs. Rolling friction is just sliding friction between two very smooth surfaces (the axle and the bearing of wheels, for example). If similar materials are used, rolling friction is much easier to overcome than sliding friction. That's why a skateboard with wheels that turn is easy to push on a sidewalk. It would be more difficult to push a skateboard if it had no wheels.

Another example:

....

Sliding Friction

Sliding friction occurs when two solid surfaces slide across each other. Sliding friction is what makes moving objects slow down and stop. Without sliding friction, a skater who falls would skid along the ground until he hit a wall!

Another example:

....

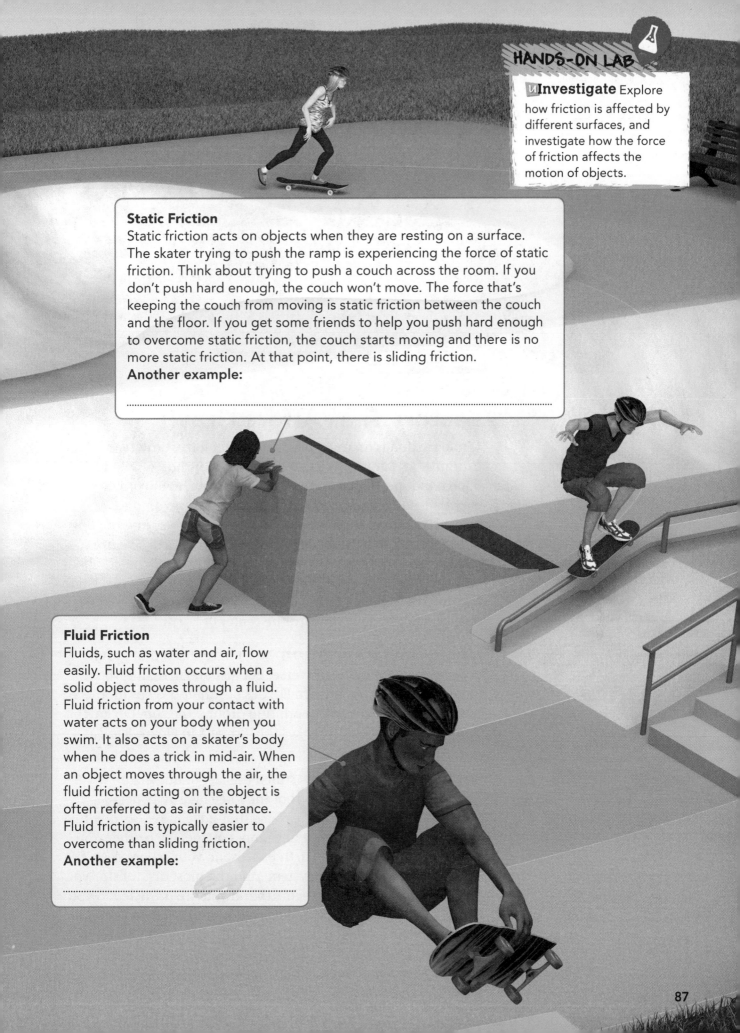

HANDS-ON LAB

и**Investigate** Explore how friction is affected by different surfaces, and investigate how the force of friction affects the motion of objects.

Static Friction

Static friction acts on objects when they are resting on a surface. The skater trying to push the ramp is experiencing the force of static friction. Think about trying to push a couch across the room. If you don't push hard enough, the couch won't move. The force that's keeping the couch from moving is static friction between the couch and the floor. If you get some friends to help you push hard enough to overcome static friction, the couch starts moving and there is no more static friction. At that point, there is sliding friction.

Another example:

....

Fluid Friction

Fluids, such as water and air, flow easily. Fluid friction occurs when a solid object moves through a fluid. Fluid friction from your contact with water acts on your body when you swim. It also acts on a skater's body when he does a trick in mid-air. When an object moves through the air, the fluid friction acting on the object is often referred to as air resistance. Fluid friction is typically easier to overcome than sliding friction.

Another example:

....

Universal Gravitation

Figure 3 How does the gravitational attraction between these people compare to the gravitational attraction between the people and Earth?

....

....

▶ **VIDEO**

Explore why the moon is able to circle Earth without falling toward it.

 READING CHECK

Summarize What is the law of universal gravitation?

....

....

....

....

Factors That Affect Gravity

While friction is an example of a contact force, gravity is an example on a non-contact force. Remember that gravity is a force that pulls objects toward each other. How is gravity experienced on Earth? You could name many examples. A basketball player shoots a ball toward the basket, and the ball falls toward Earth. Rain falls from the sky to Earth. We are so familiar with objects falling that we may not think much about why they fall. One person who thought about this was Sir Isaac Newton. He concluded that a force called gravity acts to pull objects straight down toward the center of Earth.

Universal Gravitation Newton realized that gravity acts everywhere in the universe, not just on Earth. It is the force that causes the tides in Earth's ocean and keeps all the planets in our solar system orbiting around the sun. On Earth, gravity is the force that makes the jumpers in **Figure 3** fall toward the water.

Newton's realization is now called the law of universal gravitation. This law states that the force of gravity acts between all objects in the universe that have mass. So, any two objects in the universe that have mass attract each other. You are attracted not only to Earth but also to your school desk, the other planets in the solar system, and the most distant star you can see. Earth and the objects around you are attracted to you as well. You can clearly see the gravitational effect of Earth on an object. However, you do not notice the attraction between objects on Earth because these forces are extremely small compared to the attraction between the objects and Earth itself.

Factors Affecting Gravity

What factors control the strength of the gravitational force between two objects? These factors are the mass of each object and the distance between them.

The more mass an object has, the greater the gravitational force between it and other objects. Earth's gravitational force on nearby objects is strong because the mass of Earth is so large. Gravitational force also depends on the distance between the objects' centers. As distance increases, gravitational force decreases. What happens when you drop your cell phone? You see your cell phone fall to Earth because Earth and your cell phone are close together. If your cell phone were on the moon, Earth would not exert a visible gravitational attraction to it because Earth and the phone would be so far apart. The phone would be visibly attracted to the moon instead.

Weight and Mass

Mass is sometimes confused with weight. Mass is a measure of the amount of matter in an object. **Weight** is a measure of the force of gravity on an object. Since weight is a measure of force, the SI unit of weight is a newton (N). If you know the mass of an object in kilograms, you can calculate its weight on Earth using Newton's second law. The acceleration due to gravity at Earth's surface is 9.8 m/s². The force is the weight of the object.

Net force = Mass × Acceleration

When you stand on a bathroom scale, it displays your weight—the gravitational force that Earth is exerting on you. On Earth, 1 pound equals 4.45 newtons. If you could stand on the surface of Jupiter, which has a mass around 300 times the mass of Earth, your mass would remain the same, but your weight would increase. This is because the gravitational force exerted on you is greater on Jupiter than on Earth.

Describing g-Forces

Figure 4 A lowercase g is used as the symbol for acceleration due to gravity at Earth's surface (9.8 m/s²). This symbol is used in the field of space engineering, where acceleration is often measured in "g"s. Engineers must design space shuttles considering the acceleration and forces that the crew and the shuttle itself would experience during flight.

INTERACTIVITY

Investigate how gravity affects falling objects.

Literacy Connection

Write Arguments Write an argument that explains why the pencil and notebook resting on your desk are not being pulled together by the force of gravity between them.

....

....

....

....

....

Math Toolbox

The Relationship Between Weight and Mass

Weight varies with the strength of the gravitational force. This baby elephant weighs 480 pounds on Earth, and its mass is 218 kilograms. On the moon, he would weigh about one-sixth of what he does on Earth. On Mars, he would weigh just over one-third of what he does on Earth. On Jupiter, he would weigh approximately 2.5 times as much as he does on Earth.

Analyze Relationships ✏️ Complete the table using the information about the baby elephant.

Location	Earth	Moon	Mars	Jupiter
Mass (kg)				
Weight (lbs)				

Energy, Forces, and Motion

By now, you can see how forces such as gravity and friction relate to motion. Recall that forces and motion are also related to energy.

Gravitational Potential Energy As you know, the potential energy of an object is the energy stored in the object. There are several different types of potential energy, based on different types of forces. The type of potential energy that we **associate** with gravity is called gravitational potential energy. On Earth, gravitational potential energy (GPE) is based on an object's position. In general, the higher up an object is, the greater its GPE. For example, as a diver climbs the ladder to a diving board, her GPE increases. The GPE of a skydiver increases as he rides the helicopter to his jumping point. You can calculate the GPE of an object on Earth based on the mass of the object, the acceleration due to gravity (9.8 m/s²), and the height of the object above Earth's surface.

Academic Vocabulary

Used as a verb, *associate* means to connect something to something else in one's mind. Write a sentence using *associate* as a noun.

....

....

....

....

$$\text{Gravitational potential energy (GPE)} = \text{Mass} \times \text{Acceleration due to gravity} \times \text{Height}$$

Forces and Motion When a skydiver jumps from a helicopter, a net force acts on his body as he falls. This net force is a combination of gravity and friction. Gravity pulls him down toward the ground, and fluid friction acts on him in the opposite direction as he falls through the air. However, these forces are unbalanced—the force of gravity is stronger than the air resistance, so he accelerates downward. Net force works on him as he falls, so his GPE transforms to kinetic energy, the energy of motion. As a result, his speed increases throughout his fall. As the skydiver accelerates, the force of air resistance increases until it is equal to the force of gravity. At this point, the forces on the skydiver are balanced and he falls at a constant speed the rest of the way down. This top speed is called terminal velocity. It only takes about 15 seconds for skydivers to reach 99% of their terminal velocity of 195 km/h (122 mi/h)! When skydivers open a parachute, air resistance increases. This causes the forces acting on the skydiver to balance at a much slower terminal velocity.

INTERACTIVITY

Explore the relationships among friction, gravity, tides, and Earth's rotation.

Model It

Develop Models ✏ Use what you know about energy, forces, and motion to develop a model of a falling object. Add labels to your sketch to show locations of maximum and minimum gravitational potential energy, kinetic energy, and speed. Label areas of acceleration. Draw arrows to represent the forces acting on the object. Write a caption to explain what your model shows.

SC.6.P.13.1, SC.6.P.13.2

1. Apply Scientific Reasoning Give a real-life example, not from your text, of fluid friction.

....

....

2. Determine Differences When you say that something is hard to lift, are you talking about weight or mass?

....

....

....

3. Construct Explanations Rather than push a heavy box from one room to another, a worker chooses to place the box on a wheeled cart. In terms of friction, explain why moving the box on the wheeled cart is easier than pushing.

....

....

....

....

....

4. Explain Phenomena A 4-kg ball is 2 cm away from one 1-kg ball and 6 cm away from another 1-kg ball. Use the relationships among the balls to describe two factors that affect gravity. Also explain why the balls do not move toward each other unless acted upon by another force.

....

....

....

....

....

....

....

....

....

5. Apply Concepts Paolo says that his bicycle is hard to pedal. Mia looks at the bicycle and tells him he needs to oil the chain. Explain why oiling the chain would help Paolo.

....

....

....

....

....

Quest CHECK-IN

In this lesson, you learned how different types of friction affect the movement of objects. You also learned about universal gravitation and how this scientific law applies to objects on Earth and elsewhere in the universe.

Evaluate How might friction affect the movement of bumper cars? What role does gravity play in how bumper cars move? How might you use these concepts to make bumper cars safer?

....

....

....

....

HANDS-ON LAB

Bumper Cars, Bumper Solutions

Go online to download the worksheet for this lab. Learn how friction and gravity affect vehicles on different surfaces. Then brainstorm how these factors influence the speed and direction of bumper cars.

SC.6.P.13.2, SC.6.N.3.1

Spacetime Curvature and Gravitational Waves

How does mass cause objects to attract one another? The famous scientist Albert Einstein explored this question and came up with a revolutionary theory of gravity. It explains the existence of gravitational waves, while Newton's theory could not!

In Einstein's theory, space and time are not separate from one another. They make up a four-dimensional fabric that can warp and curve. Imagine that a ball is placed on a puffy comforter. The ball sinks into the comforter so that the comforter curves around it. Objects with mass sit in spacetime in a similar way. If you roll a marble past the ball, the marble circles around the ball. The marble gets caught in a groove created by the ball. That's basically how gravity works—objects attract one another by falling into grooves of spacetime.

Now, add acceleration into the picture, and you get ripples in the fabric of spacetime! For example, when two stars circle each other, they accelerate faster and faster. This acceleration produces ripples in spacetime similar to ripples of water on a pond.

Scientists detected gravitational waves for the first time on September 14, 2015. By detecting gravitational waves, we can learn about events all around the universe, such as black holes colliding!

MY DISCOVERY

Check out magazine articles on gravitational waves at your local library.

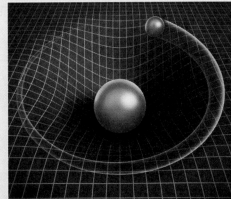

Any object with mass, such as Earth, causes the fabric of spacetime to curve. The result of this curvature is gravitational attraction.

As these stars accelerate, they create ripples in spacetime called gravitational waves.

1 Describing Motion and Force

🔘 SC.6.P.13.3, SC.6.P.13.1

1. Gabriella and Michelle are a few meters apart, at one end of a football field. Pierre is at the other end of the field, and he sees both of them moving toward him at 4 m/s. From Michelle's point of view, how is Gabriella moving?
   A. Gabriella is moving toward her at 4 m/s.
   B. Gabriella is moving away from her at 4 m/s.
   C. Gabriella is moving toward her at 8 m/s.
   D. Gabriella is not moving.

2. **Apply Concepts** A boy holds a 20 N rock while standing still on a trampoline. Suppose he hands the rock to someone else. Explain how he will move, in terms of the forces acting on him.

   ....

   ....

   ....

   ....

   ....

   ....

3. **Synthesize Information** A pendulum has its greatest velocity at the bottom of its swing. At that point, its speed is constant (it is neither accelerating nor decelerating). Draw a diagram to show why there is no acceleration at that point. Explain in terms of the pendulum's energy and the forces acting on it.

2 Speed, Velocity, and Acceleration

🔘 SC.6.P.12.1

4. A skier accelerates from a stop at a rate of 3 m/s² for 3 seconds. What is her speed at the end of that time?
   A. 9 m/s²
   B. 1 m/s
   C. 9 m
   D. 9 m/s

5. **Represent Relationships** A rolling ball decelerates at a constant rate. If you graphed its speed versus time, what would the graph look like? What point would represent its greatest instantaneous velocity?

   ....

   ....

   ....

   ....

6. A bus drove from Philadelphia to Washington, D.C. in the stages shown in the table.

Distance (km)	Time (hr)
100	2
55	1
75	2

   What was the average speed of the bus for the entire trip?

   ....

7. **Identify Criteria** A woman is walking at 4 m/s. She is accelerating at a rate of 1 m/s². To find out what her velocity is after 3 seconds, what else do you need to know?

   ....

   ....

   ....

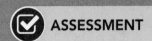
3 Newton's Laws of Motion

SC6.P.13.3

8. A volleyball accelerates due to a constant force acting on it for 5 seconds, and it reaches a speed of 60 m/s. If the mass of the volleyball is 0.25 kg, what is the constant force?

A. 3 N

B. 300 N

C. 3 m

D. 24 N

9. Synthesize Information Two billiard balls of equal masses moving with equal speeds run into each other. They hit head on, so their directions are both reversed, What can you say about their speeds after the collision?

....

....

....

....

10. Apply Concepts You have a coin sitting on a card on top of a glass. You want to put the coin into the glass, but you are not allowed to pick up the card. Think of how you can do that. Then write a short explanation of why it works that would make sense to someone who doesn't remember Newton's laws of motion.

....

....

....

....

....

....

....

....

4 Friction and Gravitational interactions

SC.6.P.13.1, SC.6.P.13.2

11. A parachutist slows down when his parachute opens. Where does the kinetic energy go?

A. It is destroyed.

B. It is transformed to heat.

C. It is transformed to gravitational potential energy.

D. It is transformed to elastic potential energy.

12. Identify Snow has been lying on a mountainside. Suddenly, it starts to move down the mountain. Which types of friction are observed in this avalanche? Where does each type occur?

....

....

....

....

....

13. Synthesize Information Suppose you are on the planet Sloth, where gravity is 1/9 the gravity on Earth. You drop a stone and measure its speed as it hits the ground. How does that speed compare to the speed the same rock would reach falling the same distance on Earth?

....

....

....

....

....

....

....

....

Circle the letter of the best answer.

At boxing practice, Ian works with his coach to improve the strength of his punch. **Use the picture below to answer questions 1, 2, 3 and 4.**

1 Which of the following is a contact force experienced by the punching bag?

A electrical

B frictional

C gravitational

D magnetic

2 Ian says that the reason the bag is heavy is so that it can absorb plenty of elastic potential energy. Is he correct?

F Yes, he is correct.

G No, the bag absorbs thermal energy.

H No, the bag absorbs GPE.

I No, the bag is heavy so that its mass will only accelerate a small amount when he punches it.

3 Ian lost his balance when he hit the bag hard. He says that the reaction force from his punch was large because the bag is heavy. Is that true?

A Yes, it is true.

B No, the large mass, not the weight, gives the reaction force.

C No, the reaction force depends only on the force of Ian's punch.

D No, the bag does not exert a reaction force, because it is flexible.

4 Emma and Maria are tossing pebbles off a bridge, and they wonder how long a pebble takes to fall. Emma says, "The kinetic energy a falling pebble has at the bottom comes from the gravitational potential energy it had at the top. So I know an equation that relates height and speed."

$Mass \times g \times Height = 1/2 \times Mass \times Speed^2$

Then Maria says, "I also know that gravity is a constant acceleration, g, so I have an equation that relates time and speed."

$g \times Time^2 = Speed$

Use the two equations to relate height and time. Correct any errors Emma or Maria may have made.

F Both girls are correct. The relation is $Height = 1/2 \times g \times Time^4$

G Maria should have written $Speed = g \times Time$. Then she would find $Height = 1/2 \times g \times Time^2$

H Emma should have written $Mass \times g \times Height = 1/2 \times Mass \times g \times Speed^2$ to find $Height = 1/2 \times Time^4$

I Emma should have written $Mass \times g \times Height = 1/2 \times Mass \times Speed$ to find $Height = 1/2 \times g \times Time$.

5 A girl is bouncing on a trampoline. Where is her gravitational potential energy a maximum, and where is her kinetic energy a maximum?

A GPE is a maximum at her highest point and KE is a maximum at her lowest point.

B GPE is a maximum at her highest point and KE is a maximum when she is halfway between lowest and highest points.

C GPE is a maximum at her highest point, and so is KE.

D GPE is a maximum at her highest point and KE is a maximum when she is just touching the trampoline.

6 This graph shows the motion of a runner. What is the acceleration of the runner?

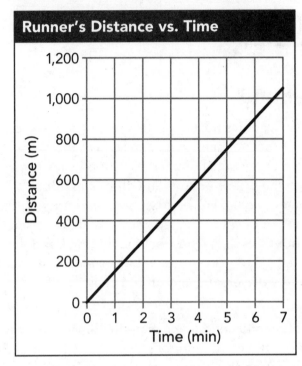

Runner's Distance vs. Time

F   0 m/min²
G   150 m/min
H   150 m/min²
I   1,000 m/min²

7 A 1,000-kg car traveling at 15 m/s brakes to a stop over a distance of 20 m. Suppose the car then speeds up to 30 m/s, and the same braking force is used. How far will the car need to stop? Use what you know about work and the conservation of energy to explain your answer.

A   Since the mass is unchanged, the distance will be the same (20 m).

B   Since the speed is doubled, the distance will be doubled (40 m).

C   Since the speed is doubled, the distance will be increased by a factor of 2², or 4 (80 m).

D   Since the speed increased by 15 m, the stopping distance increases by 15 m (35 m).

8 A bicyclist accelerates from a stop to a speed of 12 m/s in 3 seconds. What is her acceleration?

F   4 m/s²
G   4 m/s
H   36 m/s²
I   36 m/s

Quest FINDINGS

SC.6.P.13.1, SC.6.P.13.3

Complete the Quest!

Design a way to present your new bumper car design and the results of your testing to your class. Be sure to explain how you applied Newton's third law of motion to your design.

Synthesize Information Bumper cars have safety features to protect both the riders and the cars themselves. These features are built around how forces and the laws of motion affect the movement of the cars. What is another example of how forces and laws of motion impact your safety in your daily life?

....

....

....

👆 **INTERACTIVITY**

Reflect on Your Bumper Car Solution

Stopping on a Dime

How can you **design** a **basketball court** so that players don't run into band members and other spectators near the court lines?

Materials

(per group)

- tape measure
- 2 stopwatches or watches with second hands

Background

Imagine your school is hosting a championship basketball game, and the school band will be playing at the game. The band director wants the band to set up its instruments very close to the out-of-bounds line of the basketball court, so that the band will be front and center during the game. Some people at the school, however, have raised concerns about this plan. They feel that having band members so close to the court is unsafe because the members might be hit by players running off the court.

You and some of your fellow science students have been asked to design and conduct an experiment to determine whether or not the band director's plan is safe for both the band members and the players. In this experiment, you will investigate how time, distance, and average speed relate to changes in motion, and you will apply these concepts to the players on the basketball court.

Design Your Investigation

To model the basketball players running off the court, you will determine the speed of someone running a distance of 10 meters. Your will also determine how far it takes the runner to come to a complete stop after hitting the 10-meter mark. Discuss with your group how you will design and conduct the investigation. As you plan, consider the following questions with your group:

HANDS-ON LAB

и**Demonstrate** Go online for a downloadable worksheet of this lab.

1. What three properties of the players in motion do you need to consider?

2. What do you need to know to calculate the speed of a runner?

3. What tests will you perform?

4. How many trials of each test will you perform?

5. What type of data will you be collecting? How will you collect, record, and organize your data?

6. What evidence will you need to present after your investigation?

7. How will you present your evidence to communicate your results effectively?

Write your plan in the space provided on the next page. After getting your teacher's approval, conduct your investigation. Record the data you collect in your group data table.

Procedure

....
....
....
....
....
....
....
....
....

Data Table

Speed (m/s)

Stopping Distance (m)

Analyze and Interpret Data

1. **Characterize Data** Why was it important to carry out the steps of your procedure multiple times with each participant?

   ....

   ....

   ....

   ....

2. **Apply Concepts** How are unbalanced forces at work when a runner attempts to stop quickly after reaching the 10-m mark?

   ....

   ....

   ....

   ....

3. **Interpret Data** Do your data seem reasonable for representing speeds and distances traveled by basketball players on a court? Explain why or why not.

   ....

   ....

   ....

   ....

4. **Provide Critique** Compare your procedure with the procedure of another group. What did that group do differently? What would you suggest to improve that group's procedure?

   ....

   ....

   ....

5. **Construct Arguments** Write a proposal to the school that explains the importance of making sure the basketball court has enough space around it. In your proposal, suggest a strategy for making the court safer. Cite data from your investigation as evidence to support your points.

   ....

   ....

   ....

   ....

   ....

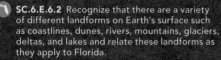
SC.6.E.6.2 Recognize that there are a variety of different landforms on Earth's surface such as coastlines, dunes, rivers, mountains, glaciers, deltas, and lakes and relate these landforms as they apply to Florida.

SC.6.E.7.4 Differentiate and show interactions among the geosphere, hydrosphere, cryosphere, atmosphere, and biosphere. (Also **SC.6.N.1.1** and **SC.6.N.3.4**)

HANDS-ON LAB

uConnect Develop a model to describe interactions among Earth's spheres.

GO ONLINE
to access your
digital course

 VIDEO

INTERACTIVITY

 VIRTUAL LAB

ASSESSMENT

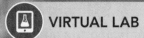 eTEXT

APP

HOW do all the things
in this photo interact
with each other?

The Essential Question

How do matter and energy cycle through Earth's systems?

How do water, rock, air, and organisms interact to make Earth's surface features and systems?

....

....

....

....

....

....

....

Quest KICKOFF

How can you predict the effects of a forest fire?

You just watched a news report about a wildfire that is burning just north of your town. The fire is not under control, and you wonder what will happen to the forest. In this problem-based Quest activity, you will take on the role of a scientist whose task is to educate and inform local residents about the harmful effects of a forest fire. You will consider how all the spheres of the Earth system interact, then use that information to make predictions about the outcome of the fire's damage. Your presentation will take the form of a poster, photo essay, or a multimedia report.

 INTERACTIVITY

Forest Fires

 SC.6.E.7.4 Differentiate and show interactions among the geosphere, hydrosphere, cryosphere, atmosphere, and biosphere. (Also **SC.6.N.1.1** and **SC.6.N.3.4**)

NBC LEARN ▶ **VIDEO**

After watching the Quest Kickoff video, which explores the effects of a forest fire, record ways in which a fire will impact Earth's spheres.

Organisms:

....

....

Ground/Earth:

....

....

Air:

....

....

Water:

....

....

Quest CHECK-IN

IN LESSON 1
How can an event in one sphere, such as the atmosphere, have an impact on another sphere? Think about the flow of energy as the fire started, then spread.

 INTERACTIVITY

Fire and Earth's Spheres

Quest CHECK-IN

IN LESSON 2
How do all of Earth's spheres interact? Consider these interactions as you learn how fire affects the geosphere.

 INTERACTIVITY

Disrupting the Geosphere

Fires are part of the natural life cycle of a forest. However, when they happen at the wrong time or burn for too long, forest fires have a devastating effect on plant and animal populations. Fires also affect the surrounding air, water, and land.

Quest CHECK-IN

IN LESSON 3

How does the hydrosphere interact with the other spheres, and vice versa? Examine the effects of fire on the hydrosphere. Then review all data and finalize your predictions.

👆 **INTERACTIVITY**

Impact on the Hydrosphere

Quest FINDINGS

Complete the Quest!

Create an engaging presentation to summarize your findings. Reflect on how the spheres influence each other—and your town.

👆 **INTERACTIVITY**

Reflect on Forest Fires

Matter and Energy in Earth's System

Guiding Questions

- What are the different components of the Earth system?
- What are the sources of energy for the processes that affect Earth?
- How can you model the cycling of matter in the Earth system?

Connections

Literacy Cite Textual Evidence

Math Interpret a Line Graph

 SC.6.E.6.2 Recognize that there are a variety of different landforms on Earth's surface such as coastlines, dunes, rivers, mountains, glaciers, deltas, and lakes and relate these landforms as they apply to Florida.

SC.6.E.7.4 Differentiate and show interactions among the geosphere, hydrosphere, cryosphere, atmosphere, and biosphere. (Also **SC.6.N.3.4**)

Vocabulary

atmosphere
geosphere
hydrosphere
cryosphere
biosphere
energy

Academic Vocabulary

system
feedback

VOCABULARY APP

Practice vocabulary on a mobile device.

Quest CONNECTION

Think about how an event, such as a fire, in one sphere can have an impact on another sphere.

Connect It !

✎ **Draw a line on the photo to indicate where the surface of the lake was in the past.**

Cause and Effect What happened to the water in this lake? Why do you think this happened?

....

....

The Earth System

Lake Mead, shown in **Figure 1**, is part of a large system consisting of the Colorado River, Hoover Dam, and Las Vegas, Nevada. A **system** is a group of parts that work together as a whole. If we zoom way out, the universe is the biggest system of all, and it contains all other systems. Earth is a system, too.

Water and Rock Cycles The Earth system involves flows of matter and energy through different components. In the water cycle, water evaporates from the ocean and other bodies of water. Then it rises into the atmosphere and eventually falls back to Earth's surface as precipitation. Rain and meltwater then flow to rivers, lakes, and the ocean. Eventually the water cycles back into the atmosphere. At each step of a cycle of matter, some change in energy occurs to keep the cycle going. Evaporation of water requires heat energy. The heat energy may come from the sun or from within Earth, as in a hot spring.

Rock also cycles through the Earth system. Hot molten material inside Earth, called magma, flows up through cracks in Earth's crust. This new material cools—loses heat energy—to form solid rock. Over time, the rock can be eroded into small pieces. If enough small pieces collect, they may get packed together to form new rock.

☑ READING CHECK **Compare and Contrast** How are the rock and water cycles similar? How are they different?

....

....

....

....

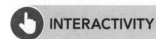

INTERACTIVITY

Explore different types of systems.

Academic Vocabulary

Much of science involves identifying components of different systems. List two systems you hear about in everyday life. What are their components?

....

....

....

....

....

....

....

....

The Cycling of Water
Figure 1 Drought has had a serious impact on Lake Mead, a reservoir in Nevada.

Literacy Connection

Cite Textual Evidence
Reread the sections about the atmosphere. Underline the evidence that supports the idea that the atmosphere affects Earth's climate.

Earth's Spheres The Earth system is made up of four main spheres, or subsystems, shown in **Figure 2**. Earth's **atmosphere** (AT muh sfeer) is the relatively thin envelope of gases that forms Earth's outermost layer. It is made of air—a mixture of gases including nitrogen, oxygen, water vapor, and carbon dioxide—and dust particles. It contains Earth's weather, and it is the foundation for the different climates around the world. Most of Earth's mass is in the form of rock and metal of the **geosphere** (GEE uh sfeer). The geosphere includes the solid metal inner core, the liquid metal outer core, and the rocky mantle and crust. All of Earth's water, including water that cycles through the atmosphere, is called the **hydrosphere** (HI druh sfeer). The **cryosphere** (CRY uh sfeer) is the frozen component of the hydrosphere. It is made up of all the ice and snow on land, plus sea and lake ice. The parts of Earth that contain all living organisms are collectively known as the **biosphere** (BI uh sfeer).

Earth's outermost layer receives energy in the form of sunlight that passes through it and from heat that rises from Earth's surface, including the ocean. Heat rising from Earth's surface creates wind, which distributes heat as well as water through the atmosphere.

Earth's rock and metal contain an enormous amount of energy. Exposed rock absorbs sunlight and radiates heat into the atmosphere. In some locations, energy and new material make up the rocky outer layer of the geosphere in the form of lava. Major eruptions can affect the atmosphere, which in turn affects the hydrosphere and biosphere.

Energy Flow The constant flow, or cycling, of matter through the Earth system requires energy. Energy is the ability to do work. The Earth system has two main sources of energy: heat from the sun and heat from Earth's interior. These energy sources drive cycles of matter in the four spheres.

HANDS-ON LAB

☑**Investigate** Model how energy flows within Earth.

☑**READING CHECK** **Use Information** Which part of each sphere do you interact with in your daily life? Give one example for each of the main spheres.

....

....

....

Earth's Spheres

Figure 2 Earth has four major spheres that cycle matter and energy and shape Earth's surface. Label each box with the correct sphere name. Then, list at least two spheres that show an interaction within the photo.

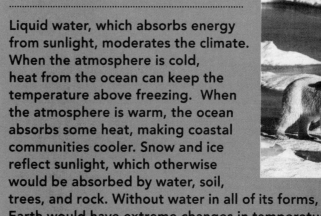

....

Liquid water, which absorbs energy from sunlight, moderates the climate. When the atmosphere is cold, heat from the ocean can keep the temperature above freezing. When the atmosphere is warm, the ocean absorbs some heat, making coastal communities cooler. Snow and ice reflect sunlight, which otherwise would be absorbed by water, soil, trees, and rock. Without water in all of its forms, Earth would have extreme changes in temperature.

....

....

....

Life has been found in virtually every part of Earth, from deep below the continental ice shelf of Antarctica to high up in the Himalayan Mountains.

....

System Feedback

Glaciers, part of the cryosphere, are large blocks of ancient ice, usually found near mountains and in polar regions. Like a freezer pack in a cooler, a glacier keeps the surrounding air and land cool. But many glaciers are melting around the world. As glaciers melt, they lose mass and volume and turn into liquid water that drains away or evaporates. This allows the land underneath to absorb more sunlight, which causes the surrounding air and land to get warmer. The warmer air makes glaciers melt even faster. This is an example of **feedback**. The system returns, or feeds back, information about itself, and that information results in change.

Positive and Negative Feedback Sometimes feedback is negative: it causes a process to slow down, or go in reverse. But some types of feedback are positive: they reinforce, speed up, or enhance the process that's already underway. Feedback may result in stability or it may cause more change. The melting glaciers are an example of positive feedback and change. A similar process is causing change in the Arctic.

READING CHECK **Cite Textual Evidence** Name a reason why melting glaciers are considered positive feedback.

....

....

Model It!

Sea Ice and Climate

Figure 3 Liquid and solid water are important factors in controlling climate. A large body of water can absorb energy from the sun, while snow or ice reflects solar energy back into space. In recent years, the amount of sea ice—frozen water—in the Arctic Circle has been dwindling because the air and water have been warmer than usual. As more of the Arctic Ocean is exposed due to loss of ice, it absorbs more sunlight and gets warmer. This makes it less likely for sea ice to form even when the air is well below freezing.

Sea Ice

Develop Models ✏ On the image provided, draw and label a cycle diagram for the feedback that is occurring in the Arctic among ice, liquid seawater, atmosphere, and solar energy.

Arctic Sea Ice

Historically, Arctic winters had long, dark nights and seawater froze. In the warmer summers, much of the sea ice melted. Today, more Arctic ice melts in summer than it has in human history. The total area of Arctic sea ice has changed in recent years as the globe has warmed. The graph shows the amount of sea ice found in the Arctic Ocean for the following years: 1986, 1996, 2006, and 2016.

1. Interpret a Line Graph What is the trend in the data?

....

2. Interpret a Line Graph What was the lowest extent of sea ice in the data, and when did it occur?

....

3. Predict What will happen to the extent of sea ice in the Arctic if temperatures continue to rise? Incorporate what you know about "feedback" into your prediction.

....

....

....

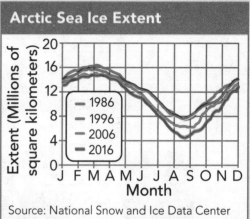

Arctic Sea Ice Extent

Source: National Snow and Ice Data Center

Interacting Spheres
An event in one sphere can affect another, which in turn can affect another. For example, Greenland is losing about 250 billion tons of ice each year. As the massive ice sheet thins, the weight of the ice decreases. As a result, in some parts of Greenland, the land is rising about 1.0 cm per year. How can this happen? Earth's rocky outer layer is floating on a denser layer of rock below the crust.

A landmass that gets heavier by gaining more water or other material will "sink," while a landmass that gets lighter by losing material will rise. It's like a boat in the water with its cargo off-loaded, as shown in **Figure 4**. As containers are removed, there's less mass on the boat. This causes the boat to sit higher in the water because it is more buoyant.

 **INTERACTIVITY**

Examine thermal energy and the cycling of matter in Earth's spheres.

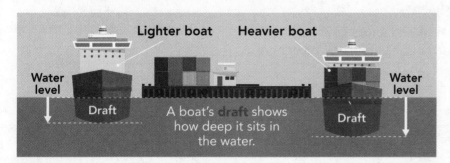

Buoyancy of Landmasses

Figure 4 A landmass can rise and sit higher on Earth's surface if it sheds a lot of mass, just like a boat floating on water.

111

☑ LESSON 1 Check

1. **Identify** Which of Earth's spheres is the frozen component of another sphere?

....

2. **Use Models** Use the rock cycle diagram below to describe how energy is involved in the cycling of matter in the geosphere.

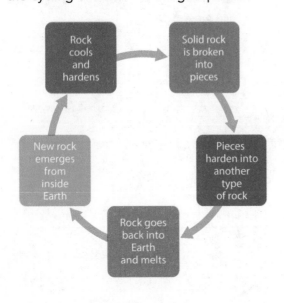

Rock cools and hardens

Solid rock is broken into pieces

Pieces harden into another type of rock

Rock goes back into Earth and melts

New rock emerges from inside Earth

....
....
....
....
....

3. **Cause and Effect** Describe the cause of precipitation and its effects on Earth's surface.

....
....
....
....
....
....
....

4. **Classify** Which of the following events of the water cycle involves the biosphere: heavy rain causing a landslide, or leaves releasing water vapor into the air? Explain.

....
....

5. **Connect to the Environment** Give an example of how changes in the cryosphere affect the biosphere.

....
....
....
....
....

Quest CHECK-IN

In this lesson, you learned about **the different spheres that make up Earth.** You also learned how **these spheres affect and shape each other, and how feedback within or between spheres produces stability or change.**

Evaluate What are three ways in which factors or events in the atmosphere could increase the damage of fire in the biosphere?

....
....
....

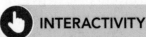 **INTERACTIVITY**

Fire and Earth's Spheres

Go online to trace how the forest fire started and discover factors that can start and spread a forest fire. Think about the flow of energy as the fire spreads and how you might use this information in your presentation.

SC.6.E.6.2, SC.6.E.7.4

When the ICE MELTS

Florida, a semi-tropical paradise far from the northern latitudes, might seem to have nothing to do with Greenland, the island of ice between the Atlantic and Arctic Oceans. But Florida is a coastal state with one of the largest populations in the United States.

And if you live near the coast, then you'll definitely want to pay attention to what's happening in Greenland. About 82 percent of Greenland is covered by an ice sheet. But in recent years, this ice sheet has been melting at an advanced rate due to warming global temperatures. When ice on land melts and runs into the ocean, it has the potential to raise sea levels around the world.

Sea levels have risen at an average rate of 1.5 cm every decade for the last century. But during the last 25 years, that rate has doubled, mostly as a result of ice melting in Greenland and Antarctica.

Higher sea levels threaten infrastructure, such as roadways or utility lines, as well as lives and property. The higher the sea level, the more vulnerable Florida is to deadly storms and coastal flooding. Government officials and scientists from a variety of fields are working together to create and implement protection measures to deal with potential problems in the future.

MY COMMUNITY

How would you deal with the problem of rising sea levels? Go online to research what Florida or another coastal state is doing to protect its coastline from the encroaching ocean.

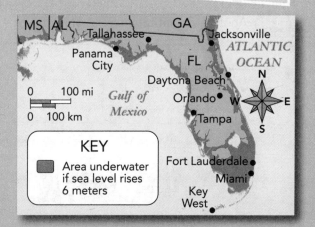

MS AL Tallahassee GA Jacksonville
Panama City FL ATLANTIC OCEAN
Daytona Beach
0   100 mi   Gulf of   Orlando   N
0   100 km   Mexico   Tampa   W   E
                                   S
KEY
■ Area underwater if sea level rises 6 meters
Fort Lauderdale
Miami
Key West

If the entire ice sheet on Greenland melted, sea levels would rise about 7 meters.

113

LESSON

2

Surface Features in the Geosphere

Guiding Questions

- What are the different landforms found on Earth?
- What forces and energy make the different landforms?
- What are the various ways to model landforms?

Connections

Literacy Write Explanatory Texts

Math Analyze Quantitative Relationships

SC.6.E.6.2 Recognize that there are a variety of different landforms on Earth's surface such as coastlines, dunes, rivers, mountains, glaciers, deltas, and lakes and relate these landforms as they apply to Florida. (Also **SC.6.N.3.4**)

Vocabulary

topography
landform
mountain
coastline
dune
river
delta
surveying

Academic Vocabulary

model

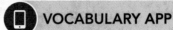

VOCABULARY APP

Practice vocabulary on a mobile device.

Quest CONNECTION

Think about how the geosphere interacts with the atmosphere and biosphere.

Connect It !

🖊 **Circle the places of high elevation in the Western and Eastern United States. What other features do you notice on the map?**

Make Observations What observations can you make about the elevations of the coasts and center of the United States?

....

....

Apply Scientific Reasoning Do you think other countries around the world also have a variety of land elevations? Explain.

....

....

Topography of the Geosphere

If you drove across the United States, you would observe many changes in topography, as shown in **Figure 1**. **Topography** (tuh PAWG ruh fee) is the shape of the land. Land can be described using elevation, relief, and landforms.

The height of a point above sea level on Earth's surface is its elevation. California has the lowest and highest points of elevation in the contiguous United States. The lowest point, found at Badwater Basin in Death Valley, is 86 meters below sea level. The highest elevation is Mount Whitney at 4,418 meters. The difference in elevation between the highest and lowest points of an area is its relief. An area's relief is the result of the different landforms found there. **Landforms** are features such as coastlines, dunes, and mountains. Different landforms have different combinations of elevation and relief.

> ☑ **READING CHECK** **Determine Central Ideas** Explain the three ways that land can be described.

....
....
....
....

HANDS-ON LAB

☑**Investigate** Model landforms to learn about elevation and relief.

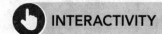

INTERACTIVITY

Think about landforms that can be found in Florida.

Relief Map
Figure 1 The United States has many different land features such as mountains, rivers, and plains.

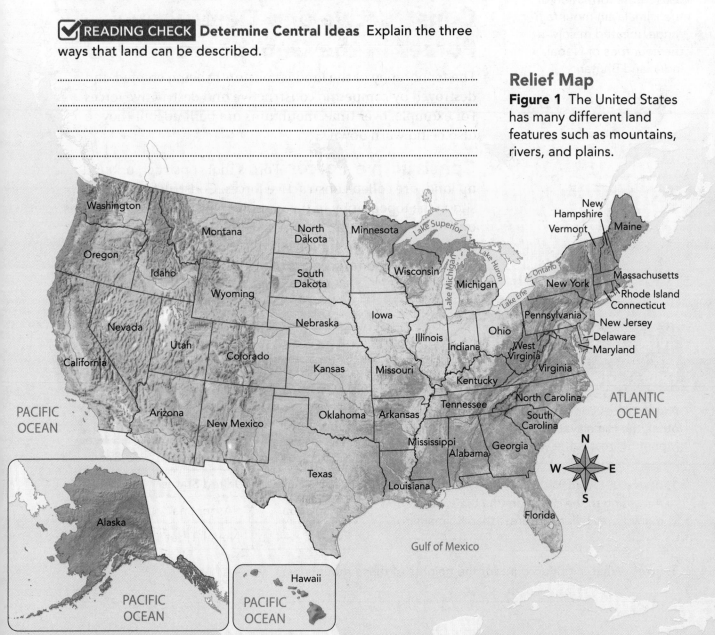

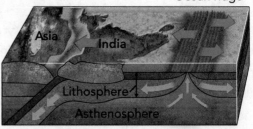

Ocean ridge

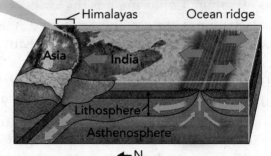

Himalayas Ocean ridge

←N

Plates Collide

Figure 2 India was pushed against Asia, which caused the formation of the Himalayan mountain range, located mainly in the countries of Nepal, India, and Bhutan.

Constructive and Destructive Forces in the Geosphere

The topography of the land is constantly being created and destroyed by competing constructive and destructive forces. For example, over time, mountains are built up, but they're also being worn down.

Constructive Forces Forces that construct, or build up land, are called constructive forces. Constructive forces shape the topography in the geosphere by creating mountains and other huge landmasses. The Himalayan mountain range in Asia formed over millions of years, as India collided with Asia and pushed up sections of the ocean floor, as shown in **Figure 2**.

Math Toolbox

Tallest Mountains

As the plates continue to push against each other, the Himalayas are still rising to new heights. Mount Everest is the world's tallest mountain.

1. **Analyze Quantitative Relationships**
   According to the data from the table, about how many times taller is Everest than Kilimanjaro?

....

2. **Infer** What might account for the heights of these mountains?

....

Mountain	Location	Height (meters)
Kilimanjaro	Tanzania	5,895
Denali	United States	6,190
Aconcagua	Argentina	6,962
Everest	Nepal/Tibet	8,850

A volcano erupts.

....

The eruption sends ash and gases into the air.

....

Lava and ash flow down into the surrounding habitats.

....

Mudflows form when ash and other volcanic material mix with water.

....

Destructive Forces

The Himalayas were formed because land was built up, but there are destructive forces that also change Earth's topography. For example, rain, wind, ice, and fire destroy and wear away landmasses and affect the geosphere.

The geosphere, atmosphere, hydrosphere, and biosphere interact with each other to affect Earth. For example, an event that occurs in the geosphere, such as the volcano in **Figure 3**, will change the other spheres. A volcano releases ash and gases into the atmosphere and volcanic material into the hydrosphere. Initially, the volcanic material and gases may kill organisms in the biosphere. However, ash can enrich the soil and give new plants more nutrients. Hardened lava may cut off old river channels but form a new lake.

☑️ **READING CHECK** **Integrate With Visuals** Refer to the art in **Figure 2** that shows the collision of India with Asia. How did changes in the geosphere cause the Himalayas to form?

....

....

A Volcano Changes Everything

Figure 3 🖊 A volcano causes changes in four spheres. Record which sphere is affected during each step in an eruption.

Literacy Connection

Write Explanatory Texts
As you read, number the steps in which an erupting volcano starts the cycle of change. Then, think about a forest fire. Explain how a fire would affect the geosphere, atmosphere, hydrosphere, and biosphere.

VIDEO

Explore the various landforms on Earth's surface.

Exploring Earth's Surface

There are a variety of landforms on Earth because Earth's surface differs from place to place. In addition, landforms change over time due to constructive and destructive forces. Some landforms are snow-capped mountains, some are giant glaciers, and others are ever-changing sand dunes. **Figure 4** shows some of the landforms found on Earth.

Many Landforms

Figure 4 ✏ There are so many different landforms, but they are all connected. Choose two landforms. Draw a line from one landform to another and tell how they are connected to each other.

....

....

....

....

Mountains A **mountain** is a landform with both high elevation and high relief. Mountains that are closely related in shape, structure, location, and age are called a mountain range. Different mountain ranges in one region make up a mountain system. The Rocky Mountains are a famous mountain system. Mountain ranges and mountain systems in a long, connected chain form a larger unit called a mountain belt.

Plateaus and Plains Landforms that have high elevation and low relief are called plateaus. Streams and rivers may cut into the plateau's surface. Landforms that have low elevation and low relief are called plains. A plain that lies along a seacoast is called a coastal plain. In North America, the Atlantic coastal plain extends from Florida all the way up to Cape Cod in Massachusetts.

Plateau

Lake

Plain

Dune

Coastlines The boundary between the land and the ocean or a lake is the **coastline**. Among the 50 states, the mainland of Alaska has the longest coastline at 10,686 kilometers. The mainland of Florida has the second longest coastline, measuring 2,170 kilometers.

Dunes The land that extends from a coastline may be rocky cliffs, sandy beaches, or dunes. A **dune** is a hill of sand piled up by the wind. Dunes in the coastal regions are parallel to the coastline and protect the land from ocean waves.

Rivers and Deltas A **river** is a natural stream of water that flows into another body of water such as an ocean, lake, or another river. When a river reaches an ocean, the water slows and sand, clay, and sediment in the water sink. When the sediment builds up, it makes a landform called a **delta**. In Florida, the Apalachicola River supplies sand to St. Vincent's Island, a barrier island and wildlife refuge.

☑ READING CHECK **Compare and Contrast** How are dunes and deltas similar and different?

....

....

Mountain

Glacier

River

Plain

Coastline

Delta

Modeling Landforms

Before modern technology, scientists and mapmakers studied
the land and drew maps by hand. They spent hundreds of
hours walking over landforms or sailing along coastlines
to **model** what they saw. Then people used a process called
surveying. In **surveying**, mapmakers determine distances and
elevations using instruments and the principles of geometry.
Today, people use computers to create topographic and other
maps from aerial photography and satellite imagery.

Topographic Maps Imagine that you are in a plane
flying high above the United States. How does it look? A
topographic map portrays the surface features of an area as if
being viewed from above. Topographic maps provide accurate
information on the elevation, relief, and slope of the ground, as
shown in **Figure 5**.

Contour Lines Topographic maps have contour lines to show
elevation, relief, and slope. A contour line connects points of
equal elevation. Contour lines also show how steep or gradual
a slope is. Contour lines that are far apart represent flat areas
or areas with gradual slopes. Lines that are close together
represent areas with steep slopes.

The change in elevation from one contour line to the next is
called a contour interval. On a given map, the contour interval
is always consistent. Every fifth contour line is known as an
index contour. These lines are darker and heavier than the
other lines.

**Topographic Map
of Mt. Grinnell**

Figure 5 The contour lines
on the map can be used
to determine a feature's
elevation. Use the contour
lines to determine the
elevation of Mt. Grinnell.

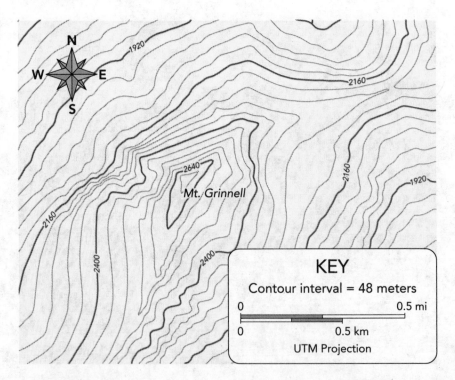

KEY

Contour interval = 48 meters

0   0.5 mi

0   0.5 km

UTM Projection

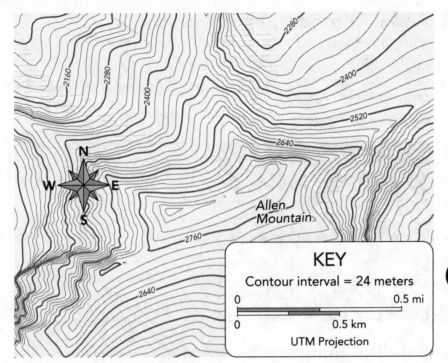

Shape of Contour Lines

Figure 6 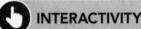 The area around Allen Mountain has many features. Circle the hilltops. Mark the steepest slopes with an X.

INTERACTIVITY

Investigate how constructive and destructive forces affect Earth's landforms.

Reading a Topographic Map In the United States, the scale of many topographic maps is 1 centimeter on the map for every 0.24 kilometers on the ground. This scale allows mapmakers to show land features such as rivers and coastlines. Large human-made structures, such as airports and highways, appear as outlines, while small structures, such as houses, are represented with symbols.

To find the elevation of a feature on the map in **Figure 6**, begin at an index contour line and count the number of lines up or down the feature. The shape of contour lines also provides information. V-shaped contour lines pointing away from a summit indicate a ridge line. V-shaped contour lines pointing toward a summit indicate a valley. A contour line that forms a closed loop indicates a hilltop. A closed loop with dashes inside indicates a depression, or hollow in the ground.

Model It !

A map is a way to model Earth. What features are modeled by the topographic map in **Figure 6**?

Develop Models ✎ Use the topographic map to create a drawing of the features it represents. Use the contour lines to help determine whether the area has a steep or gradual elevation. Be sure to label your illustration with the elevation of each feature.

Aerial Photography

When photographs are taken with cameras mounted in airplanes, it is called aerial photography. As the airplane flies, the camera takes pictures of strips of land. These picture strips are fitted together like a large puzzle to form an accurate picture of a large area of land, as shown in **Figure 7**.

Aerial Photograph

Figure 7 🖊 Mapmakers use aerial photographs such as this one to create a map. Use the photo to make a street map of the neighborhood in the photograph. Be sure to add your own street names.

Satellite Imagery

With the creation of computers, mapping has become easier and more accurate. Mapmakers can make maps of Earth using computers that interpret satellite data. Mapping satellites use electronic devices to collect data about the land surface. Pictures of the surface based on these data are called satellite images. These images are made up of pixels, and each pixel has information about the color and brightness of a part of Earth's surface, as shown in **Figure 8**.

Satellites orbit Earth collecting and storing data. Then, computers use the data to create images. Satellite images show details including plants, soil, rock, water, snow, and ice that cover Earth's surface.

Satellite Image of North America

Figure 8 🖊 Scientists and mapmakers identify special features on an image by their color and shape. For example, forests appear green, water may be blue or black, and snow is white. Draw an *X* to show where your state is.

Interpret Photos Write about the features you see in the satellite image.

....

....

....

....

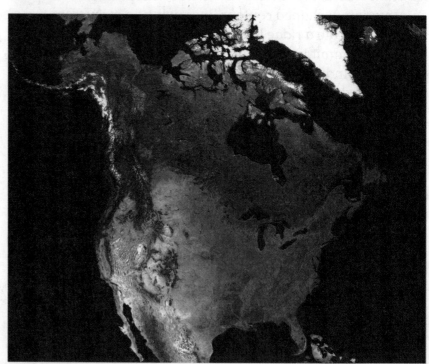

GPS The Global Positioning System, or GPS, is a navigational system that uses satellite signals to fix the location of a radio receiver on Earth. GPS helps anyone with a receiver locate his or her position anywhere on or above Earth.

You may have used GPS on a phone or in a car to navigate, but do you know how it works? Twenty-four orbiting satellites continuously send their current location and time to a GPS receiver on Earth. A user's receiver, such as a phone, needs information from at least three satellites to determine its location.

GIS A Geographic Information System, or GIS, is a system of computer hardware and software used to produce interactive maps. GIS uses GPS, satellite images, statistics about an area, and other maps to display and analyze geographic data.

The different types of information stored in a GIS are called data layers. The data layers help scientists and city planners to solve problems by understanding patterns, relationships, and trends. **Figure 9** shows how GIS could be used to determine a neighborhood's flood risk by analyzing data layers about the location of a river, its floodplain boundary, and the streets in a neighborhood.

INTERACTIVITY

Explore how maps can help solve problems.

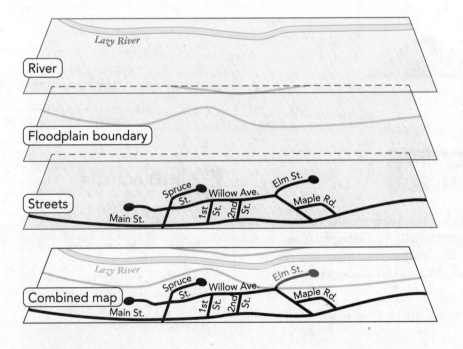

GIS Map

Figure 9 🖉 A GIS map has many data layers that can be used to analyze how different systems interact. Shade in the floodplain on the combined map. Where should a city planner avoid building houses? Why?

....

....

☑ READING CHECK **Write Explanatory Texts** Explain ways in which GPS and GIS are more useful than a topographic map.

....

....

....

SC.6.E.6.2

1. Identify A mountain is a landform with both

   high .... and high ....

2. Compare and Contrast How are plains and plateaus similar and different?

   ....
   ....
   ....
   ....

3. Interpret a Diagram ✐ Match each set of contour lines to the correct drawing.

4. Infer The owner of a car wash wants to open a new location in a different neighborhood. How could the owner use GIS to choose the best location? Explain what information should be included in the data layers.

   ....
   ....
   ....
   ....

5. Plan an Investigation You are hired to survey and map a volcanic island. What would you want to learn about the island before you choose your surveying and map-making tools? Explain.

   ....
   ....
   ....
   ....
   ....
   ....
   ....
   ....

Quest CHECK-IN

In this lesson, you learned about the topography of the geosphere and the various landforms. You learned how different forces shape these landforms. You also discovered how scientists model landforms to better understand the topography.

Evaluate How might a fire have a destructive effect on the geosphere?

....
....
....
....

👆 INTERACTIVITY

Disrupting the Geosphere

Go online to determine how the interactions among the geosphere, atmosphere, and biosphere affect the course of the forest fire and the damage it causes.

A DARING BRIDGE

Do you know how to build a bridge with some tough budget and environmental constraints? You engineer it! Plans for the Bixby Bridge in California show us how.

The Challenge: To design a cost-effective bridge across a canyon that withstands the elements.

Every winter, people in Big Sur, California, were trapped. Bad weather made the Old Coast Road impossible to travel. That changed in the 1930s when the state built a bridge across the canyon cut by Bixby Creek.

In designing the bridge, engineers weighed its impact on the environment. Then they considered costs and appearance. The country had entered the Great Depression. Funds were scarce, and a steel bridge would be costly. Also, a steel bridge so close to the Pacific Ocean would rust.

Finally, the engineers decided on an uncovered arch bridge 713 feet long and more than 260 feet above the canyon floor. They used concrete—45,000 sacks of it. Its appearance fit better alongside the area's stone cliffs. This design was also much less expensive. The Bixby Bridge reached completion on time and under budget—a success for any building project!

VIDEO

Learn how engineers considered each sphere when building the Bixby Bridge.

During the 1930s and 1940s, the lack of good roads and bridges could sometimes make traveling by car impossible.

DESIGN CHALLENGE

Can you design a bridge? Go to the Engineering Design Notebook to find out!

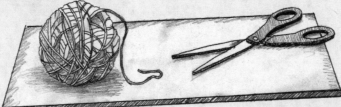

3 The Hydrosphere

Guiding Questions

- Where and in what features is water found on Earth?
- How does water cycle through Earth's systems?

Connection

Literacy Determine Central Ideas

 SC.6.E.6.2 Recognize that there are a variety of different landforms on Earth's surface such as coastlines, dunes, rivers, mountains, glaciers, deltas, and lakes and relate these landforms as they apply to Florida.

SC.6.E.7.4 Differentiate and show interactions among the geosphere, hydrosphere, cryosphere, atmosphere, and biosphere. (Also **SC.6.N.3.4**)

Vocabulary

water cycle
evaporation
transpiration
condensation
precipitation
watershed
aquifer
well

Academic Vocabulary

process

📱 **VOCABULARY APP**

Practice vocabulary on a mobile device.

 Quest CONNECTION

Think about how the hydrosphere interacts with the other spheres and how fire affects them all.

Connect It !

✏️ **Circle the different areas of water in this photo.**

Infer Why is water important to human beings?

....

....

....

Apply Scientific Reasoning Why is water important to our planet?

....

....

....

The Water Cycle

Without water, life as we know it would not exist. As shown in **Figure 1**, water is an important characteristic of Earth. All living things require water to live. Fortunately, Earth has its own built-in water recycling system: the water cycle.

The **water cycle** is the continuous process by which water moves from Earth's surface to the atmosphere and back again. This movement is driven by energy from the sun and by gravity. In the water cycle, water moves through the geosphere, the biosphere, the hydrosphere, and the atmosphere.

Evaporation The sun heats up the surface of bodies of water and causes water molecules to undergo a change. The process by which molecules at the surface of a liquid absorb enough energy to change to a gas is called **evaporation**. Water constantly evaporates from the surfaces of bodies of water.

Elements of the geosphere and biosphere can also add water vapor to the atmosphere. Water evaporates from soil in the geosphere. Animals in the biosphere release water vapor as they breathe. Water even evaporates from your skin.

Plants also play a role in this step of the water cycle. Plants draw in water from the soil through their roots. Eventually the water vapor is given off through the leaves in a process called **transpiration**.

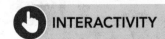

INTERACTIVITY

Discuss ways you depend on the hydrosphere.

Importance of Water
Figure 1 Water makes life on Earth possible.

The Water Cycle

Figure 2 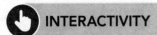 This diagram shows some of the major processes that make up the water cycle. Draw arrows to show the way that water moves through the cycle. Then, in the blank spaces, write the process that is at work.

INTERACTIVITY

Review all of the processes of the water cycle.

Literacy Connection

Determine Central Ideas As you read, underline the central idea of each paragraph. Note how this idea is developed through examples and details.

Condensation After a water molecule evaporates into the atmosphere, warm air carries the water molecule upward. **Condensation** is the process by which water vapor becomes liquid water. As water vapor rises into the colder air, some water vapor cools and condenses into liquid or solid water. Droplets of liquid water and ice crystals collect around solid particles in the air, forming clouds. Eventually, this results in precipitation.

Precipitation As more water vapor condenses, the water droplets and ice crystals grow larger. Eventually, they become so heavy that gravity causes them to fall back to Earth in the form of precipitation. Water that forms in clouds and falls to Earth as rain, snow, hail, or sleet is called **precipitation**. Once it falls, it collects in rivers, lakes, and streams. It is also absorbed by the soil in the geosphere. Precipitation is the source of almost all fresh water on and below Earth's surface.

For millions of years, the total amount of water cycling through the Earth's system has remained fairly constant—the rates of evaporation and precipitation are balanced. That means that the water you use today is the same water that your ancestors used.

✓ READING CHECK **Draw Evidence** The biosphere interacts with the hydrosphere within the water cycle. Cite one example of that interaction.

....

....

....

Distribution of Earth's Water

Most of the water in the hydrosphere—roughly 97 percent—is salt water found mostly in the ocean. Only 3 percent is fresh water, as shown in **Figure 3**.

Fresh Water Of the 3 percent that is fresh water, about two-thirds is frozen in huge masses of ice near the North and South poles. Much of Earth's fresh water is frozen into thickened ice masses called glaciers. Massive glacial ice sheets cover most of Greenland and Antarctica.

About a third of Earth's fresh water is underground. A tiny fraction of fresh water occurs in lakes and rivers. An even tinier fraction is found in the atmosphere, most of it in the form of invisible water vapor, the gaseous form of water.

Most precipitation falls directly into the ocean. Of the precipitation that falls on land, most evaporates. A small amount of the remaining water runs off the surface into streams and lakes in a **process** called runoff, but most of it seeps into the ground. After a long time, this groundwater eventually comes to the surface and evaporates again.

Salt Water Atlantic, Indian, Pacific, and Arctic are the names for the different parts of the ocean. The Pacific Ocean is the largest, covering an area greater than all the land on Earth. Smaller saltwater bodies are called seas. Seas are generally inland and landlocked. A small percentage of Earth's salt water is found in some saline lakes.

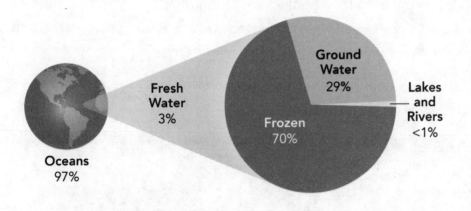

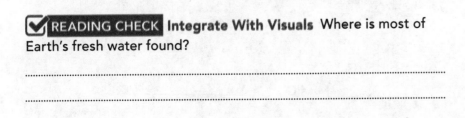

✓ READING CHECK **Integrate With Visuals** Where is most of Earth's fresh water found?

....

....

....

HANDS-ON LAB

☑**Investigate** Model the distribution of water on Earth.

Academic Vocabulary

A process is a series of actions or operations leading toward a particular result. List some processes you are familiar with in your daily life.

....

....

....

....

Water Resources
Figure 3 Most of the water on Earth is salt water in the ocean.

Reflect NASA satellite data show that the ice sheets are melting at a rate of about 350 billion tons of ice each year, which is far above historic averages. What do you think is causing this to happen? What effect would this increased amount of ice melt have on the ocean?

Surface Water

Surface water includes all the water found on the surface of Earth. The ocean, rivers, lakes, and ponds are all part of the surface water in the hydrosphere.

Rivers Even large rivers, such as the Mississippi River or St. Johns River, start as a trickle of water that originates from a source—an underground stream, runoff from rain, or melting snow or ice. Gravity causes these tiny streams to flow downhill. These small streams join others to form a larger stream. Larger streams join others to form a river that flows into the ocean. The streams and smaller rivers that feed into a main river are called tributaries. A river and all the tributaries that flow into it make up a river system, as shown in **Figure 4**.

Watersheds The land area that supplies water to a river system is called a **watershed**. When rivers join another river system, the areas they drain become part of the largest river's watershed. **Figure 5** shows the major watersheds that cover the United States.

Divides Watersheds stay separated from each other by a ridge of land called a divide. Streams on each side of the divide flow in different directions. The Great Divide, the longest divide in North America, follows the Rocky Mountains. West of this divide, water flows toward the Pacific Ocean. Some water stays in the Great Basin between the Rocky and Sierra Nevada Mountains. East of the divide, water flows toward the Mississippi River and into the Gulf of Mexico, joining rivers flowing from the Appalachian Mountains.

The Mississippi River
Figure 4 Many tributaries contribute to the Mississippi River.

▶ **VIDEO**

Discover how an aquaculture manager helps meet the needs of people while protecting the habitats of living things.

Watersheds
Figure 5 ✏ This map shows the watersheds of some large rivers in the United States. Draw a line on the map to represent the Great Divide. Use arrows to show the direction in which the water flows on each side of the divide.

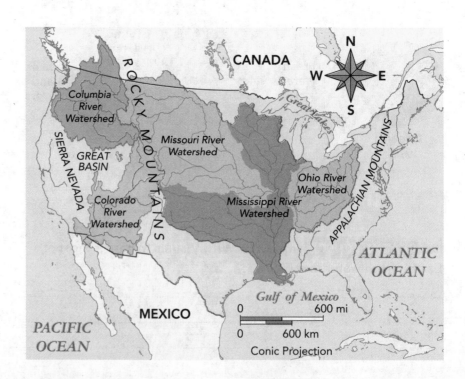

Ponds and Lakes Ponds and lakes form when water collects in hollows and low-lying areas of land. Unlike streams and rivers, ponds and lakes contain mostly still water. Ponds are smaller and shallower than lakes. Like other bodies of water, lakes and ponds are supplied by rainfall, melting snow and ice, and runoff. Some are fed by rivers or groundwater.

Lakes, such as the ones in **Figure 6**, form through several natural processes. When a river bends, a new channel may form, cutting off a loop to form an oxbow lake. Some lakes, such as the Great Lakes, formed in depressions created by ice sheets that melted at the end of the Ice Age. Other lakes were created by movements of Earth's crust that formed long, deep valleys called rift valleys. Lakes can also form in the empty craters of volcanoes.

✅ **READING CHECK** **Summarize** How do river systems, watersheds, and divides interact?

....

....

....

....

....

....

Lakes in Mountains
Figure 6 Lakes are important because they hold some of Earth's fresh water.

Plan It!

Building a Reservoir

Research ✏ A reservoir is a storage space for water. Consider why people build reservoirs. Do some research to help you plan how to build a reservoir in your region of the country. Use the space provided to draw a diagram showing the features of your reservoir. Write out the steps of your plan below.

....

....

....

....

Groundwater

Figure 7 ✏ This diagram shows how water travels underground. Add arrows to identify the paths that water takes.

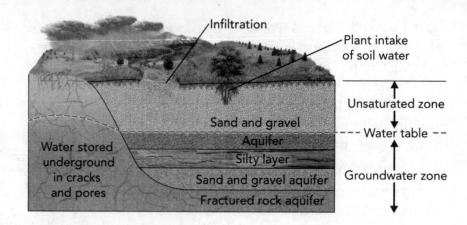

INTERACTIVITY

Explore how the Floridan aquifer formed and describe its importance today.

VIDEO

Learn more about the role of groundwater in the water cycle.

Groundwater

A large portion of fresh water in the hydrosphere is underground, as shown in **Figure 7**. Water that fills the cracks and spaces in soil and rock layers is called groundwater. Far more fresh water is located underground than in all of Earth's rivers and lakes.

Aquifers As precipitation falls to Earth, it moves through the soil and the small spaces within underground rock layers. These layers contain air as well as water, so they are not saturated, or filled, with water. This top layer is called the unsaturated zone.

Eventually, the water reaches a level where the openings in the layers are filled with water, or saturated. The upper level of the saturated zone is called the water table. Below the saturated zone there are layers of rock that hold water called **aquifers**.

Aquifers range in size from a small patch to an area the size of several states. Aquifers and other groundwater sources provide 55 percent of the drinking water for the United States. In rural areas, aquifers provide as much as 99 percent of the water used.

Wells People can get groundwater from an aquifer by digging a well that reaches below the water table. A **well** is a hole sunk into the earth to reach a supply of water. Long ago, people dug wells by hand and used buckets to bring up the water. Today, most wells are created with drilling equipment and the water is retrieved using mechanical pumps that run on electricity.

✓ READING CHECK **Determine Central Ideas** What is an aquifer?

....

....

....

....

Exploring the Ocean

There are several ways that the ocean is unique in the hydrosphere. The water in Earth's ocean varies in salinity, temperature, and depth.

Salinity The total amount of dissolved salts in a sample of water is the salinity. Near the ocean's surface, rain, snow, and melting ice add fresh water, lowering the salinity. Evaporation, on the other hand, increases salinity. Salinity is also higher near the poles because the forming of sea ice leaves some salt behind in the seawater.

Salinity affects ocean water in different ways. For instance, fresh water freezes at 0°C but ocean water freezes at about –1.9°C because the salt interferes with the formation of ice. Salt water also has a higher density than fresh water. Therefore, seawater lifts, or buoys up, less dense objects floating in it.

Temperature The broad surface of the ocean absorbs energy from the sun. Temperatures at the surface of the ocean vary with location and the seasons. Near the equator, surface ocean temperatures often reach 25°C, about room temperature. The temperatures drop as you travel away from the equator.

Depth The ocean is very deep—3.8 kilometers deep on average. That's more than twice as deep as the Grand Canyon. As you descend through the ocean, the water temperature decreases. Water pressure, the force exerted by the weight of water, increases by 1 bar, the air pressure at sea level, with each 10 meters of depth. Use **Figure 8** to explore temperature, pressure, and depth.

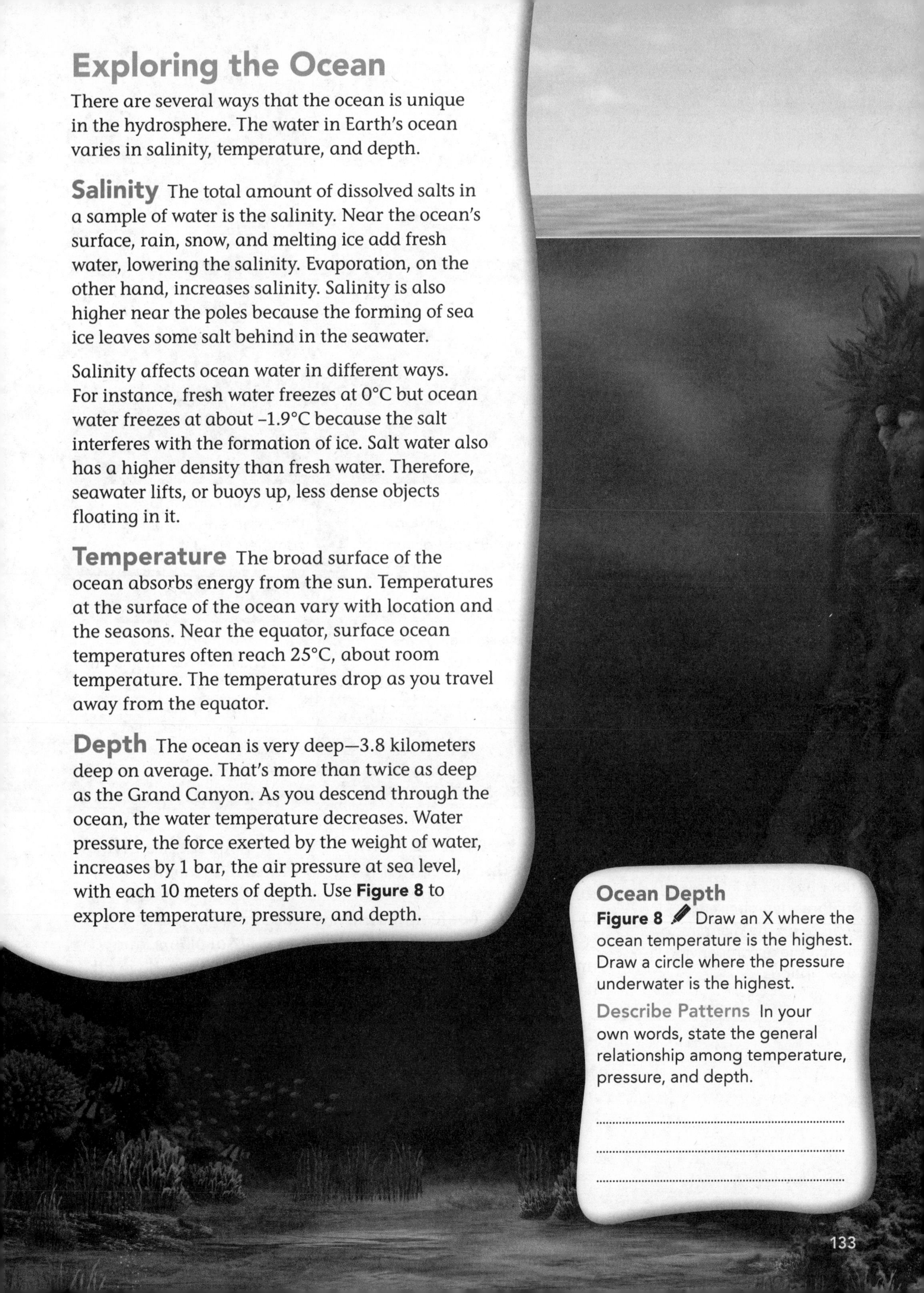

Ocean Depth

Figure 8 🖊 Draw an X where the ocean temperature is the highest. Draw a circle where the pressure underwater is the highest.

Describe Patterns In your own words, state the general relationship among temperature, pressure, and depth.

....

....

....

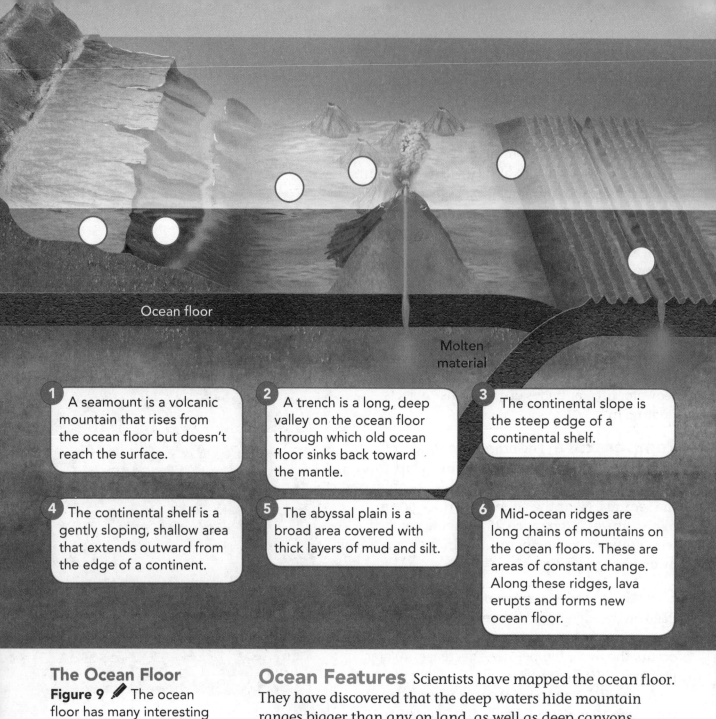

Ocean floor

Molten material

1 A seamount is a volcanic mountain that rises from the ocean floor but doesn't reach the surface.

2 A trench is a long, deep valley on the ocean floor through which old ocean floor sinks back toward the mantle.

3 The continental slope is the steep edge of a continental shelf.

4 The continental shelf is a gently sloping, shallow area that extends outward from the edge of a continent.

5 The abyssal plain is a broad area covered with thick layers of mud and silt.

6 Mid-ocean ridges are long chains of mountains on the ocean floors. These are areas of constant change. Along these ridges, lava erupts and forms new ocean floor.

The Ocean Floor

Figure 9 ✏️ The ocean floor has many interesting features. Number each feature on the diagram to match the accompanying descriptions.

Ocean Features Scientists have mapped the ocean floor. They have discovered that the deep waters hide mountain ranges bigger than any on land, as well as deep canyons. Major ocean floor features include seamounts, trenches, continental shelves, continental slopes, abyssal plains, and mid-ocean ridges. These features, shown in **Figure 9**, have all been formed by the interaction of Earth's plates.

☑ READING CHECK **Draw Conclusions** How do the temperature and pressure most likely differ at the top of a seamount and the bottom of a trench?

....

....

....

....

SC.6.E.6.2, SC.6.E.7.4

1. **Cause and Effect** Explain how evaporation of surface water in one location can result in groundwater being replenished in a distant location.

....
....
....
....
....
....

2. **Compare and Contrast** ✏ Create a Venn diagram comparing fresh water and salt water, including the amounts of each on Earth.

3. **Identify** What are some of the important phases of the water cycle?

....
....
....

4. **Infer** A chemical pollutant released near a stream in the Appalachian Mountains is later detected in the Atlantic Ocean. What can you infer about the pollutant and how it moved?

....
....
....
....
....
....
....

5. **Plan an Investigation** Describe how you would trace the path of water that begins as a trickle of melting snow near a glacier high in a mountain range.

....
....
....
....
....

Quest CHECK-IN

In this lesson, you learned how the water of the hydrosphere is cycled and how it interacts with the other spheres. You also learned about the characteristics of each portion of the hydrosphere, including surface water, ocean water, and groundwater.

Evaluate How might a natural disaster, such as a forest fire, affect the elements of the hydrosphere?

....
....
....
....

☞ INTERACTIVITY

Impact on the Hydrosphere

Go online to examine how the hydrosphere interacts with other spheres and the effect of a forest fire on those interactions. Then review the data and finalize your predictions about the fire's damage.

SC.6.E.6.2, SC.6.E.7.4, SC.6.N.3.4

FLORIDA'S Barrier Islands

Many people from all over the world flock to Florida to enjoy the magnificent beaches. Florida may seem like a vacation paradise, but it is also literally in the path of destruction. How do all of the magnificent beaches, salt marshes, and mangrove swamps that form Florida's coastline stay intact?

Much of the coastline is guarded by barrier islands. These narrow masses of sand and marine sediment protect the coast by absorbing the brunt of the wind and wave action that hurricanes and other storms bring. But shifting ocean currents or brutal storms may reshape barrier islands or wash them away altogether. Some of these islands may reform as loose sand and other sediment accumulate off the coast.

Many of Florida's world-famous beaches happen to be on barrier islands. As a result, towns and cities have developed on land that is subject to flooding and damaging winds. How wind, water, land, and people continue to interact will determine the future of these important features of Florida's coast.

Barrier islands can protect the coastline from flooding and other destruction caused by storms.

Use the map to answer the following questions.

Hurricane Matthew's Path

1. Characterize Data Describe how the strength of the hurricane changed along its path to Florida.

....

....

....

....

KEY
- 39–73 mph wind
- 74–95 mph wind
- 96–110 mph wind
- 111–130 mph wind
- 131–155 mph wind
- 156+ mph wind

2. Cause and Effect What role do you think barrier islands played in this hurricane? How might they have been impacted by the hurricane?

....

....

....

....

3. Solve Problems Most of Florida's coast suffers damage from flooding and storms. What are some strategies that you think can be used to strengthen the barrier islands and minimize the damage?

....

....

4. Construct Arguments Make an argument for or against restrictions that limit the number of homes and businesses that can be built on barrier islands.

....

....

....

☑ TOPIC 3 Review and Assess

1 Matter and Energy in Earth's System

SC.6.E.6.2, SC.6.E.7.4

1. The cycles of matter in Earth's systems are driven by movement of
   A. heat.   B. rock.
   C. water.   D. air

2. Which of the following is an example of positive feedback in an Earth system?
   A. Exercise makes a person warm. They perspire, which cools their body.
   B. Warm weather heats a rain forest, causing water vapor to rise and condense into clouds. The clouds shade the forest from sunlight, and causing the temperature to cool.
   C. Warm air melts sea ice, exposing more sea water to sunlight, which warms the water. The warm water is harder to freeze when the air temperature drops.
   D. A field of grass absorbs sunlight, grows tall, produces seeds, and releases the seeds to produce a new generation of grass.

3. Explain Phenomena As ice melts from Greenland into the surrounding ocean, Greenland appears to rise by about 1 cm per year. If the sea level is rising, how can Greenland be rising, too?

   ....
   ....
   ....
   ....

4. Summarize Give an example of an interaction involving the cycling of matter between spheres.

   ....
   ....
   ....
   ....

2 Surface Features in the Geosphere

SC.6.E.6.2, SC.6.E.7.4

5. Florida is part of a landform of the southeast portion of North America that consists of mostly flat landscape not much higher than sea level. This is called a
   A. prairie.
   B. watershed.
   C. plateau.
   D. coastal plain.

6. With .... technology you can find your precise location on a digital map if your device can receive signals from three satellites. A ....
   map is a low-tech tool for visualizing the contours and elevations of a landform.

7. Construct Arguments Write a brief proposal for why GPS technology and surveying should be used to study changes on a low-lying area of the coast.

   ....
   ....
   ....
   ....
   ....

8. Explain Phenomena Explain how a volcano can produce both destructive and destructive forces on Earth's surface.

   ....
   ....
   ....
   ....
   ....
   ....

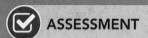
3 The Hydrosphere

SC.6.E.6.2, SC.6.E.7.4

9. When ocean water reaches the poles, some of it turns to ice if air temperatures are frigid. Some salt gets trapped between ice crystals, but most is left behind in the unfrozen seawater. This causes an increase in the seawater's
   A. evaporation.
   B. salinity.
   C. pressure.
   D. temperature.

10. **Plan an Investigation** Describe how you could use technology to monitor and map the cryosphere.

   ....
   ....
   ....
   ....
   ....

11. **Summarize** Describe the makeup of the hydrosphere in terms of percentages that are fresh water and salt water, and where those types of water are found.

   ....
   ....
   ....
   ....
   ....
   ....
   ....
   ....

12. In the photo, the .... is interacting with the .... by wearing down the rocks as the water flows. The water that fills the river was delivered to higher elevations when the

   .... released precipitation

   in the form of rain or ....

13. **Develop Models** How might water from a lake move through the water cycle and eventually fall as rain? Draw a diagram to model the cycle.

Science Assessment Practice

Circle the letter of the best answer.

1 About 530 million years ago, land that would later become Florida formed through both volcanic activity and the buildup of sediment. Over hundreds of millions of years, this land was repeatedly submerged as glaciers melted and the sea level rose, and then exposed as temperatures cooled and glaciers reformed. When the land was submerged, more sediment, shells, and coral reefs accumulated. Which spheres interacted most to make the land that is now Florida?

A geosphere, hydrosphere, biosphere

B geosphere, hydrosphere, cryosphere, biosphere

C geosphere, hydrosphere, cryosphere

D geosphere, hydrosphere, atmosphere

2 The contour map shows land topography of a mountain in the Appalachian range. What is the elevation of the point marked X, the top of the mountain, on the map?

F about 1,500 meters

G about 1,485 meters

H about 1,525 meters

I about 1,545 meters

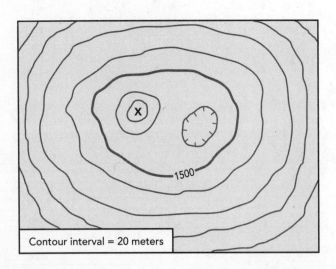

Contour interval = 20 meters

Use the watershed map to answer questions 3 through 6.

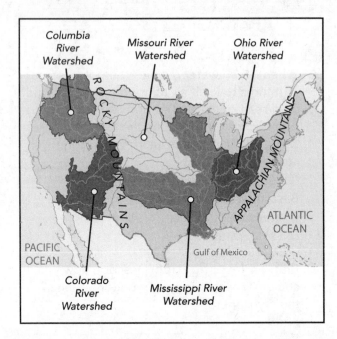

3 If there is a disruption to precipitation patterns in the Rocky Mountains, which of the following regions of the United States would probably be least affected?

A southeast (Florida, South Carolina)

B northwest (Washington, Oregon)

C southwest (Arizona, New Mexico)

D midwest (Iowa, Illinois, Ohio)

4 Your selection in Question 3 was based on that region

F being in the Mississippi Watershed, which is too far from the Rocky Mountains to be impacted.

G receiving water from the Ohio River Watershed, which is unaffected by the Rocky Mountains.

H being part of the Appalachian Mountain Watershed, which is separate from all of the others that receive water from the Rockies.

I receiving all of its moisture from the Atlantic Ocean.

5 Which of the following is the most reasonable explanation for why most of Texas is not part of the major river watersheds shown on the map?

  A Most of Texas is too dry to be considered part of any watershed.

  B Differences in elevation and relief set most of Texas apart from those watersheds.

  C The nearby watersheds are at higher elevations.

  D The nearby watersheds are at lower elevations.

6 If a major water pollution event occurred in a lake in Florida, why wouldn't the pollution pose much of a threat to the Mississippi River Watershed?

  F Florida is not part of that watershed. The pollution would either stay within Florida or drain to the surrounding ocean.

  G The pollution would be cleaned up before it could threaten any other states.

  H Lakes do not drain anywhere, so the pollution would stay put.

  I The Appalachian Mountains separate Florida from the Mississippi River Watershed.

7 Warmer temperatures are reducing the amount of water that has been locked in glaciers and ice caps for thousands of years. This melting of the cryosphere could directly

  A increase the total amount of water in the hydrosphere.

  B force the biosphere to absorb more water.

  C drain groundwater from the world's aquifers.

  D increase the amount of liquid surface water, including the volume of the oceans.

Quest FINDINGS

SC.6.E.7.4

Complete the Quest!

Determine the best way to present your findings with data and evidence, such as a map or a multimedia presentation.

Summarize   How does a forest fire demonstrate how the different spheres of Earth interact with each other?

....

....

....

....

....

....

....

👆 **INTERACTIVITY**

Reflect on Forest Fires

141

SC.6.E.7.4, SC.6.N.1.1, SC.6.N.3.4

Modeling a Watershed

How can you **model** the effects of **pollution** on a watershed?

Materials

(per group)

- small wooden or plastic blocks
- paper or plastic drinking cups
- newspaper
- markers
- craft sticks
- plastic CD cases
- light paper
- aluminum foil
- plastic wrap
- large pan
- water
- red food coloring
- metric ruler
- tape
- digital camera (optional)
- goggles
- apron
- gloves

Background

A factory has released pollutants into a nearby river. You discovered dead fish far downstream from the factory. But the factory claims that it can't be responsible because the fish were found so far away. You have been asked to help biologists demonstrate that when contaminated water enters one part of a watershed, it can affect the entire watershed.

In this investigation, you will model the effects of pollution on surface water in a watershed and demonstrate the importance of protecting watershed areas.

Procedure

HANDS-ON LAB

ⁿ**Demonstrate** Go online for a downloadable worksheet of this lab.

☐ 1. Use the materials provided by your teacher to design and build a model watershed for your demonstration. Use a camera or drawings to record and analyze information to show how pollution affects an entire watershed.

☐ 2. Consider the following questions before you begin planning your model:

- How can the materials help you to model a watershed?

- How will you form highlands in your model?

- How can you include streams and rivers in your model?

- How can you use food coloring to represent the effects of pollution on surface water in the watershed?

- What are some ways that a watershed can be polluted?

☐ 3. Once you have worked out a design, draw a sketch of your model. Label the objects in your model and identify the materials you are using.

☐ 4. Write a short procedure that details the steps you will follow to model how pollution can affect surface water in a watershed.

☐ 5. Once your teacher has approved your design and procedure, carry out the investigation. If possible, use a camera to photograph your model during the investigation. Record observations about how your model represents the effects of pollution in a watershed.

Sketch   Design and sketch your model here.

Observations

....
....
....
....
....
....
....
....
....
....
....
....

Analyze and Interpret Data

1. **Use Models** Describe the path that the food coloring took through your model. What does the pattern of the food coloring's path tell you about the effect of pollution on surface water in a watershed? Based on your observations and evidence, could the factory's pollution have caused the fish to die?

....

....

....

....

2. **Cause and Effect** What other human activity takes place in the watersheds that might lead to pollution?

....

....

....

3. **Identify Limitations** Compare your model to other models. How can you improve your model based on other examples? What parts of a watershed, if any, are missing from your model?

....

....

....

4. **Construct Explanations** Explain the importance of laws that restrict and punish individuals or businesses that pollute healthy watersheds. Include a description of any cause-and-effect relationships that you think scientists might observe when pollutants are introduced into a watershed area. Use your model and your observations in this lab as evidence for your answer.

....

....

....

....

....

TOPIC
4

Energy in the Atmosphere and Ocean

SC.6.E.7.1 Differentiate among radiation, conduction, and convection, the three mechanisms by which heat is transferred through Earth's system.

SC.6.E.7.3 Describe how global patterns such as the jet stream and ocean currents influence local weather in measurable terms such as temperature, air pressure, wind direction and speed, and humidity and precipitation.

SC.6.E.7.5 Explain how energy provided by the sun influences global patterns of atmospheric movement and the temperature differences between air, water, and land.

SC.6.E.7.8 Describe ways human beings protect themselves from hazardous weather and sun exposure.

SC.6.E.7.9 Describe how the composition and structure of the atmosphere protects life and insulates the planet. (Also **SC.6.N.1.1**, **SC.6.N.1.5**, and **SC.6.N.3.4**)

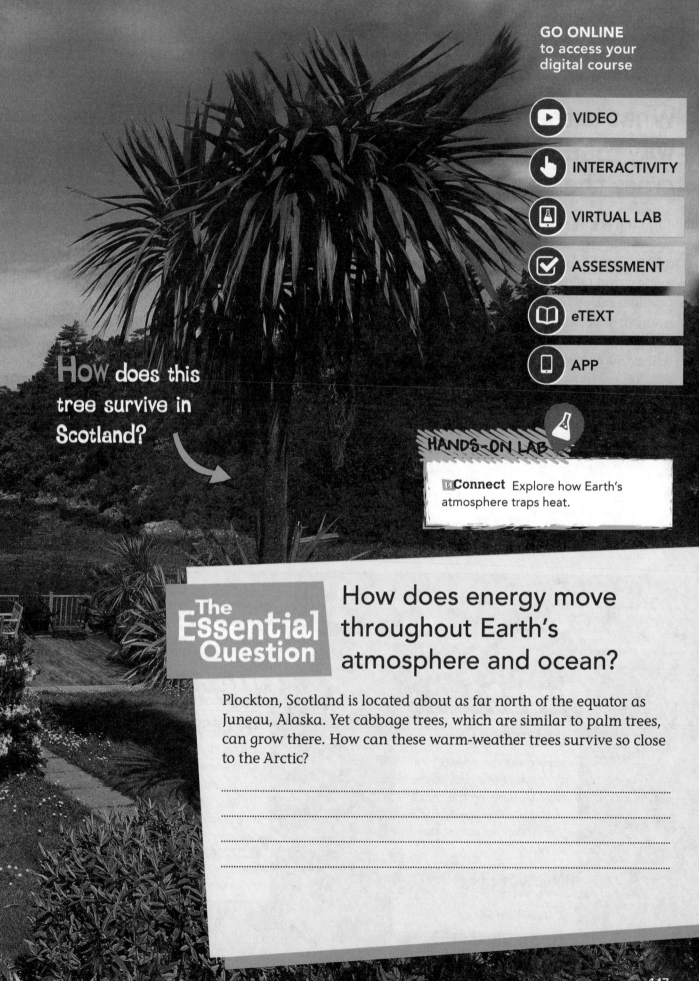

GO ONLINE
to access your
digital course

▶ VIDEO

👆 INTERACTIVITY

🔬 VIRTUAL LAB

☑ ASSESSMENT

📖 eTEXT

📱 APP

How does this tree survive in Scotland?

HANDS-ON LAB

🔲**Connect** Explore how Earth's atmosphere traps heat.

The Essential Question

How does energy move throughout Earth's atmosphere and ocean?

Plockton, Scotland is located about as far north of the equator as Juneau, Alaska. Yet cabbage trees, which are similar to palm trees, can grow there. How can these warm-weather trees survive so close to the Arctic?

....

....

....

....

Quest KICKOFF

What is the most efficient way for a container ship to cross the Atlantic?

Shipping is a very cost-effective mode of transporting goods. But trips across the ocean can be dangerous, and it is up to the ship's captain and its officers to plan and follow safe navigation routes. In this problem-based Quest activity, you will plot a round-trip ocean journey across the Atlantic Ocean for a container ship. In digital activities and labs, you will evaluate data on fuel consumption and the effects of wind patterns and ocean currents. Finally, you will develop and present a recommended route.

 INTERACTIVITY

Crossing the Atlantic

 SC.6.E.7.5 Explain how energy provided by the sun influences global patterns of atmospheric movement and the temperature differences between air, water, and land. (Also **SC.6.N.1.5** and **SC.6.N.3.4**)

NBC LEARN ▶ VIDEO

After watching the Quest Kickoff video about the work involved in navigating a ship, identify three dangers a container ship might face at sea.

1

....

....

....

2

....

....

....

3

....

....

....

....

Quest CHECK-IN

IN LESSON 1

How does the speed of a ship affect the cost of the trip? Determine the most cost-effective speed for a ship traveling across the Atlantic.

HANDS-ON LAB

Choose Your Speed

Quest CHECK-IN

IN LESSON 2

How does wind affect a ship's speed? Consider how using wind can help to decrease the time of the ship's journey.

 INTERACTIVITY

Wind at Your Back

Each container on this ship is equivalent to the back of a semi-trailer truck.

Quest FINDINGS

Complete the Quest!

Present your recommended route and explain the factors that you considered when planning the route.

 INTERACTIVITY

Reflect on Crossing the Atlantic

Quest CHECK-IN

IN LESSON 3

How do global ocean currents affect navigation routes? Analyze the patterns of currents in the northern Atlantic Ocean, and then finalize your route.

 INTERACTIVITY

Find Your Advantage

Energy in Earth's Atmosphere

Guiding Questions

- How does the sun's energy reach and move through Earth's atmosphere?
- How is heat transferred in Earth's atmosphere?
- What role does the atmosphere play in allowing life to thrive on Earth?

Connections

Literacy Determine Central Ideas

Math Convert Measurement Units

SC.6.E.7.1 Differentiate among radiation, conduction, and convection, the three mechanisms by which heat is transferred through Earth's system.

SC.6.E.7.8 Describe ways human beings protect themselves from hazardous weather and sun exposure.

SC.6.E.7.9 Describe how the composition and structure of the atmosphere protects life and insulates the planet. (Also **SC.6.N.1.1**, **SC.6.N.1.5**, and **SC.6.N.3.4**)

Vocabulary

electromagnetic wave
greenhouse effect
thermal energy
convection
conduction
radiation

Academic Vocabulary

absorb

 VOCABULARY APP

Practice vocabulary on a mobile device.

Quest CONNECTION

Think about the most cost-effective speed for a ship crossing the Atlantic.

Connect It!

 Circle the correct terms to complete the statement in the box.

Draw Conclusions Suppose you observe puddles on the ground after a brief rainstorm. A few hours after the sun comes out, the puddles are no longer there. What has happened to them?

....

....

....

Energy from the Sun

Most of the energy that is moving within Earth's atmosphere and across Earth's surface comes from the sun. The sun's energy travels to Earth as electromagnetic radiation, a form of energy that can move through the vacuum of space. **Electromagnetic waves** consist of an electric field and a magnetic field.

When you use a microwave oven or watch television, you are using the energy created by electromagnetic waves. The waves are classified according to wavelength, or distance between wave peaks. Most of the electromagnetic waves that travel from the sun and reach Earth are in the form of visible light, which you can see in **Figure 1,** and infrared radiation. A smaller amount arrives as ultraviolet (UV) radiation.

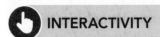

INTERACTIVITY

Investigate how sand and water absorb light energy.

Electromagnetic Waves

Figure 1 Energy from the sun travels to Earth in the form of radiation.

Sunlight (warms / cools) the ice, causing it to (freeze / melt).

Academic Vocabulary
What other things can be absorbed?

....

....

....

....

....

....

Literacy Connection

Determine Central Ideas
As you proceed through the lesson, keep track of how energy moves and changes by underlining relevant sentences or passages.

Sunlight and the Atmosphere

In order for the sun's energy to reach Earth's surface and sustain life, it must first get through the atmosphere. Earth's atmosphere is divided into layers based on temperature. Some sunlight is **absorbed** or reflected by the different levels of the atmosphere before it can reach the surface, as shown in **Figure 2**.

Some UV wavelengths are absorbed by the topmost layer of the atmosphere, called the thermosphere. More UV energy, along with some infrared energy, is absorbed in the next layer, the mesosphere. Below that, in the stratosphere, ozone absorbs more infrared and UV energy. Without the ozone layer, too much UV radiation would reach Earth's surface and threaten the health of organisms. However, the amount of UV radiation that reaches Earth's surface can still be damaging, which is why humans benefit from wearing clothing, sunscreen, and sunglasses.

By the time sunlight reaches the troposphere, there is some infrared radiation, some UV radiation, and visible light. Some light has been reflected into space by clouds. The daytime sky on a cloudless day appears blue because gas molecules scatter short wavelengths of visible light, which are blue and violet, more than the longer red and orange wavelengths.

Layers of Atmosphere
Figure 2 Much of the energy in sunlight that reaches the atmosphere does not reach Earth's surface.

Make Inferences What would happen if all of the sun's energy were to reach Earth?

....

....

....

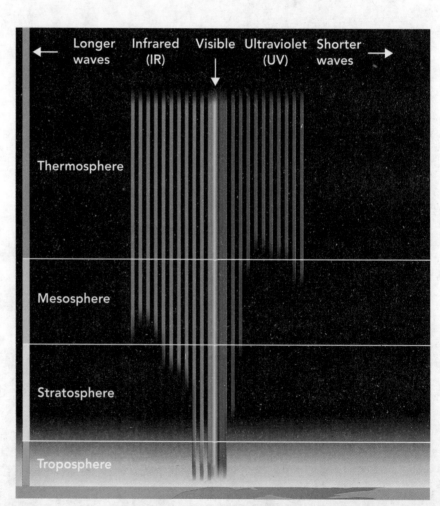

Earth's Energy Budget Of the radiation that travels from the sun to the troposphere, only about 50 percent is absorbed by land and water and converted, or transformed, to heat. The rest, as shown in **Figure 3**, is reflected by clouds and other particles in the atmosphere (25%), absorbed by gases and particles (20%), or reflected by the surface itself (5%). Snow, ice, and liquid water reflect some sunlight back into the atmosphere, where some will be absorbed by clouds and particles that the energy missed on the way down.

Only a tiny fraction of the visible light that reaches Earth's surface is transformed to chemical energy in plants and other photosynthetic organisms. The rest is absorbed by Earth and re-emitted into the atmosphere as infrared radiation. Earth's surface absorbs and re-emits equal amounts of energy so that its energy remains in balance over time.

☑ READING CHECK **Determine Central Ideas** Describe the atmosphere's role in moderating the amount of electromagnetic radiation necessary to sustain life on Earth.

....

....

The Sun's Energy
Figure 3 🖊 Label the different percentages of energy that are absorbed or reflected.

Make Meaning

When the sun goes down, a real-world greenhouse may need an alternative source of light or heat to keep the plants alive. How is this similar to Earth's surface at night?

The Greenhouse Effect Have you ever been to a greenhouse to buy plants? The glass walls and roof of a greenhouse allow sunlight inside. Some sunlight is absorbed by plants and transformed into chemical energy. Most of the sunlight is converted to heat. Much of the heat is contained by the glass panes of the greenhouse, keeping the interior at an acceptable temperature for plant growth.

Earth's atmosphere plays a similar role. Sunlight is absorbed and transformed into heat within the atmosphere and in the materials at Earth's surface, such as rock and water. The surface reradiates all of that energy, and Earth's total energy remains in balance over time. (Otherwise, Earth would continually heat up and turn into molten rock.) Gases in the atmosphere trap some of the heat near Earth's surface, while some heat escapes into space. This **greenhouse effect** is shown in **Figure 4**.

Overall, Earth's atmosphere keeps our planet at a temperature that is adequate to support life. Organisms are adapted to specific ranges of temperatures. Surface features such as the sea level and the amounts of trapped ice have been relatively constant for thousands of years. However, changes to the composition of the atmosphere—those gases that absorb the infrared energy radiated from Earth's surface—can result in changes in temperature. Most scientists who study the atmosphere and the climate think that humans have been enhancing the greenhouse effect by increasing the amounts of carbon dioxide and methane in the atmosphere. This has caused an increase in the average temperature of Earth, which in turn is causing changes to sea level and melting ice in polar regions and in glaciers.

Earth as a Greenhouse

Figure 4 Fill in the boxes in the diagram to describe how the atmosphere, Earth's surface, sunlight, and space interact.

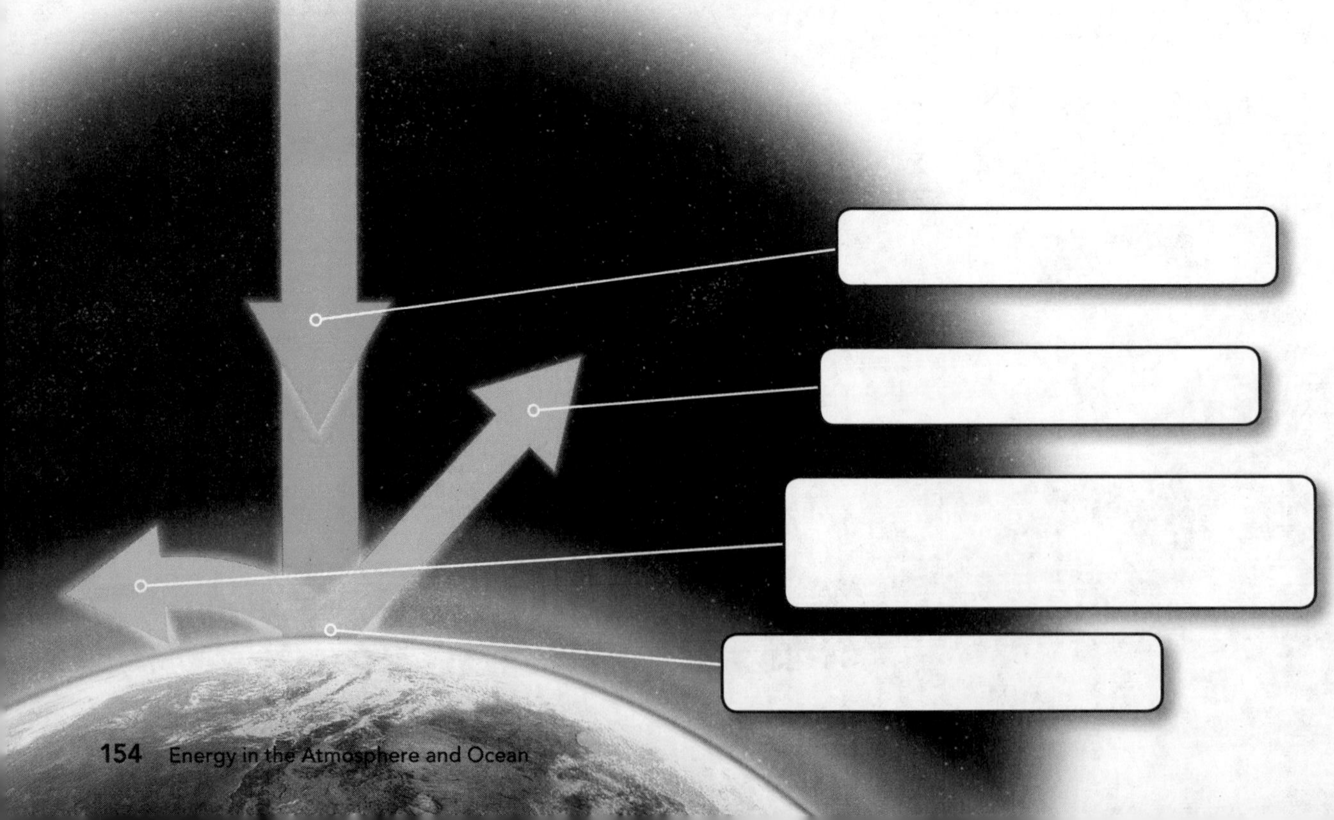

Daily Air Temperature

Convert Measurement Units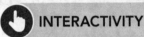
Grace records the air temperature throughout the day in a table. Convert Grace's measurements from degrees Fahrenheit (°F) to degrees Celsius (°C) using the formula shown below.

$$(\text{Temp } °F - 32) \times \frac{5}{9} = \text{Temp } °C$$

Time	Temperature	
	°F	°C
8:00 AM	52	
11:00 PM	56	
2:00 PM	60	
5:00 PM	55	
8:00 PM	50	

Heat Transfer in the Atmosphere

All matter is made up of particles that are constantly moving. The faster the particles move, the more energy they have. Temperature is the *average* amount of energy of motion of each particle of a substance. **Thermal energy** is the total energy of motion in the particles of a substance.

It may seem odd to think that particles in solids are moving, but they are vibrating in place. Even the water molecules in a block of ice, or the atoms of iron and carbon in a steel beam, are moving ever so slightly.

When a substance reaches its melting point, the substance has enough energy of motion to reach a new state—liquid. And when the substance reaches its boiling point, it changes into a gas, which has even more energy of motion. The energy that first reaches Earth as sunlight drives many processes on Earth, including the freezing, melting, and evaporation of water.

✅READING CHECK **Determine Conclusions** Which has more thermal energy: a 1-kilogram block of ice or a 1-kilogram volume of water vapor? Why?

....

....

INTERACTIVITY

Find out how convection currents form in the atmosphere.

HANDS-ON LAB

☑**Investigate** Develop and test a hypothesis about the heating and cooling rates of land and water.

▶ VIDEO

Explore radiation, conduction, and convection.

Methods of Heat Transfer

We often talk about heat as though it is the same as thermal energy. Heat is actually energy that transfers into an object's thermal energy. Heat only flows from a hotter object to a cooler one. Heat transfers in three ways: **convection**, **conduction**, and **radiation,** as shown in **Figure 5**.

Things Are Heating Up
Figure 5 A campfire can illustrate all three types of heat transfer.

Convection

In fluids such as a hot campfire's smoke, particles move easily from one place to another, taking energy with them. Convection is the transfer of heat by the movement of a fluid.

Convection

Radiation

The transfer of energy by electromagnetic waves is called radiation. The energy that is transferred from the sun to Earth is radiation. Likewise, the light and heat that are emitted by a campfire to toast a marshmallow or cook a hot dog is radiation.

Conduction

Radiation

Conduction

The transfer of heat between two substances that are in direct contact, such a between a hot metal prong and a hot dog or your hand, is called conduction. The closer together the molecules are in a substance, the better they conduct heat. This is why conduction works well in some solids, such as metals, but not as well in liquids and gases whose particles are farther apart.

Heat Transfer at Earth's Surface

The sun's radiation is transformed at Earth's surface into thermal energy. The surface may get warmer than the air above it. Air doesn't conduct heat well. So only the first few centimeters of the troposphere are heated by conduction from Earth's surface to the air. When ground-level air warms up, its molecules move more rapidly. As they bump into each other, they move farther apart, making the air less dense. The warmer, less-dense air rises, and cooler, denser air from above sinks toward the surface.

The cool air then gets warmed by the surface, and the cycle continues. If the source of heat is isolated in one place, a convection current can develop. This occurs in Earth's atmosphere as a result of radiation, conduction, and convection working together. The horizontal movement of the convection current in the atmosphere is what we call wind. Convection currents are especially powerful if Earth's radiant surface is much warmer than the air above it. This is related to why storms can arise much more suddenly and be more severe in warmer regions of Earth. For example, hurricanes tend to form in tropical areas where the sea is very warm and the air above it is relatively cool.

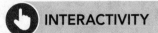
INTERACTIVITY

Discover patterns in the wind and how they relate to energy transfer in the atmosphere.

☑ **READING CHECK** **Translate Information** Explain how a pot of heated water could demonstrate convection.

....

....

....

Model It!

Develop Models ✏ Use different arrows or other illustration techniques to draw the three types of heat transfer that are occurring at this beach. Label each type of heat transfer.

☑ LESSON 1 Check

SC.6.E.7.1, SC.6.E.7.8, SC.6.E.7.9

1. **Identify** What three types of heat transfer occur on Earth?

   ....

   ....

2. **Construct an Explanation** If the amounts of carbon dioxide and methane continue to increase in Earth's atmosphere, what will happen to Florida's coastline? Explain.

   ....

   ....

   ....

   ....

3. **Summarize** How do the gases in Earth's atmosphere keep the amount of energy that Earth receives from the sun from being too much, or more than Earth and its organisms can tolerate?

   ....

   ....

   ....

   ....

   ....

4. **Plan an Investigation** The manufacturer of a new convection oven claims that his product will bake things 25 percent faster than a conventional oven that relies mainly on radiation. How could you test this claim?

   ....

   ....

   ....

   ....

   ....

   ....

   ....

5. **Design a Solution** You want some ice cream, but the carton you removed from the freezer is frozen solid. It's difficult to dig the metal ice cream scooper into the ice cream. How could you apply what you know about heat transfer to get some ice cream without waiting?

   ....

   ....

   ....

   ....

   ....

𝒬𝓊𝑒𝓈𝓉 CHECK-IN

In this lesson, you learned how the sun's energy is reflected, absorbed, transformed, and transferred by Earth's atmosphere and surface.

Evaluate Why is it important to know how the sun's energy affects the lower atmosphere if you are planning to harness the power of moving air?

....

....

....

....

HANDS-ON LAB

Choose Your Speed

Do the Hands-On Lab to determine the most cost-effective speed for a ship traveling across the Atlantic and how the sun's energy affects moving air.

Measure Radiation with a Cube

This RAVAN can measure incoming energy from the sun and outgoing energy from Earth in the form of radiation. A difference in the amounts, called Earth's radiation imbalance, can affect the planet's climate.

Right now, satellites the size of toasters are circling Earth. Each one is collecting data about the planet's atmosphere. These small cube satellites, or CubeSats, give scientists a new way to measure changes in Earth's climate. Different teams have built their own CubeSats, even students.

One team launched a CubeSat called RAVAN to measure the amount of radiation energy leaving Earth's atmosphere. Data from the satellite will allow the team to compare the amount of energy coming in from the sun with the amount of energy leaving Earth. This energy balance reveals a lot about Earth's climate. So tracking the energy balance will help scientists to predict future climate changes.

RAVAN is only the beginning. The team hopes to launch 30 to 40 cubes that will collect data from every part of Earth's atmosphere.

MY DISCOVERY

Anyone can submit an idea for a CubeSat to NASA. Elementary students at St. Thomas More Cathedral School in Arlington, Virginia, built, tested, and launched their own CubeSat. Everyone in the entire school participated for more than three years to launch it. Search the Internet to learn more about the St. Thomas More CubeSat. Can you think of a school project where a CubeSat would come in handy?

CubeSats are so small that most of their scientific instruments are about the size of a deck of cards.

LESSON

2 Patterns of Circulation in the Atmosphere

Guiding Questions

- What causes winds?
- How does the sun's energy affect wind characteristics?
- How do winds redistribute energy around Earth?

Connections

Literacy Translate Information

Math Analyze Relationships Using Tables

 SC.6.E.7.3 Describe how global patterns such as the jet stream and ocean currents influence local weather in measurable terms such as temperature, air pressure, wind direction and speed, and humidity and precipitation.

SC.6.E.7.5 Explain how energy provided by the sun influences global patterns of atmospheric movement and the temperature differences between air, water, and land. (Also **SC.6.N.1.1**, **SC.6.N.1.5**, and **SC.6.N.3.4**)

Vocabulary

wind
sea breeze
land breeze
Coriolis effect
jet stream

Academic Vocabulary

area
model

 VOCABULARY APP

Practice vocabulary on a mobile device.

Quest CONNECTION

Consider how wind might affect a container ship on the ocean.

Connect It !

✏ **Without wind, there wouldn't be any kite surfing. Draw an arrow to show the direction you think the wind is blowing.**

Construct Explanations What are some ways that you rely on the wind?

....

....

....

Winds

The surfer in **Figure 1** is moving over the top of a fluid, water. But the surfer is also moving through another fluid, called air. Air, like water, flows from place to place and does not have a fixed shape. But what causes air to flow?

Causes of Winds

Air, like most things, moves away from high pressure **areas** to low pressure areas. When there is a difference in air pressure, air moves and wind is created. **Wind** is the movement of air parallel to Earth's surface.

Higher and lower pressure areas are results of the unequal heating of the atmosphere. Air over the heated surface expands, becomes less dense, and rises. As the warm air rises, its air pressure decreases. Meanwhile, if another area is not heated as much, then the air in that area is cooler and denser. The denser air sinks and air pressure increases. The cool, dense air with a higher pressure flows underneath the warm, less dense air. This difference in pressure forces the warm air to rise.

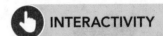

INTERACTIVITY

Explore how Earth's rotation affects wind.

Academic Vocabulary

The word *area* is used in mathematics and in everyday life. How are the two ways to use the word *area* related?

....

....

....

....

Catching the Wind
Figure 1 Kite surfers need wind to move across the water.

Anemometer

Figure 2 The higher the wind speed, the faster the cups spin around on the anemometer, shown in the top left side of the image.

Measuring Wind Wind is a valuable resource, and understanding wind can put this resource to work for us. To identify winds, they are named using the direction from which they originate and their speed. A wind vane is helpful in seeing which way the wind is blowing. The arrow on the wind vane points in the direction from which the wind is blowing. Winds can blow from any of the four directions: north, south, east, and west, and they are named by the direction from which they are blowing. For example, a north wind blows from the north to the south.

Wind speed and pressure can be measured with an anemometer like the one in **Figure 2**. An anemometer has three or four cups mounted at the ends of horizontal spokes that spin on an axle. The force of the wind against the cups turns the axle. The anemometer tracks the number of rotations, and that number is used to calculate wind speed.

☑ READING CHECK **Summarize Text** What causes wind?

....

....

Math Toolbox

Windchill Factor

The wind blowing over your skin removes body heat. The increased cooling that a wind causes is called the windchill factor.

1. Analyze Relationships Using Tables A weather reporter says, "It is 20 degrees Fahrenheit. But with a wind speed of 30 miles per hour, the windchill factor makes it feel much colder." Use the table to determine how cold the air will feel with the windchill factor accounted for.

....

2. Predict Will it feel colder with an air temperature of 15°F with wind speeds of 40 mph or with an air temperature of 10°F with wind speeds of 25 mph? Explain.

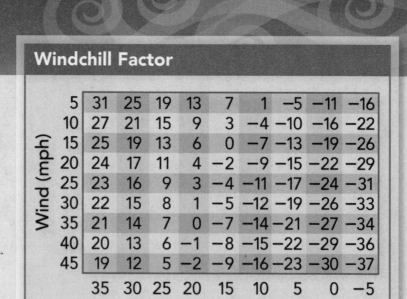

Windchill Factor

Wind (mph)	35	30	25	20	15	10	5	0	−5
5	31	25	19	13	7	1	−5	−11	−16
10	27	21	15	9	3	−4	−10	−16	−22
15	25	19	13	6	0	−7	−13	−19	−26
20	24	17	11	4	−2	−9	−15	−22	−29
25	23	16	9	3	−4	−11	−17	−24	−31
30	22	15	8	1	−5	−12	−19	−26	−33
35	21	14	7	0	−7	−14	−21	−27	−34
40	20	13	6	−1	−8	−15	−22	−29	−36
45	19	12	5	−2	−9	−16	−23	−30	−37

Temperature (°F)

....

Local Winds and Global Winds

Because of Earth's shape, surfaces, and tilt, the sun cannot evenly warm all of Earth at the same time. Different parts of Earth are warmed at different times and rates. This unequal heating and Earth's rotation affect wind and weather conditions on land, both in local areas and over global regions. Scientists use this understanding to make a **model**, such as a diagram or a map, to describe and predict wind patterns and their effects.

Local Winds Have you ever noticed a breeze at the beach on a hot summer day? Even if there is no wind inland, there may be a cool breeze blowing in from the water. Winds that blow over short distances and affect local weather are called local winds. The unequal heating of Earth's surface within a local area causes local winds. These winds form only when the global winds in an area are weak.

Two types of local winds are sea breezes and land breezes, which are illustrated in **Figure 3** below. When sunlight reaches the surface of Earth, land warms up faster than water. The air over the land gets warmer than the air over the water. As you know, warm air is less dense, and it rises, creating a low-pressure area. Cool air blows inland from over the water and moves underneath the warm air, causing a sea breeze. A **sea breeze** or a lake breeze is a local wind that blows from an ocean or lake.

At night, the land cools faster than water. The air above the land begins to cool and move under the warm air rising off the water. The flow of air from land to a body of water forms a **land breeze**.

Academic Vocabulary

Model can be a noun that means "a picture or other representation of a complex object or process." Or it can be a verb that means "to represent something." Write sentences using the term first as a noun and then as a verb.

....

....

....

....

....

Sea Breeze and Land Breeze

Figure 3 🖊 Fill in the labels to indicate how a sea breeze and a land breeze develop.

The .... air rises.

The .... air moves to take .... air's place.

The .... air rises.

At night, the .... air moves off land.

163

INTERACTIVITY

Construct a model to show atmospheric cirulation.

VIDEO

Learn about general circulation and wind belts.

Global Winds

The patterns of winds moving around the globe are called global winds. Like local winds, global winds are created by the unequal heating of Earth's surface. However, unlike local winds, global winds occur over a large area.

Figure 4 models how the sun's radiation strikes Earth. Direct rays from the sun heat Earth's surface intensely near the equator at midday. Near the poles, the sun's rays strike Earth's surface less directly. The sun's energy is spread out over a larger area, so it heats the surface less. As a result, temperatures near the poles are much lower than they are near the equator.

Global winds form from temperature differences between the equator and the poles. These differences produce giant convection currents in the atmosphere. Warm air rises at the equator, and cold air sinks at the poles. Therefore, air pressure tends to be lower near the equator and greater near the poles. This difference in pressure causes winds at Earth's surface to blow from the poles toward the equator. Away from Earth's surface, the opposite is true. Higher in the atmosphere, air flows away from the equator toward the poles. Those air movements produce global winds.

Model It

Earth Is Heating Up

Figure 4 Depending on where you are on Earth's surface, the sun's rays may be stronger or weaker and you may be hotter or colder. These temperature differences produce convection currents in the atmosphere.

1. **Identify** ✏ Label the areas where the sun hits Earth most directly (M) and least directly (L).

2. **Identify** Describe how cool and warm air moves in the atmosphere.

....

....

3. **Develop Models** ✏ Draw a convection current in the atmosphere north of the equator. Use arrows to show the direction of air movement.

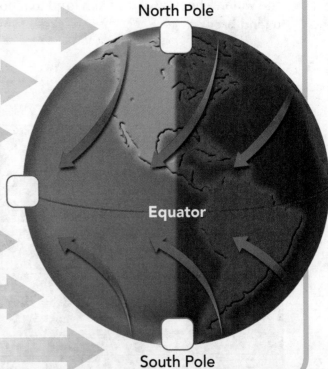

North Pole

Equator

South Pole

Earth's Rotation If Earth did not rotate on its axis, global winds would blow in straight lines. Instead, global winds get deflected or shifted by Earth's rotation. As the winds blow, Earth rotates from west to east underneath them, making it seem as if the winds curve. The way Earth's rotation makes winds curve is called the **Coriolis effect** (kawr ee OH lis ih FEKT) as shown in **Figure 5**. Because of the Coriolis effect, global winds in the Northern Hemisphere gradually turn toward the right. A wind blowing toward the south gradually turns toward the southwest. In the Southern Hemisphere, winds curve toward the left.

INTERACTIVITY

Explain how local wind patterns form.

READING CHECK **Translate Information** How do **Figure 5** and the text support the concept that winds do not follow a straight path due to the Coriolis effect?

....

....

....

....

No rotation

Modeling the Coriolis Effect

Figure 5 The Coriolis effect is the result of Earth's rotation. Without it, global winds would travel in straight lines away from their sources. With it, global winds turn to the right in the Northern Hemisphere and to the left in the Southern Hemisphere.

With rotation

Global Wind Belts

The Coriolis effect, global convection currents, and other factors combine to produce a pattern of calm areas and global wind belts around Earth, as shown in **Figure 6**. The calm areas where air rises or sinks include the doldrums and the horse latitudes. The major global wind belts are the trade winds, the polar easterlies, and the prevailing westerlies. These wind belts are not stationary and can shift about from month to month.

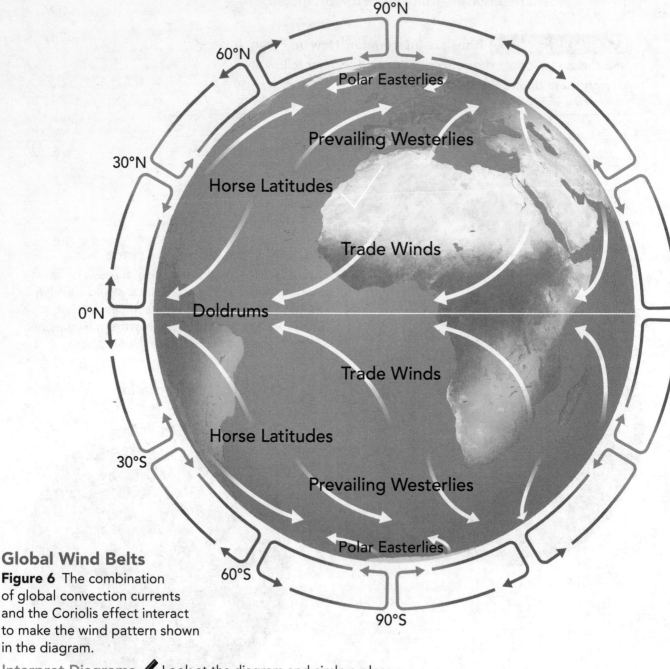

Global Wind Belts

Figure 6 The combination of global convection currents and the Coriolis effect interact to make the wind pattern shown in the diagram.

Interpret Diagrams ✎ Look at the diagram and circle a place where warm air is rising. Draw a square around a place where cool air is sinking. Draw a triangle on a place that shows winds turning right in the Northern hemisphere. Place a check mark on a place where winds along Earth's surface are calm.

Effects of Global Wind Belts Global winds affect local weather by moving masses of air from one place to another. The air masses affect the temperature, rainfall, and air pressure. Overall, the global wind belts move energy away from the equator and toward the poles. This helps to equalize the temperature, allowing life to survive in a larger range of latitudes on Earth.

Jet Streams About 10 kilometers above Earth's surface are bands of high-speed winds called **jet streams**. They generally blow from west to east at speeds of 200 to 400 kilometers per hour. As jet streams travel around Earth, they wander north and south along wavy paths that vary over time.

The jet streams greatly affect local weather. As shown in **Figure 7**, the jet streams traveling over North America bring a variety of weather conditions. Weather forecasters track the jet streams to predict temperature and precipitation. If the polar jet stream wanders farther south than usual in winter, it could mean colder temperatures and snowy conditions for areas north of the jet stream. If the jet stream wanders farther north than usual, then warmer air moves up from the south and warmer temperatures are predicted for areas south of the jet stream.

HANDS-ON LAB

ʀ**Investigate** Explore precipitation in the United States.

Literacy Connection

Translate Information As you read, underline the text that describes how the jet stream pictured in **Figure 7** can be used to predict weather.

Jet Streams

Figure 7 ✏ The changing positions of the jet streams over the United States influence local weather, particularly in winter. The map shows the position of the polar jet stream on a winter day.

1. **Interpret Diagrams** The weather in Boise, Idaho, is most likely (colder/warmer) than usual.

2. **Interpret Diagrams** The weather in Cheyenne, Wyoming, is most likely (colder/warmer) than usual.

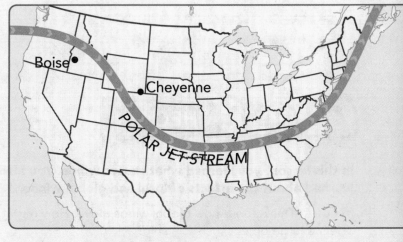

☑ **READING CHECK** **Integrate With Visuals** How does the map help you to understand the path of the jet stream?

....

....

SC.6.E.7.3, SC.6.E.7.5

1. **Identify** What is wind?

....
....
....
....

2. **Develop Models** Describe how you could use a globe and your hand to model the path of a global convection current in the atmosphere.

....
....
....
....
....
....
....
....

3. **Cause and Effect** A storm near Florida turns into a hurricane that spins clockwise. How is this related to the rotation of Earth?

....
....
....
....
....
....
....

4. **Predict** It's a hot, sunny morning in a coastal town in South Florida. Warm air is rising up from the land. Large, puffy clouds are forming overhead. Which way do you think the wind will be moving this afternoon, and what do you think will happen to the temperature?

....
....
....
....
....

Quest CHECK-IN

In this lesson, you learned what causes winds. You also learned about the effects of local and global winds.

Predict Think about how global winds move. How might they affect a large object such as a ship?

....
....
....
....

INTERACTIVITY

Wind at Your Back

Go online to explain why a container ship's captain might want to travel in the direction the wind is blowing rather than against the wind.

Windmills of the Future

 VIDEO

Visualize the inner workings of a turbine.

Windmills are great when winds are steady and strong. But how can you capture energy from swirling winds? You engineer it!

The Challenge: To make a wind turbine that produces electricity from swirling winds.

A company in Spain has come up with a way to capture swirling winds. As wind moves around a tall, slim mast, it vibrates. Magnets located inside a cone at the top of the mast amplify this movement. When wind pushes the mast one way, the magnets push it in the opposite direction so that the whole turbine swirls. The energy of this movement is then converted to electricity. The turbine works no matter the wind direction or speed.

This new turbine needs only a mast, which means no spinning blades, so it doesn't pose a danger to birds and is totally silent. It also costs less, because there are fewer parts to make and maintain. And many more bladeless turbines can fit in one area, so they won't take up as much space. One day soon, forests of these windmills of the future may capture wind energy in a location near you!

The circular mast is light enough to oscillate due to the wind.

The carbon-fiber rod is strong, but also flexible.

The generator housed inside the bottom of the mast converts the mast's motion into electricity.

 **DESIGN CHALLENGE**

Can you design and build a wind turbine? Go to the Engineering Design Notebook to find out!

3 Patterns of Circulation in the Ocean

Guiding Questions

- What causes ocean currents?
- How do ocean currents redistribute Earth's energy?

Connections

Literacy Integrate With Visuals

Math Analyze Quantitative Relationships

SC.6.E.7.3 Describe how global patterns such as the jet stream and ocean currents influence local weather in measurable terms such as temperature, air pressure, wind direction and speed, and humidity and precipitation. (Also **SC.6.N.1.1**, **SC.6.N.1.5**, and **SC.6.N.3.4**)

Vocabulary

current
El Niño
La Niña

Academic Vocabulary

gradually

 VOCABULARY APP

Practice vocabulary on a mobile device.

Quest CONNECTION

Think about how global ocean currents might affect a container ship's navigation route.

Connect It!

✏️ **In the space provided, identify how you think ocean currents, water temperature, and weather might affect a sea turtle.**

Apply Scientific Reasoning How do factors such as ocean currents, water temperature, and weather affect you in your daily life?

....

....

....

Surface Currents

You probably know that ocean water moves as waves. It also flows as currents. A **current** is a large stream of moving water that flows through the ocean. Both waves and currents can affect ocean ecosystems, such as the one shown in **Figure 1**. Unlike waves, currents carry water from one place to another. Some currents move water deep in the ocean. Other currents, called surface currents, move water at the surface of the ocean.

Surface currents are driven mainly by global winds and affect water to a depth of several hundred meters. They follow Earth's global wind patterns. Surface currents move in circular patterns in the five major ocean basins.

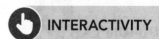
INTERACTIVITY

Describe what it would be like to swim against a current.

Riding the Currents
Figure 1 Sea turtles travel long distances by riding ocean currents.

weather

ocean currents

water temperature

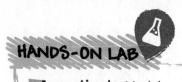

Investigate Model how surface and deep ocean currents form.

Reflect Along which surface current in **Figure 2** would you most like to float in a boat? In your science notebook, explain why.

Factors Affecting Surface Currents

Global wind belts affect surface currents. Unequal heating and the rotation of Earth combine to produce global wind belts. Because global winds drive surface currents, unequal heating and Earth's rotation also drive patterns of ocean circulation. Warm currents moving away from the equator redistribute energy to keep temperatures moderate. Cold currents move toward the equator to complete the circle, as shown in **Figure 2**.

You learned that as Earth rotates, the paths of global winds curve. This effect, known as the Coriolis effect, also applies to surface currents. In the Northern Hemisphere, the Coriolis effect causes the currents to curve to the right. In the Southern Hemisphere, the Coriolis effect causes the currents to curve to the left.

As ocean currents are moved by the winds, the continents stop the movements and redirect the currents. Winds push currents, but once the currents meet land, they have to find a new path.

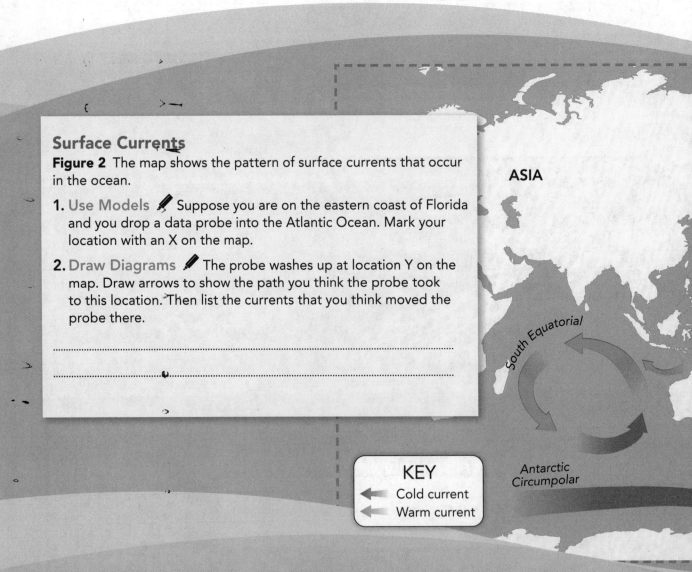

Surface Currents

Figure 2 The map shows the pattern of surface currents that occur in the ocean.

1. Use Models ✏ Suppose you are on the eastern coast of Florida and you drop a data probe into the Atlantic Ocean. Mark your location with an X on the map.

2. Draw Diagrams ✏ The probe washes up at location Y on the map. Draw arrows to show the path you think the probe took to this location. Then list the currents that you think moved the probe there.

....

....

ASIA

South Equatorial

KEY
← Cold current
← Warm current

Antarctic Circumpolar

Effects on Climate The Gulf Stream is the largest and most powerful surface current in the North Atlantic Ocean. It originates from the Gulf of Mexico and brings warm water up the east coast of North America and across the Atlantic. This large, warm current is caused by powerful winds from the west and is more than 30 kilometers wide and 300 meters deep. When the Gulf Stream crosses the Atlantic, it becomes the North Atlantic Drift.

The Gulf Stream and other surface currents redistribute heat from the equator to the poles. These currents have a great impact on local weather and climates. Climate is the temperature and precipitation typical of an area over a long period of time. For example, the North Atlantic Drift brings warm water to Northern Europe. The warm water radiates heat and brings warm temperatures and wet weather. This is why England is warmer and wetter than other countries at the same latitude, such as Canada and Russia. In a similar way, when cold surface currents bring cold water, they cool the air above them. Because cold air holds less moisture than warm air, it results in a cool and dry climate for the land areas.

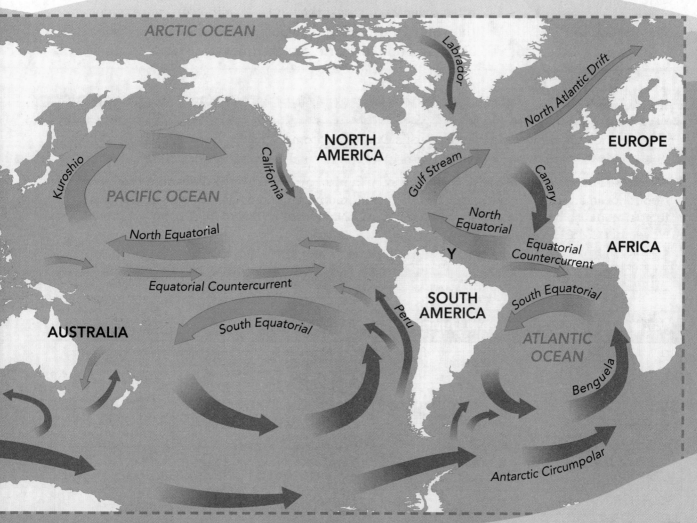

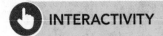

INTERACTIVITY

Discover how deep ocean currents affect weather and climate.

El Niño

Figure 3 The image shows the surface temperatures of water in the Pacific Ocean during the 2015–2016 El Niño. Red indicates the warmest temperatures and blue the coolest.

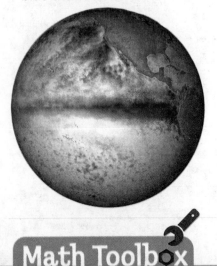

El Niño and La Niña Changes in wind patterns and ocean currents can have major impacts on weather conditions on nearby land. One example is **El Niño**, a climate event that occurs every two to seven years in the Pacific Ocean.

Near the equator, winds usually blow east to west. During El Niño, the winds along the equator weaken and reverse direction. This change allows warm, tropical water from the Pacific Ocean to flow east toward the South American coast and prevents the cold, deep water from moving to the surface. El Niño conditions can last for one to two years.

El Niño's effects on the atmosphere and ocean cause shifts in weather patterns. The most recent El Niño in 2015 and 2016, shown in **Figure 3**, was one of the three strongest on record. It increased rainfall and snowfall in California and caused flooding in California and Texas.

When surface waters in the eastern Pacific are colder than normal, a climate event known as **La Niña** occurs. A La Niña event is the opposite of an El Niño event. During a La Niña, stronger winds blow above the Pacific Ocean, causing more warm water to move west. This allows lots of cold water to rise to the surface. This change in the ocean temperature affects weather all over the world. La Niña can cause colder than normal winters and greater precipitation in the Pacific Northwest and the north central United States.

Math Toolbox

Analyzing El Niño Data

The graph shows how much warmer the Pacific Ocean was from 2015 to 2016 than the average temperature from 1981 to 2010.

1. **Analyze Quantitative Relationships** About how many degrees did water temperature rise between January and November 2015?

....

....

2. **Interpret Diagrams** Why does the temperature most likely decrease between November 2015 and April 2016?

....

....

....

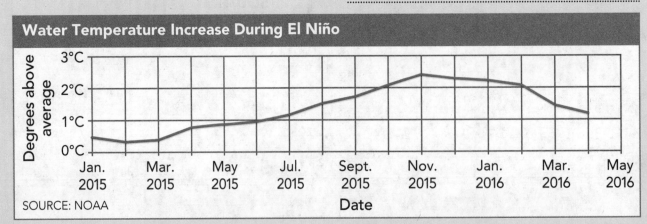

Water Temperature Increase During El Niño

SOURCE: NOAA

Deep Ocean Currents

Deep below the ocean surface, another type of current causes the movement of cold waters across the ocean floor. Deep currents are caused by differences in the density of ocean water.

Temperature, Salinity, and Density The density of ocean water varies with its temperature and salinity. Water is dense if it is cold or salty. Dense water sinks, which drives deep ocean currents. When a warm surface current moves from the equator toward one of the poles, it **gradually** gets denser because it both cools and becomes saltier as water evaporates. As ice forms near the poles (see **Figure 4**), the salinity of the water increases even further. This is because the ice contains only fresh water, leaving the salts in the water. The cold salty water sinks and flows along the ocean floor as a deep current. Like surface currents, deep currents are affected by the Coriolis effect, which causes them to curve.

Deep currents move and mix water around the world. They carry cold water from the poles toward the equator. Deep currents flow slowly. They may take longer than 1,000 years to make one full trip around their ocean basins.

INTERACTIVITY

Explore ocean habitats.

Academic Vocabulary
Use the term *gradually* in a sentence describing Earth's movements.

....

....

....

....

Sea Ice
Figure 4 Sea ice forms different shapes. This ice is called pancake ice.

Plan It !

Sea Ice and Salinity
Plan Your Investigation How can you use the set up below to investigate how ice formation affects the salinity of ocean water? Summarize your plan.

....

....

Make Observations 🖊 Each glass of water contains the same amount of salt. Circle the glass that contains water with the greatest salinity?

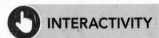

Global Ocean Conveyor

The ocean currents move in a loop around Earth's bodies of water. The movement looks like a conveyor belt, as shown in **Figure 5**, and results from density differences due to variations in temperature and salinity. The movement of the currents circulates oxygen that is essential for marine life.

The ocean's deep currents mostly start as cold water in the North Atlantic Ocean. This is the same water, called the North Atlantic Deep Water, that moved north across the Atlantic as part of the Gulf Stream. It sinks and flows southward toward Antarctica. From there it flows northward into both the Indian and Pacific oceans. There, deep cold water rises to the surface, warms, and eventually flows back along the surface into the Atlantic.

This system circulates water and transfers heat throughout the interconnected ocean basins and thus around Earth from the equator to the poles and back again.

✓ READING CHECK **Integrate With Visuals** How does the map in **Figure 5** relate to the text on this page?

....

....

Global Conveyor Belt

Figure 5 Deep currents and surface currents form a global system of heat distribution through Earth's interconnected ocean basins.

1. **Develop Models** 🖊 Draw arrows on the conveyor to indicate the direction of both cold and warm water movement.

2. **Predict** What might happen if the global conveyor stopped?

....

....

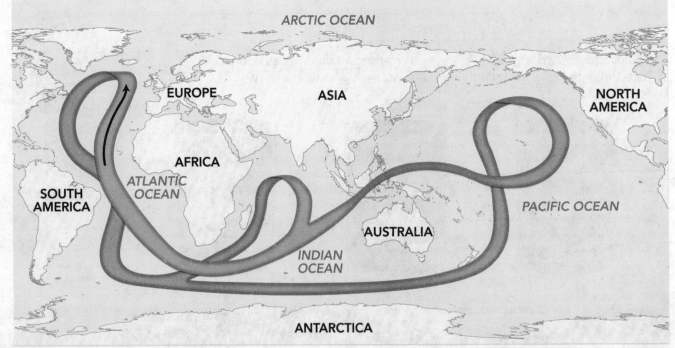

1. **Identify** What is the main driver of surface currents in the ocean?

....

2. **Patterns** What is the connection between the direction in which many surface currents move in the Northern Hemisphere and the direction of global winds?

....

....

....

3. **Construct an Explanation** Why are the west coasts of England, Ireland, and Norway warmer and wetter than the inland areas of the same countries or even parts of Europe that lie further the south?

....

....

....

....

....

4. **Plan an Investigation** Suppose you were being sent to another country to study the weather of a coastal region. Describe what you would want to know about global patterns of ocean winds and currents before focusing on the specific region.

....

....

....

....

....

....

....

....

....

....

....

....

Quest CHECK-IN

In this lesson, you learned about how surface currents and deep ocean currents form. You also discovered how they affect weather and climate.

Apply Concepts Which ocean currents are most likely to affect your container ship? Why?

....

....

....

....

....

....

👆 **INTERACTIVITY**

Find Your Advantage

Go online to analyze the path of the Gulf Stream.

SC.6.E.7.3, SC.6.N.3.4

HURRICANES in the Making

You've probably seen images of enormous hurricanes swirling over the Atlantic Ocean. Where will the next one strike? Thankfully, these giant storms often follow predictable patterns. That's because the development and movement of hurricanes is affected by air and ocean currents.

How Hurricanes Form

Hurricanes form over the North Atlantic Ocean where the water temperature is at least 80°F. As the warm ocean air rises, it leaves an area of low air pressure in its place. Air rushes in to fill the low pressure area, and then it heats up and rises, too, which makes the air begin to swirl and spin.

Hurricanes move with Earth's air currents. Most hurricanes form in a current of westward-flowing air near the equator called the trade winds. If a low pressure area forms off the coast of Africa, it can then catch a ride on the trade winds. As the low pressure area moves westward across the warm ocean waters, it grows in strength. By the time it reaches the southern United States, the low pressure area has become a hurricane.

Tracking Hurricanes

A hurricane may take different paths. A hurricane moving northward might run into westerly winds that blow across the United States. These winds will cause the hurricane to turn eastward, back out to sea. Sometimes a northward hurricane also lines up with the Gulf Stream, the warm ocean current running northward up the coast. When that happens, a hurricane can travel up to New England.

Other hurricanes may take a path westward across Florida. Some travel into the Gulf of Mexico, where westerly winds may turn a hurricane back eastward, across Louisiana, Alabama, or Florida.

Hurricanes that impact the eastern United States usually form off the western coast of Africa or in the Caribbean Sea.

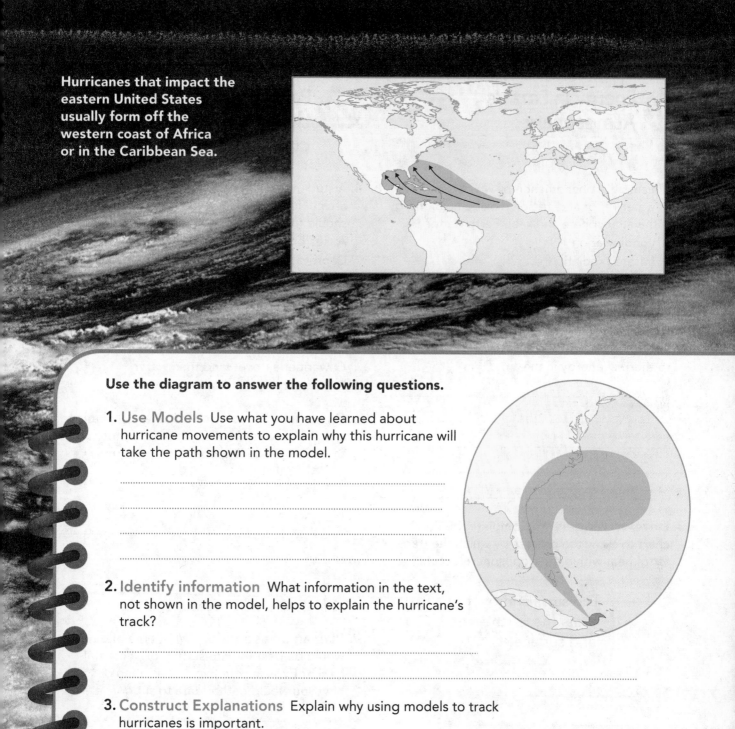

Use the diagram to answer the following questions.

1. Use Models Use what you have learned about hurricane movements to explain why this hurricane will take the path shown in the model.

....

....

....

....

2. Identify information What information in the text, not shown in the model, helps to explain the hurricane's track?

....

....

3. Construct Explanations Explain why using models to track hurricanes is important.

....

....

....

4. Develop Models Meteorologists now predict calmer westerly winds for the next few days. Draw a new track for the hurricane based on this information.

☑ TOPIC 4 Review and Assess

1 Energy in Earth's Atmosphere

SC.6.E.7.1, SC.6.E.7.9

1. Which is the phenomenon by which gases such as water vapor and carbon dioxide hold energy in the atmosphere and keep Earth warm?
A. condensation
B. infrared radiation
C. ultraviolet radiation
D. the greenhouse effect

2. Use Concepts Describe how infrared waves are involved in changing energy from the sun to thermal energy in the air.

....

....

....

....

....

3. Develop Models ✏ Complete the flow chart to show the process by which the transfer of heat within the troposphere occurs.

The sun's energy heats the Earth's land surface.

2 Patterns of Circulation in the Atmosphere

SC.6.E.7.3, SC.6.E.7.5

4. A student makes a model of global winds that affect Florida. Which of the following winds should *not* be included in the student's model?
A. sea breezes   B. trade winds
C. prevailing westerlies   D. polar easterlies

5. Which unequal condition causes a sea breeze to develop?
A. drier air over land than water
B. drier air over water than land
C. warmer air over land than water
D. warmer air over water than land

6. Cause and Effect How do unequal heating and the movement of air at the equator and at the poles produce global wind patterns?

....

....

....

....

....

....

7. Plan an Investigation What time of day would be best for kite surfing off a coastal beach? Explain your hypothesis, then describe how you would gather data to support it.

....

....

....

....

....

....

....

....

....

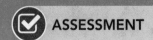
③ Patterns of Circulation in the Ocean

SC.6.E.7.3

8. What drives deep ocean currents?

   A. surface winds   **B.** global winds

   C. unequal heating   **D.** density differences

9. Construct Explanations Describe how a shift of the polar jet stream can bring icy weather to orange groves in Florida during the winter.

....

....

....

....

....

10. Predict Meteorologists have identified an El Niño event in the equatorial area of the Pacific Ocean. What do you think this will do to the precipitation pattern in California?

....

....

11. Cause and Effect Explain how cold, salty seawater of the Arctic Ocean can end up as warm surface seawater of the Indian Ocean hundreds of years later.

....

....

....

....

....

....

....

....

....

12. Develop Models ✎ Draw a diagram of a major warm ocean surface current flowing along a coastal area. Label the current and type of climate you would most likely find in the area. Show how the current influences the area's climate.

◑ Science Assessment Practice

Circle the letter of the best answer.

Use the following information to answer questions 1–3.

The following map shows the location of the polar jet stream in the Northern Hemisphere over the United States on two different days of the same week during winter. The map shows the jet stream on Monday and then its more northerly location three days later.

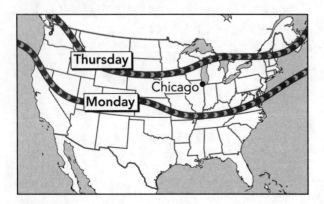

1 As a result of the change in location of the jet stream shown in the map, which statement most likely describes how the weather on Thursday in Chicago compares to the weather on Monday?

A It got colder.

B It got wetter.

C It got warmer.

D The weather did not change.

2 If Chicago experienced a major snowstorm on Monday, what other areas of the U.S. were likely to get snow on Tuesday and Wednesday due to the jet stream position and its effect on local weather?

F Florida and the southeast

G New York and southern New England

H Texas and New Mexico

I Northern California

3 Why would a commercial airline be concerned about the exact position of the jet stream if one of its planes was going to fly from the East Coast to Chicago?

A The jet stream has high winds blowing west to east. These could slow a westbound plane's progress to Chicago.

B Bad weather is associated with the jet stream. The airline would want its planes to steer clear of the jet stream at all times.

C The jet stream carries moisture with it, which means a plane flying in the jet stream would be encountering heavy rains throughout the flight.

D The jet stream is the upper portion of a convection current, meaning it contains very warm air. It would be dangerous for a plane to fly in the jet stream.

4 Ozone is a form of oxygen that can damage lungs and lead to a type of pollution called "smog" in the lower atmosphere. At the same time, it is considered beneficial to the health of organisms. Why?

F It allows visible light to pass through all layers of the atmosphere so organisms can see.

G By allowing heat to escape, it keeps temperatures from getting to warm.

H By enhancing the greenhouse effect, it keeps temperatures from getting too cold at night.

I It absorbs harmful ultraviolet radiation before it reaches Earth's surface.

5 Suppose you are standing on a beach on Florida's Atlantic coast. It is in the afternoon on a hot, sunny day. You feel a strong breeze coming from the east. To which of the following categories does the wind you feel most likely belong?

A trade winds

B sea breezes

C land breezes

D prevailing westerlies

6 During an El Niño event, winds weaken and reverse direction, blowing from west to east. What kind of ocean current would this affect?

F gulf stream current

G surface current

H deep ocean current

I rip current

7 Based on what you know about circulation in oceans, which of the following mechanisms is the best explanation for how water circulates in a freshwater lake?

A Heat exchange between the lake water and the air, and the amount of sunlight, cause the surface water to warm or cool as weather and seasons change. The changing density of the surface water causes the lake's layers to mix, as cool water sinks and warm water rises.

B The wind churns up the surface water, causing surface currents that turn into deep-lake currents. The deep-lake currents mix the different layers of the lake.

C Salt seeps into the lake from the shore and increases the density of the surface water, causing it to sink. Less-salty water rises from lower layers to the surface. This mixes all layers of the lake.

D Wind mixes the top layer of water but otherwise there is little to no mixing or circulation of water in a lake.

8 Which of the following describes an example of conduction?

F how energy travels from a campfire to your body

G how the first few centimeters of the troposphere get heated

H how most of the energy from the sun travels to Earth's surface

I how energy moves along with rising carbon dioxide particles in air

Quest FINDINGS

SC.6.E.7.3, SC.6.E.7.5

Complete the Quest!

Write a report that recommends a speed and route for the container ship crossing the Atlantic Ocean. Be sure to include evidence that justifies your recommendations and explain the factors that affect your recommendations.

Construct Explanations Explain why you think your recommendations will or will not still be valid in a year.

....

....

....

....

....

....

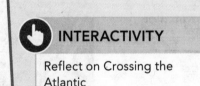

👆 **INTERACTIVITY**

Reflect on Crossing the Atlantic

183

SC.6.E.7.5, SC.6.N.1.1, SC.6.N.3.4

Not All Heating Is Equal

How can you use a model to **demonstrate** the amount of **solar energy** that different places on **Earth** receive?

Background

As an engineer at a solar energy company, you must help choose a location for a new solar farm. The company has identified three possible sites: near Yellowknife, Canada; La Paz, Mexico; or Quito, Ecuador. In this investigation, you will model how sunlight hits Earth to determine the best location for the solar farm.

Design and Plan Your Investigation

HANDS-ON LAB

и**Demonstrate** Go online for a downloadable worksheet of this lab.

1. Look at the diagram. Then predict how you think the amount of solar energy received at each of the three spots is related to its location. Which of the three locations do you think is best suited for a solar farm? Record your prediction in the space provided.

Yellowknife

La Paz

Equator

Quito

2. Design your model to test your predictions. Sketch your model and identify the materials you will use. Use your model to measure the temperature of surfaces that face a light source at different angles. (Hint: Assume that the temperature of black construction paper will increase after about 15 minutes when a light shines on it from 30 cm away.) Consider the following questions as you design and plan your investigation:

   • How will you represent the sun and Earth in your model?

   • What two variables will you investigate?

   • How will you make sure that you test only one variable?

   • How will you measure the amount of solar energy each location receives?

3. Write a detailed procedure describing how you will use your model to test your predictions about how the amount of solar energy received at each of the three spots is related to its location. (Hint: Plan to use some of the available materials to determine how the temperature of the black paper is affected by its position on your model.) Record your procedure in the space provided.

4. Have your teacher approve your procedure. Then make your model and conduct the investigation to test your prediction. Use the data table to record your data.

Prediction

....

....

Sketch of Model

Procedure

....

....

....

....

....

Data Table

Location	Temperature after 15 minutes (°C)
A (Yellowknife)	
B (La Paz)	
C (Quito)	

Analyze and Interpret Data

1. **Develop Models** Summarize how you developed your model to test your prediction.

....

....

....

....

2. **Interpret Data** In which locations did you observe the highest and lowest temperatures?

....

....

....

....

3. **Cause and Effect** How does the temperature of each location relate to the amount of solar energy it receives? Explain.

....

....

....

....

4. **Patterns** Based on your results, explain how the location of an area on Earth affects the amount of solar energy it receives. Then describe how your results compare to your prediction.

....

....

....

....

5. **Construct Explanations** Based on your results, which of the three locations is the best site for the new solar farm? Use evidence from your observations to support your answer.

....

....

....

....

Weather and Climate

SC.6.E.7.2 Investigate and apply how the cycling of water between the atmosphere and hydrosphere has an effect on weather patterns and climate.

SC.6.E.7.3 Describe how global patterns such as the jet stream and ocean currents influence local weather in measurable terms such as temperature, air pressure, wind direction and speed, and humidity and precipitation.

SC.6.E.7.6 Differentiate between weather and climate.

SC.6.E.7.7 Investigate how natural disasters have affected human life in Florida.

SC.6.E.7.8 Describe ways human beings protect themselves from hazardous weather and sun exposure (Also **SC.6.N.1.1** and **SC.6.N.3.4**)

HANDS-ON LAB

uConnect Explore what happens to water in a puddle when sunlight acts upon it.

What happened
to this house?

GO ONLINE
to access your
digital course

▶ VIDEO

👆 INTERACTIVITY

🧪 VIRTUAL LAB

☑ ASSESSMENT

📖 eTEXT

📱 APP

The Essential Question

What determines weather and climate on Earth?

One of the first things you might have done this morning was to look out the window to see what the weather was like. It might be warm and sunny, or you might be expecting a severe storm. Is your weather today typical for the climate in which you live? List some ways in which your life depends on weather and climate.

....
....
....
....
....
....

Quest KICKOFF

How can you prepare for severe weather?

Severe weather can put people's lives and property at risk. Part of the job of a meteorologist, or a scientist who studies the weather, is to help keep the public safe by informing them about severe weather events. In this Quest activity, you will explore the factors that cause severe weather and the ways people can protect themselves and reduce damage during these weather events. Applying what you learn in each lesson, you will develop a public service announcement (PSA) to teach people about severe weather and what they can do to prepare for it and stay safe. In the Findings activity, you will present your PSA and reflect on your work.

 INTERACTIVITY

Preparing a Plan

 SC.6.E.7.8 Describe ways human beings protect themselves from hazardous weather and sun exposure. (Also **SC.6.N.2.2 and SC.6.N.2.3**)

NBC LEARN ▶ **VIDEO**

After watching the video, which explores the tools that meteorologists use to study and predict the weather, complete the 3-2-1 activity.

3 tools that a meteorologist uses

....

....

....

2 types of severe weather that a meteorologist might predict

....

....

....

1 question I have for the meteorologist

....

....

....

Quest CHECK-IN

IN LESSON 1

How is the water cycle involved in severe weather? Consider the information you should include in your PSA.

 INTERACTIVITY

Weather and Severe Weather

Quest CHECK-IN

IN LESSON 2

What happens when different air masses interact? Explore how tornadoes form and decide what information about air masses you will include in your PSA.

 INTERACTIVITY

All About Air Masses

Quest CHECK-IN

IN LESSON 3

How can forecasts help people to prepare for severe weather? Record ideas about weather predictions that your PSA should address.

 INTERACTIVITY

Predicting Severe Weather

A tornado is one of the most destructive types of severe weather that occurs in the United States.

Quest CHECK-IN

IN LESSON 4

How does examining past data help prepare people for future weather hazards? Analyze historical data about tornadoes in the United States.

HANDS-ON LAB

The History of Hazardous Weather

IN LESSON 5

How can knowing about the climate of a region help prepare people for severe weather? Consider how people who live in certain regions on Earth need to be prepared for specific types of severe weather.

Quest FINDINGS

Complete the Quest!

Create your PSA to help people to understand, predict, prepare for, and avoid the dangers of severe weather.

 INTERACTIVITY

Reflect on Your PSA

Water in the Atmosphere

Guiding Questions

- What processes make up the water cycle?
- How does energy drive the processes of the water cycle?
- How does the water cycle affect weather?

Connections

Literacy Summarize Text

Math Convert Measurements

SC.6.E.7.2 Investigate and apply how the cycling of water between the atmosphere and hydrosphere has an effect on weather patterns and climate. (Also **SC.6.N.3.4** and **SC.6.N.2.1**)

Vocabulary

water cycle
evaporation
condensation
dew point
humidity
relative humidity
precipitation

Academic Vocabulary

cycle

VOCABULARY APP

Practice vocabulary on a mobile device.

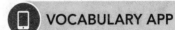 **Quest** CONNECTION

Think about how the water cycle can affect severe weather.

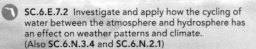 Connect It !

✏️ **Circle the organisms in the photo. Do the organisms have any effect on the water in the stream?**

Construct Explanations How does the grass in the photo affect the movement of water?

....

....

....

Apply Scientific Reasoning How might the cattle affect the movement of water?

....

....

Water Enters the Atmosphere

During a humid day, the air around you may feel moist and thick. On a clear, cloudless day, the air may feel dry. The difference between these feelings is caused by the amount of water in the air. Water is always moving between the surface of Earth and the atmosphere. This process is known as the **water cycle**. A **cycle** is any series of events that repeat in the same order over and over again.

In one phase of the water cycle, water vapor enters the atmosphere through a number of processes. One of these processes is **evaporation**. During evaporation, molecules of liquid water in oceans, lakes, and other bodies of water are heated by the sun. The energy of the sun causes the water molecules to speed up and collide more often. As the molecules collide, some of them "escape" and enter the surrounding air.

The stream in **Figure 1** is not the only source of water for the atmosphere. Plants and animals also release water vapor into the air. In plants, water enters through the roots, rises to the leaves, and is released into the air as water vapor. This is known as transpiration. Animals (and people!) release water vapor into the air every time they breathe out, or exhale. This is known as respiration.

HANDS-ON LAB

Explore the conditions under which water vapor becomes liquid water.

Academic Vocabulary

How do the four seasons also represent a cycle?

....

....

....

Water Enters the Atmosphere

Figure 1 Water is released into the atmosphere as water vapor from bodies of water such as this stream and living things, such as grass and cattle.

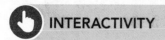

INTERACTIVITY

Investigate the stages of the water cycle.

HANDS-ON LAB

Investigate Investigate how clouds and fog form.

Forming a Cloud

Figure 2 ✏ Complete the diagram to show how clouds form when warm, moist air rises and cools. Use the following terms: *evaporation, cooling air, condensation,* and *particles.*

Condensation

Condensation Recall that water vapor is a gas mixed in with the rest of the air. **Condensation** occurs when water vapor changes into liquid water.

For condensation to occur, tiny particles must be present in the atmosphere so that the water has a surface on which to condense. Most of these particles are salt crystals, dust from soil, bacteria, or particles contained in smoke. During condensation, molecules of water vapor mix with these particles.

Temperature is also a major factor in condensation. Warm air can hold more water vapor than cold air can. Therefore, as warm air cools, the amount of water vapor it can hold decreases, and the water vapor starts to condense. Liquid water that condenses from the air onto a cooler surface is called dew. The temperature at which condensation begins is called the **dew point**. If the dew point is above freezing, the water vapor forms droplets. If the dew point is below freezing, the water vapor may change directly into ice crystals called frost.

One result of condensation of water vapor in the atmosphere is cloud formation. Clouds form when water vapor in the air condenses to form liquid water or ice crystals. When you look at a cloud, such as the one in **Figure 2,** you are seeing millions of these tiny water droplets or ice crystals. When water vapor condenses near ground level, it can take the form of fog. Water can condense as dew on any solid surface, such as a blade of grass or a window pane.

Relative Humidity Meteorologists often warn of high or low humidity during their weather forecasts. **Humidity** is a measure of the amount of water vapor in the air.

The ability of air to hold water vapor depends on temperature. Warm air can hold more water than cool air. So, in their weather reports, meteorologists usually refer to the amount of water vapor in the air as relative humidity.

Relative humidity is the percent of water vapor in the air compared to the maximum amount of water vapor the air can hold at a particular temperature. For example, suppose that 1 cubic meter of air at a particular pressure holds 8 grams of water vapor at 10°C. If there are 8 grams of water vapor in the air, then the relative humidity is 100 percent and the air would be said to be saturated. Similarly, the relative humidity would be 50 percent if the air had only 4 grams of water vapor per cubic meter.

Relative humidity is a better reflection of how the air feels than humidity. For example, air that holds 4 grams of water vapor per cubic meter can feel moist on a cold day or dry on a hot day. Relative humidity reflects this feeling. It would be near 100 percent on a cold day, and much lower on a hot day.

Relative humidity can be measured using a psychrometer. It is a device made up of two thermometers, a wet-bulb thermometer and a dry-bulb thermometer. As shown in **Figure 3**, a moist cloth covers the wet bulb. When the psychrometer is "slung," or spun around, air flows over both thermometers. The wet-bulb thermometer is cooled by evaporation, causing its temperature reading to fall. If the relative humidity is high, evaporation occurs slowly and the wet-bulb temperature does not change much. If the relative humidity is low, evaporation occurs rapidly and the wet-bulb temperature drops by a large amount. Relative humidity is measured by comparing the temperatures of the two bulbs.

✔️ **READING CHECK** **Determine Conclusions** Suppose the two thermometers on a sling psychrometer show almost identical readings. Was the psychrometer more likely used on a Florida beach or in an Arizona desert? Explain your answer.

....

....

....

👆 **VIRTUAL ACTIVITY**

Observe how water moves in the water cycle.

Literacy Connection

Summarize Text As you read, underline sentences that contain information you consider important to remember.

Tools for Measuring Humidity

Figure 3 Digital hygrometers and sling psychrometers like the ones shown are used to find relative humidity.

Write About It
What are the different types of precipitation you encounter in your daily life? In your science notebook, describe how precipitation impacts your life.

Water Leaves the Atmosphere

Water is continually evaporating and condensing in the atmosphere, and this process forms clouds. When enough condensation occurs within a cloud, water droplets form. At first, the droplets are very small, but they grow larger as condensation continues. Depending on temperature and other conditions in the atmosphere, the droplets may grow heavy enough that gravity pulls them down toward Earth's surface. When this happens, precipitation occurs. **Precipitation** is any form of water that falls from clouds and reaches Earth's surface.

Types of Precipitation The most common kind of precipitation is rain. Rain comes in various forms depending on the size of the water droplets that form, as seen in **Figure 4**. Rain starts out as cloud droplets. When cloud droplets grow a bit bigger, they become mist. When droplets reach a size of 0.05 to 0.5 millimeters in diameter, they are known as drizzle. Drops of water are called rain when they are larger than 0.5 millimeters in diameter.

Water Droplets

Figure 4 🖊 On the diagram, label the drops as *mist, rain, drizzle,* or *droplet.*

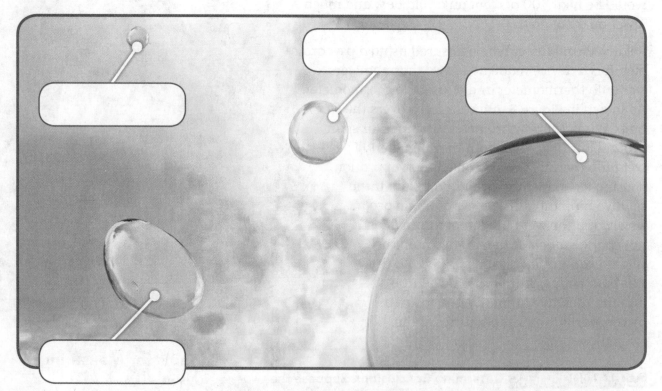

Temperature is a very important factor in determining the type of precipitation an area may get at any given time. In warm climates, precipitation is almost always rain. However, there are many other types of precipitation. In colder regions, precipitation often falls as snow or ice. Besides rain, common types of precipitation include sleet, freezing rain, snow, and hail, as shown in **Figure 5**.

Freezing Precipitation

Figure 5 Draw a check mark on the photos showing the precipitation that occurs when the air temperature is above 0°C and the ground temperature is below 0°C. Draw an *X* on the photos showing the precipitation that occurs when the air temperature is below 0°C and the ground temperature is above 0°C. Draw a triangle on the photos showing the precipitation that occurs when both air and ground temperature are below 0°C.

Freezing Rain Raindrops sometimes freeze when they hit a cold surface. This kind of precipitation is called freezing rain.

Hail A hailstone is a round pellet of ice at least 5 millimeters in diameter. Hail starts as an ice pellet inside a cold region of a cloud. Strong updrafts of wind carry the hailstone up through the cold region many times, adding ice in layers to the outside of the hailstone. Eventually the hailstone becomes heavy enough for gravity to pull it to the ground.

Sleet Raindrops that fall through a layer of air below 0°C freeze into solid particles of ice before they hit the ground. Ice particles smaller than hailstones are called sleet.

Snow Snow forms when water vapor in a cloud is converted directly into ice crystals that clump together. The clumps fall in the form of ice crystals called snowflakes.

VIDEO

Watch a single drop of water as it moves through the water cycle.

Measuring Precipitation If a town receives a large snowfall, meteorologists need to track how much snow fell to determine how safe it is to travel. Similarly, if a big storm delivers a lot of rain, people would need to know how much rain fell to determine whether flooding might occur.

Rain can be measured by using a rain gauge, which is an open-ended tube that collects rain. The amount of rain is measured either by dipping a ruler into the water in the tube or by reading a scale printed on the tube. Snowfall is usually measured in two ways: by using a simple measuring stick or by melting collected snow and measuring the depth of water it produces. On average, 10 centimeters of snow contain about the same amount of water as 1 centimeter of rain. However, light, fluffy snow contains far less water than heavy, wet snow does.

✅ **READING CHECK** **Determine Central Ideas** How are snow and rain formation similar? How are they different?

....

....

....

....

Math Toolbox

Measuring Precipitation

In late September and early October of 2016, Hurricane Matthew brought a huge amount of rain to the Caribbean and then the southeastern United States, causing major flooding and damage. The table shows approximate rainfall during the hurricane. Use the table to answer the questions about this powerful storm.

1. **Convert Measurements** ✏ Complete the table. Use the fact that 1 inch is equal to 25.4 millimeters.

2. **Draw Conclusions** Do the data in the table support the conclusion that the rainfall lessened before reaching the United States? Explain.

Rainfall During Hurricane Matthew		
Location	Rain in mm	Rain in inches
Hewanorra, Saint Lucia		12.6
Santo Domingo, Dominican Republic		9.21
Fayetteville, NC, United States	355	

....

....

The Water Cycle

The water cycle describes the way that water moves through Earth's systems and affects our lives in many ways. As the sun heats the land, ocean, lakes, and other bodies of water, its energy changes the amount of water in the atmosphere. Through evaporation, transpiration, and respiration, water rises up and forms clouds. Rain, snow, and other forms of precipitation fall from the clouds toward Earth's surface. The water then runs off the surface or moves through the ground, back into lakes, streams, and eventually the ocean. As seen in **Figure 6**, gravity and energy from the sun together drive water molecules through this never-ending cycle.

INTERACTIVITY

Examine your own role in the water cycle.

✓ READING CHECK **Summarize Text** What role does energy play in the water cycle?

....

....

....

Model It!

Figure 6 Identify Patterns ✏ Study this diagram of the water cycle in action. Label the various processes you see in the diagram.

☑LESSON 1 Check

1. Generalize Besides energy from the sun, what force helps move water molecules through the water cycle?

....

2. Explain Explain in terms of the water cycle the cause of the general trend in water level from 2000 to 2015 shown in the graph.

....

....

....

3. Identify Suppose you use a sling psychrometer in two different locations. How would you know which location has lower relative humidity?

....

....

....

4. Use Models ✏ Create a diagram that shows how water cycles through the environment around your neighborhood. Label sources of evaporation, transpiration, condensation, and precipitation.

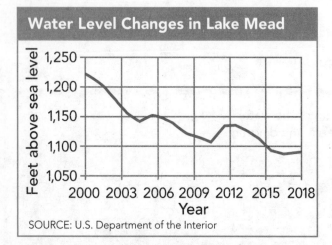

Water Level Changes in Lake Mead

SOURCE: U.S. Department of the Interior

Quest CHECK-IN

In this lesson, you learned how water cycles through Earth's systems. You also discovered that the water cycle can influence the weather.

Evaluate How does each part of the water cycle contribute to the weather?

....

....

....

....

....

....

 INTERACTIVITY

Weather and Severe Weather

Go online to analyze how the water cycle is involved in weather, especially severe weather. Then consider possible causes and effects of various weather events, and suggest how people can prepare for those events.

SC.6.E.7.In.2, SC.6.N.1.1, SC.6.N.1.4

CATCHING WATER
With a Net

INTERACTIVITY

Explore the factors affecting the amount of water that a dew catcher can collect.

How can you provide safe drinking water for small villages far from any clean water source? By extracting it from the air!

The Challenge: To reclaim clean drinking water from humidity in the air.

You can get a fresh drink of water almost anywhere in the United States simply by turning on a faucet. However, in many villages and cities around the world, people have to go a long way to find clean water that is safe to drink.

Scientists have taken up the challenge of bringing water to these people through the ancient method of collecting dew. Recall that dew is the moisture that condenses on surfaces as a result of cooling temperatures and the available humidity in the air.

In rural villages across the world, people are putting up nets. Cooler night temperatures cause moisture in the air from higher humidity or fog to condense and cover the nets with water. The water drains into a container, providing a lifeline to thirsty communities. The water is safe for drinking, cooking, bathing, and tending crops.

Members of the Swakopmund People of the Topnaar tribe work on a fog collection system in the Namib Desert in Namibia.

DESIGN CHALLENGE

Can you build a device to catch dew from the air? Go to the Engineering Design Notebook to find out!

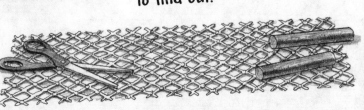

② Air Masses

Guiding Questions

- How do global patterns, such as the jet stream, affect air masses?
- How do air masses interact to form fronts?
- How do the interactions of air masses result in changes in weather?

Connections

Literacy Read and Comprehend

🖊 **SC.6.E.7.2** Investigate and apply how the cycling of water between the atmosphere and hydrosphere has an effect on weather patterns and climate.

SC.6.E.7.3 Describe how global patterns such as the jet stream and ocean currents influence local weather in measurable terms such as temperature, air pressure, wind direction and speed, and humidity and precipitation. (Also **SC.6.N.1.1** and **SC.6.N.1.5**)

Vocabulary

air mass
jet stream
front
cyclone
anticyclone

Academic Vocabulary

prevailing
stationary

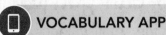 **VOCABULARY APP**

Practice vocabulary on a mobile device.

Quest CONNECTION

Think about how interacting air masses can cause severe weather.

Connect It !

🖊 **Make a checkmark on something in the picture that indicates whether the air is warm or cool. Make an X on something that indicates the relative humidity.**

Construct Explanations Do you think the air at this beach is humid or dry? Why do you think so? Explain.

....

Apply Scientific Reasoning What factors affect the temperature at this beach?

....

....

Major Air Masses

Look outside your window. What is the weather like where you are today? The weather you see is happening due to the influence of air masses. An **air mass** is a huge body of air that has similar temperature, humidity, and air pressure at any given height. Scientists classify air masses based on temperature and humidity.

The characteristics of an air mass depend on the temperature and moisture content of the region over which the air mass forms. Whether an air mass is humid or dry depends on whether it forms over water or dry land. For example, an air mass that forms above the ocean in **Figure 1** would have different characteristics than an air mass that forms over a desert.

How Air Masses Move Air masses are always on the move. In the continental United States, air masses are commonly moved by the **prevailing** westerlies and jet streams.

In general, the major wind belts over the continental United States, known as the prevailing westerlies, push air masses from west to east. For example, cool, moist air masses from the Pacific Ocean may be blown onto the West Coast, bringing low clouds and showers. Embedded within the prevailing westerlies are jet streams. A **jet stream** is a band of high-speed winds about 6 to 14 km above Earth's surface. As jet streams blow from west to east, the surface air masses beneath them are carried along. The movement of these air masses, and their interactions have a great impact on weather.

INTERACTIVITY

Explore the characteristics of air masses.

Academic Vocabulary
Think about the meaning of *prevailing* in terms of wind. Keeping this in mind, what might be the prevailing noise at a concert?

....

....

....

Air Masses

Figure 1 Air masses near this beach have specific temperature and humidity profiles based on conditions where the air masses formed.

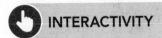

Describe the properties and characteristics of the different kinds of air masses.

Types of Air Masses
Figure 2 These four major types of air masses affect North American weather.

Integrate with Visuals 🖊 Label each type of air mass with two words that describe its temperature and humidity such as *warm* and *dry*.

Types of Air Masses
Is it often windy or rainy where you live? Your local weather, and all the weather in North America, is influenced by one of four major types of air masses: maritime tropical, continental tropical, maritime polar, and continental polar. These air masses are shown in **Figure 2**.

Tropical, or warm, air masses form in the tropics and have low air pressure. Polar, or cold, air masses form in the high latitudes and have high air pressure. Maritime air masses form over the ocean and are very humid. Continental air masses have less exposure to large amounts of moisture, and are drier than maritime air masses. The high and low temperatures in continental air masses can be more extreme than the temperatures in maritime air masses. This is because large bodies of water moderate air temperatures.

☑ **READING CHECK** **Read and Comprehend** What types of air masses affect the weather in North America?

....

....

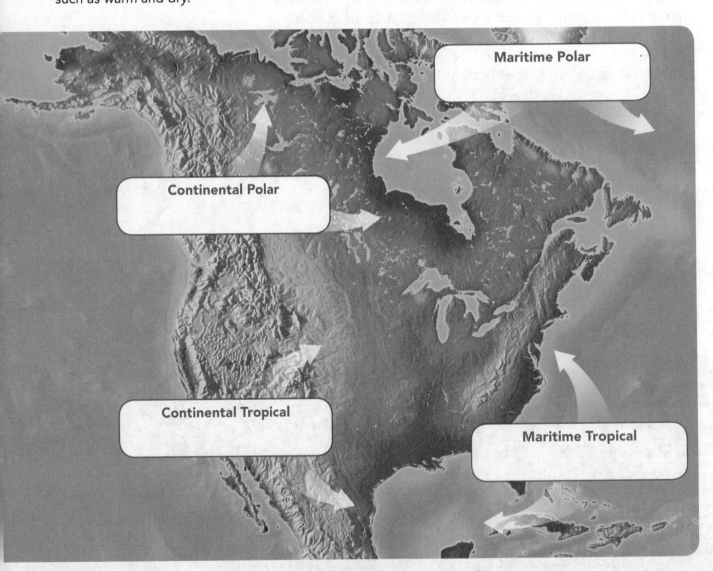

Types of Fronts

Think about a bottle of oil and water. What happens when you shake the bottle? If you try this, you will see that the two substances do not mix—the less-dense oil winds up floating on top of the water. Air masses of different temperatures and humidity act the same way. Although they move across the land and frequently collide with each other, they do not mix easily. Instead, the boundary where the air masses meet becomes a **front**. Storms and changeable weather often develop along fronts like the one in **Figure 3**.

The weather may be different when you leave school this afternoon than it was when you arrived in the morning. The change might be due to a front passing through your area. Colliding air masses can form four types of fronts: cold fronts, warm fronts, stationary fronts, and occluded fronts, as shown on the next two pages in **Figure 4**. The kind of front that develops depends on the characteristics of the air masses and the direction in which they move.

How a Front Forms
Figure 3 A front may be 15 to 600 km wide and extend high into the troposphere.

Predict What kind of weather would develop along the front shown in the photo?

....

....

HANDS-ON LAB

Investigate Model the behavior of cold and warm fronts.

Cold Front

Warm Front

Literacy Connection

Read and Comprehend
As you read about each type of front, underline any effects caused by its formation. Think about how the interactions of these fronts affect the weather.

Academic Vocabulary

A *stationary* front occurs when two air masses meet but neither one can move the other. Knowing that, in what way would a population be said to be stationary?

....

....

....

....

....

Cold Fronts A cold front forms when a cold air mass runs into a warm air mass. Because cold air is denser than warm air, the warm air is pushed up rapidly as the colder air slides beneath it. Cold fronts can result in abrupt and hazardous weather such as heavy rains and winds, thunderstorms, and even tornadoes. After the front passes, the weather usually cools and the skies become clear.

Warm Fronts A warm front forms when a fast-moving warm air mass overtakes a slower-moving cold air mass. Because the warm air mass is less dense, it rises above the cold air mass. Along the front, light rain or snow can fall if the warm air is humid. Scattered clouds can form if the warm air mass is dry. These fronts often move slowly, so there may be rain and clouds for a few days. The weather usually is warmer and more humid after a warm front moves by.

Occluded Fronts Sometimes, a warm air mass gets caught between two cold air masses, forming an occluded front. Because the cooler air is denser, it moves under the warm air, causing the warm air to rise. When the two cold air masses meet, they mix together. Air temperature drops as the warm air mass becomes occluded, or prevented from reaching the ground. As the warm air mass rises and cools, clouds gather, and rain or snow may fall.

Stationary Fronts Sometimes cold and warm air masses meet, but neither one can move the other. This non-moving front is called a **stationary** front. Where the warm and cool air meet, water vapor in the warm air condenses into rain, snow, fog, or clouds. A stationary front may bring many days of clouds and precipitation.

✓ **READING CHECK** **Determine Central Ideas** What do all of these different types of fronts have in common?

....

....

Occluded Front

Stationary Front

Model It

Develop Models ✏ Draw a diagram to model what would happen when a cold air mass moving from the south collides with a warm air mass moving from the north.

Types of Fronts

Figure 4 Different types of fronts occur, depending on how the different air masses interact.

Synthesize Information How are cold and warm fronts different?

....

....

....

....

 VIDEO

Watch how the different fronts could affect the weather.

Cyclone

Figure 5 ✎ This image shows a specific type of Northern Hemisphere cyclone known as a hurricane. On the image, draw arrows to show the direction the cyclone is swirling. How do you know this picture is of a cyclone and not an anticyclone?

....

....

....

....

INTERACTIVITY

Identify the types of weather that take place in different locations.

📓 **Write About It** Watch water swirl down a drain. In your science notebook, describe how this swirling water is related to a cyclone.

Cyclones and Anticyclones

When air masses collide, they form fronts that can sometimes become distorted by surface features, such as mountains, or by strong winds, such as the jet stream. When this happens, the air begins to swirl, causing a low-pressure center to form. Areas of relatively low air pressure can also form in other ways.

Cyclones As shown in **Figure 5**, a swirling center of low air pressure can form a **cyclone**. As warm air at the center of a cyclone rises, the air pressure decreases. Cooler air blows inward from nearby areas of higher air pressure. Winds spiral inward toward the center. In the Northern Hemisphere, the Coriolis effect deflects these winds towards the right, so the cyclone winds spin counterclockwise when viewed from above. As air rises in a cyclone, the air cools, forming clouds and precipitation.

Anticyclones An **anticyclone** is the opposite of a cyclone. It is a high-pressure center of dry air, shown by an H on a weather map. In an anticyclone, winds spiral outward from the center, moving toward areas of lower pressure. The Coriolis effect, which is the deflection of the winds towards the right, causes the winds in an anticyclone to spin clockwise in the Northern Hemisphere. As air moves out from the center, cool air moves downward from higher in the atmosphere. As the cool air warms up, its relative humidity drops, so no clouds form and the weather is clear and dry.

✔️ **READING CHECK** **Read and Comprehend** How do cyclones and anticyclones differ?

....

....

....

1. **Compare and Contrast** What is the difference between an air mass and a front?

....

....

....

....

....

2. **Explain** One summer vacation morning, the weather was warm and humid. About 3:00, heavy clouds formed, and then there was a severe thunderstorm with rain and hail. After the storm, the sun came out, but the temperature had dropped 15°C. Explain each change in the day's weather.

....

....

....

....

....

....

....

....

....

....

3. **Cause and Effect** A state often has cold, snowy winters and cool, rainy summers. Is this state more likely to be New York or Nebraska? Explain your answer.

....

....

....

....

....

4. **Apply Concepts** What types of data would a meteorologist need to collect to demonstrate the presence of a cyclone in a specific region? Support your answers.

....

....

....

....

....

....

....

....

Quest CHECK-IN

In this lesson, you learned that air masses interact at fronts. You also discovered that interacting air masses can cause severe weather.

Infer Why is it important for people to understand how interacting air masses can affect the weather?

....

....

....

....

INTERACTIVITY

All About Air Masses

Go online to explore what happens when different air masses interact. Then find out how and where tornadoes form.

Predicting Weather Changes

Guiding Questions

- How do meteorologists use the interactions of air masses to forecast changes in weather?
- How does technology aid in collecting and analyzing weather data?
- How do weather maps help to model current weather and predict future weather?

Connections

Literacy Determine Central Ideas

Math Analyze Quantitative Relationships

 SC.6.E.7.2 Investigate and apply how the cycling of water between the atmosphere and hydrosphere has an effect on weather patterns and climate.

SC.6.E.7.3 Describe how global patterns such as the jet stream and ocean currents influence local weather in measurable terms such as temperature, air pressure, wind direction and speed, and humidity and precipitation. (Also **SC.6.N.2.2** and **SC.6.N.2.3**)

Vocabulary

meteorologist

Academic Vocabulary

synthesize

 VOCABULARY APP

Practice vocabulary on a mobile device.

Quest CONNECTION

Think about how weather forecasts help people to prepare for severe weather.

Connect It !

🖊 **On two different places in the photo, draw a symbol to indicate the type of weather occurring in that location.**

Make Observations What details in the photo support your predictions?

....

....

....

How To Predict Weather

Whether you're planning on going on a hike, driving to an amusement park, or having a picnic in the park, you'll need to know the day's weather to make your plans. Before you're able to predict the weather, you'll first need to collect data, either through direct observations or by using special instruments, such as a barometer. A barometer measures air pressure. If the reading is falling, meaning the air pressure in the area is decreasing, then you can expect stormy weather.

Making observations is a simple way of predicting how the weather might change. Looking at the sky shown in **Figure 1** might make you wonder how you can use your observations to forecast weather. You might read signs of changing weather in the clouds. On a warm day, you may see clouds that slowly grow larger and taller, which could indicate that a thunderstorm is on the way. If you can see thin, high clouds in the sky, a warm front may be approaching.

Usually, your observations won't tell you everything you need to know. Even careful observers often turn to meteorologists for weather information. A **meteorologist** (mee tee uh RAHL uh jist) is a scientist who studies and predicts weather.

INTERACTIVITY

Explore some of the factors that make it difficult to predict the weather.

Predicting Weather Changes
Figure 1 Meteorologists forecast the weather using direct observations about the conditions.

HANDS-ON LAB

ИInvestigate Consider how barometric pressure is related to weather conditions.

Weather Technology

Figure 2 Technological improvements in gathering weather data have improved the accuracy of weather forecasts.

Weather Balloons Weather balloons carry instruments for collecting weather data high into the atmosphere where human observation is not feasible.

Automated Weather Stations Weather stations in many locations can gather real-time weather data.

Weather Satellites Satellites orbit high above Earth collecting data as well as images of Earth's surface and atmosphere.

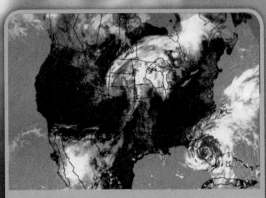

Computer Forecasts Computers process weather data quickly, which

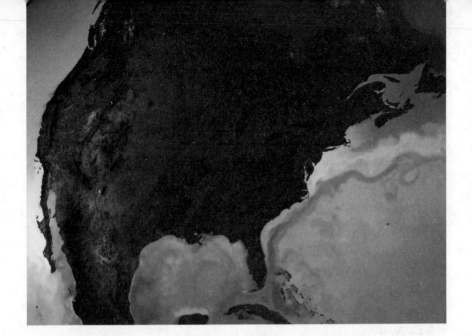

Ocean Surface Temperatures

Figure 3 This satellite image uses red color to show the warm waters of the Gulf Stream ocean current as it moves north along the Florida coast into the cooler waters of the North Atlantic.

Weather Technology In recent years, new technologies have been developed to help meteorologists predict the weather, as shown in **Figure 2**. Short-range forecasts—forecasts for up to five days—are now fairly reliable. Meteorologists can also make somewhat accurate long-range predictions.

Global Patterns and Local Weather

Recognizing patterns is another component of weather forecasting. A large part of the job of a meteorologist is to determine how global patterns affect the local weather. Meteorologists look at many different factors, including temperature, wind, air pressure, humidity, and precipitation. They closely observe and track the movements of jet streams and ocean currents to help predict future weather changes.

Jet streams help to move air masses and weather systems around the globe. While the weather may be warm and sunny one day, a jet stream can push a cold, moist air mass into the area and change the forecast to cooler, stormy days.

Ocean currents, which move warm and cold water around the world, also affect local weather. Warm ocean currents cause the air masses above them to become warmer, while cold currents lower the temperature of air masses above them. These currents affect local air temperatures and precipitation, and they also cause changes in wind speed and direction. Observe **Figure 3** to see how one ocean current, the Gulf Stream, influences the temperatures on the east coast of North America.

 INTERACTIVITY

Discover how air masses can be used to predict weather.

 VIDEO

Learn how weather satellites are used in meteorology.

✓ **READING CHECK** **Determine Conclusions** Based on the image in **Figure 3**, how does the Gulf Stream most likely affect temperatures on the East Coast?

....

....

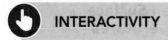

INTERACTIVITY

Practice developing your own weather predictions.

Academic Vocabulary

What do you think it means to synthesize a chemical?

....

....

Learning from Weather Maps

Do you ever check the weather on your phone or a tablet? In addition to telling you the temperature and atmospheric conditions, many apps will show you a weather map. A weather map is a model that shows the weather conditions at a particular time over a large area. There are many types of weather maps.

Reading Weather Maps
Data from many local weather stations all over the country are **synthesized** into weather maps at the National Weather Service. Some weather maps show curved lines. These lines connect places with similar conditions of temperature or air pressure. Isobars are lines joining places on the map that have the same air pressure. Isotherms are lines joining places that have the same temperature.

Figure 4 shows a typical newspaper weather map. Standard symbols on weather maps show many features, including fronts, areas of high and low pressure (measured in millibars), types of precipitation, and temperatures.

Math Toolbox

Isobars

The black lines on this map of the United States are isobars, which connect points of equal air pressure, measured in millibars.

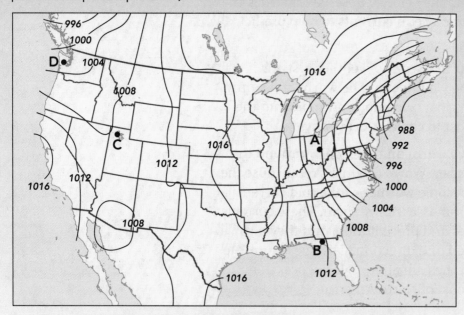

Analyze Quantitative Relationships Use the locations A, B, C, and D from the map to answer the questions about air pressure.

1. Which two locations have approximately the same air pressure? _____

2. Which two locations have the greatest difference in air pressure?_____

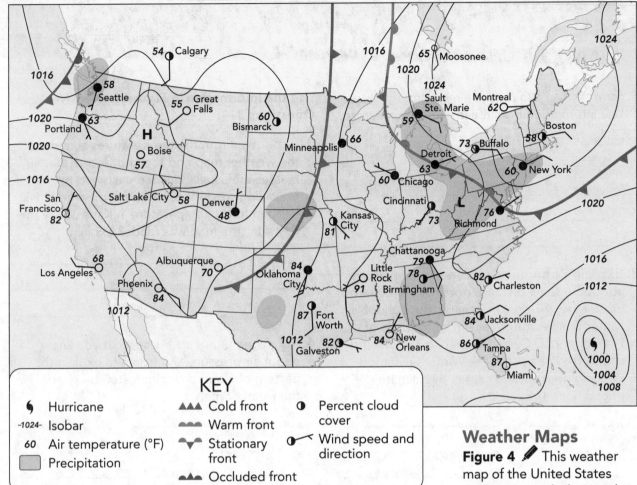

KEY

🌀	Hurricane
-1024-	Isobar
60	Air temperature (°F)
▨	Precipitation
▲▲▲	Cold front
⌒⌒	Warm front
▽▽	Stationary front
▲▲▲	Occluded front
◑	Percent cloud cover
◖—<	Wind speed and direction

The Future of Meteorology As computers, satellites, and radar technologies become more sophisticated, scientists can make better forecasts. But even with these advanced tools, no forecaster will ever be one hundred percent accurate. This is because the atmosphere works in such a way that a small change in the weather today can mean a larger change in the weather a week later! A tiny event might cause a larger disturbance that could—eventually—grow into a large storm.

✅ **READING CHECK** **Determine Central Ideas** How are isobars and isotherms alike? How are they different?

....

....

....

Weather Maps

Figure 4 🖉 This weather map of the United States uses many symbols. Use the key to interpret the symbols. Underline the cities with the highest and lowest temperatures. (Note that the temperatures are given in degrees Fahrenheit.) Then circle the area showing the highest levels of atmospheric pressure.

Literacy Connection

Determine Central Ideas Compare the information you read about weather forecasts in the text with the information you gained about forecasts from looking at the weather map. Use the central idea from the reading and map reading to compare the information.

☑ LESSON 3 Check

SC.6.E.7.2, SC.6.E.7.3

1. **Summarize** What does a meteorologist do? Use information from the lesson to summarize.

....

....

....

....

....

2. **Explain Phenomenon** London, England, is about the same distance north of the Equator as Calgary, Alberta, in Canada. But London's winter temperatures are similar to those of Washington, D.C., and Calgary is so cold and snowy they've hosted the Winter Olympics! Which global pattern causes this climate phenomenon? Explain.

....

....

....

....

....

....

....

....

Use the information in Figure 4 to answer Questions 3–4.

3. **Patterns** From the temperatures shown on the weather map and the knowledge that air masses are usually pushed eastward by the prevailing westerlies, what do you predict will happen to the temperature in Kansas City the day after the map was made? Explain.

....

....

....

4. **Interpret Diagrams** Use what you know about air pressure and fronts to explain the pattern of cloud cover indicated by symbols in the weather map.

....

....

....

....

....

....

Quest CHECK-IN

In this lesson, you learned how meteorologists use observations, patterns, and tools to predict the weather.

Infer How might accurate weather forecasting help people who work as farmers or fishers? How does it help everyone?

....

....

....

....

....

👆 INTERACTIVITY

Predicting Severe Weather

Go online to determine how weather forecasts help people to prepare for severe weather. Then identify which weather conditions you should address in your PSA.

Watching the CLOUDS GO BY

People have been trying to predict the weather for thousands of years. In ancient times, people observed the clouds, the wind, and the temperature changes. They recognized patterns that helped them to forecast the weather with some accuracy.

Today, forecasting the weather combines data collection with the old skill of pattern recognition. Scientists called meteorologists collect weather data using computers and other tools. They analyze and interpret the data and compare it to their knowledge and experience. This process allows meteorologists to make predictions about the weather days and even weeks in advance.

There are many different types of meteorologists. Broadcast meteorologists report the weather on television. Research meteorologists work at government agencies and study particular issues related to weather and climate. Forensic meteorologists are called upon to research past weather events for court cases or insurance claims.

Meteorologists often have a good background in subjects such as physics, astronomy, and math. It also helps if you like different kinds of weather and if you are observant and curious!

 VIDEO

Find out how a meteorologist predicts the weather in an area.

Meteorologists check instruments at an automated weather station in a remote desert location at the Jornada Biosphere Reserve in southern New Mexico.

MY CAREER

Type "meteorologist" into an online search engine to learn more about this career.

Severe Weather and Floods

Guiding Questions

- How does severe weather affect human life?
- How do humans protect themselves from severe weather?

Connections

Literacy Cite Textual Evidence

 SC.6.E.7.7 Investigate how natural disasters have affected human life in Florida.
SC.6.E.7.8 Describe ways human beings protect themselves from hazardous weather and sun exposure. (Also **SC.6.N.1.1** and **SC.6.N.1.5**)

Vocabulary

storm
thunderstorm
hurricane
tornado
storm surge
flood
drought

Academic Vocabulary

approximate

 VOCABULARY APP

Practice vocabulary on a mobile device.

Quest CONNECTION

Think about how data from past events might help to prepare people for future weather hazards.

Connect It!

✏ **Label the center, or eye, of this North Atlantic hurricane.**

Explain Phenomena In what direction are the winds swirling around the location you identified?

....

Predict How might this storm affect people living near its path?

....

....

Types of Severe Storms

In October 2016, Hurricane Matthew struck the Caribbean and the southeastern United States with torrential rains and winds that reached **approximate** speeds of 250 km/h. Shown in the satellite image in **Figure 1**, it was one of the most intense storms ever to hit that part of the United States.

The death toll due to Hurricane Matthew surpassed 1000, with most of those deaths occurring in Haiti. In the United States, approximately 40 people died, more than half of these in North Carolina. Florida did not receive the extremely strong winds that some areas did, but the hurricane dropped between 7 and 10 inches of rain in the eastern half of the state.

In addition to casualties, property damage from the hurricane was extreme. Many areas were battered by winds or flooded for days. Many buildings were blown down and roads washed away.

A hurricane is one example of a storm. A **storm** is a violent disturbance in the atmosphere. Storms involve sudden changes in air pressure, which cause rapid air movements and often precipitation. There are several types of severe storms: winter storms, thunderstorms, hurricanes, and tornadoes.

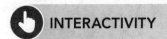

INTERACTIVITY

Write about your experiences with severe weather.

Academic Vocabulary

What is the difference between an approximate and an exact number?

....

....

....

Hurricane Matthew

Figure 1 This satellite image shows Hurricane Matthew swirling north of Cuba and beginning to engulf the Florida peninsula.

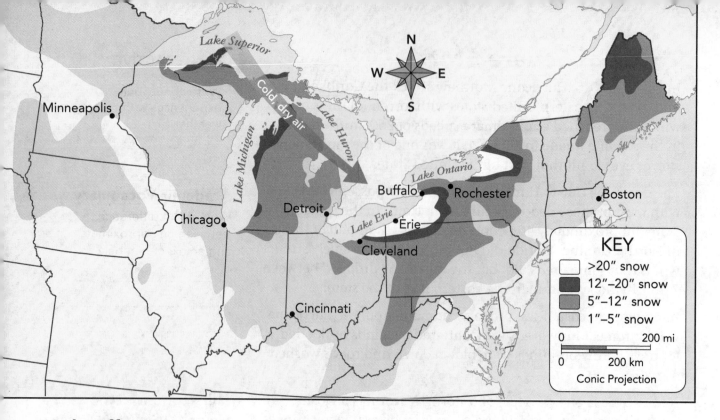

Lake Superior

Cold, dry air

Lake Michigan

Lake Huron

Lake Ontario

Lake Erie

Minneapolis

Chicago

Detroit

Buffalo

Rochester

Erie

Cleveland

Boston

Cincinnati

KEY

>20" snow

12"–20" snow

5"–12" snow

1"–5" snow

0   200 mi

0   200 km

Conic Projection

Lake-Effect Snow

Figure 2 This map shows the snow totals after a certain winter storm. The higher totals are a result of lake-effect snow. Draw arrows on the map to represent the wind blowing across the lakes.

Write About It Identify the actions you can take to remain safe during a severe storm of any kind.

Winter Storms

In the winter in the northern United States, most of the precipitation that occurs is in the form of snow. If the air is colder than 0°C all the way to the ground, the precipitation falls as snow. Heavy snow can block roads, trap people in their homes, and delay emergency vehicles. Extreme cold can cause water pipes to burst.

Some places, such as Erie, Pennsylvania, get more snow than other places relatively close by. In an average winter, nearly 118 inches of snow fall on these cities due to lake-effect snow, as shown in **Figure 2.**

In the fall and winter, the land near the Great Lakes cools much more rapidly than the water in the lakes. When a cold, dry air mass moves southeast across the lakes, it picks up water vapor and heat. As soon as the air mass reaches the other side of the lake, the air rises and cools again. The water vapor condenses and falls as snow.

Some winter storms are more intense than others. In February 1978, a huge blizzard hit the northeastern United States. During this storm, weather stations recorded hurricane-force winds and record-breaking amounts of snow. The storm hovered over New England, and heavy snow fell for almost 33 hours without letting up.

People driving on highways abandoned their cars when the snow became too deep. Rescuers traveled on cross-country skis and snowmobiles to help stranded drivers. It was almost a week until the roads opened again.

Thunderstorms Spring and summer are often associated with clear, warm weather, but they are also the times when hazardous thunderstorms can form.

A **thunderstorm** is a localized storm often accompanied by heavy precipitation, frequent thunder, and dangerous lightning. It usually forms when warm air carrying lots of moisture is forced upward along a cold front. The warm, humid air rises rapidly, forming dense thunderheads. Thunderstorms can bring heavy rain and hail.

During a thunderstorm, positive and negative electrical charges build up and discharge in the thunderheads. Lightning occurs as these charges jump between parts of a cloud, between nearby clouds, or between a cloud and the ground, all of which are shown in **Figure 3**.

The loud booms of thunder that can keep us up at night are produced when lightning heats the air near it to as much as 30,000°C. That's hotter than the sun's surface! The rapidly heated air expands explosively, creating the shockwave we call thunder in the surrounding air as it is compressed.

Thunderstorms cause severe damage. Their heavy rains may flood low-lying areas. Large hailstones ruin crops, damage property such as cars and windows, and may even cause fatalities to people and animals out in the open. Lightning strikes start fires and damage structures or sometimes just the electrical equipment within a structure. If lightning strikes a person, it can cause unconsciousness, serious burns, and even death.

Thunder and Lightning
Figure 3 Lightning strikes can cause severe damage during thunderstorms.

Model It

How Thunderstorms Form

Develop Models Draw a labeled diagram to show the formation of a thunderstorm.

Hurricanes

When a cyclone's winds exceed 119 km/h, we call it a hurricane. A **hurricane** can stretch more than 600 kilometers across and it may have winds as strong as 320 km/h. In the western Pacific Ocean, these storms are called typhoons. When they occur in the Indian Ocean, they are known simply as cyclones.

A typical hurricane that strikes the United States forms in the Atlantic Ocean north of the equator during the late summer. It begins as a low-pressure area, or tropical disturbance, over ocean water warmed by solar radiation.

A hurricane draws its energy from the warm, humid air near the warm ocean's surface. This air rises, forming clouds and drawing surrounding air into the area, as shown in **Figure 4**. Bands of heavy rains and high winds spiral inward toward the area of lowest pressure at the center. The lower the air pressure at the center of the storm, the faster the winds blow toward it.

Hurricane winds are strongest in a narrow band or ring of clouds at the storm's center called the eyewall, which encloses the storm's "eye." When the eye arrives, the weather changes suddenly, growing calm and clear. After the eye passes, the storm resumes, but the winds blow from the opposite direction.

Hurricanes often result in severe flooding, which in turn contaminates drinking water supplies. Wind damage and severe flooding often mean that travel after the storm will be difficult. Residents of hurricane-prone areas are encouraged to stock a three-day supply of drinking water, ready-to-eat food, and any other necessary items, such as medications or diapers, to help them through the aftermath of a hurricane.

Literacy Connection

Cite Textual Evidence
Textual evidence is information or clues that reinforce or support an idea. Reread the third and fourth paragraphs on this page. Underline the evidence that supports the statement that hurricane winds are strongest around the storm's center.

Formation of a Hurricane

Figure 4 ✏️ Draw arrows to show how warm, humid air rises to form clouds and how winds spiral toward the area of low pressure.

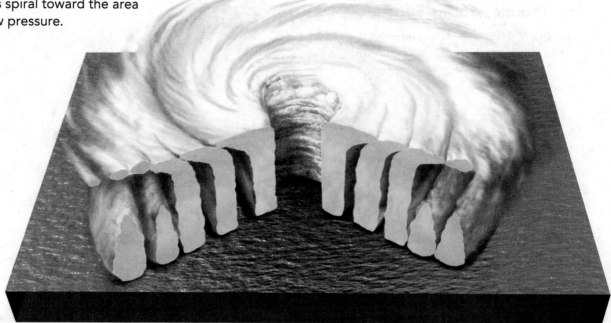

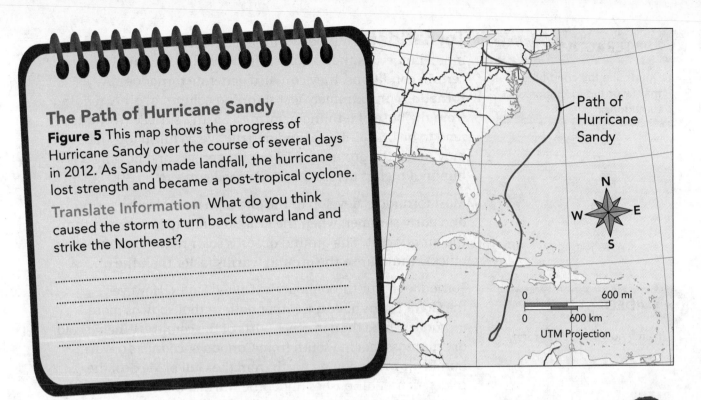

The Path of Hurricane Sandy

Figure 5 This map shows the progress of Hurricane Sandy over the course of several days in 2012. As Sandy made landfall, the hurricane lost strength and became a post-tropical cyclone.

Translate Information What do you think caused the storm to turn back toward land and strike the Northeast?

....

....

....

....

Path of Hurricane Sandy

0   600 mi

0   600 km

UTM Projection

How Hurricanes Move

Hurricanes are long-lasting storms, existing for a week or more. They can travel thousands of kilometers from where they originally formed. Hurricanes that form in the Atlantic Ocean are usually steered by easterly trade winds toward the Caribbean islands and then up toward the southeastern and eastern United States, as was Hurricane Sandy in 2012 (**Figure 5**). Once a hurricane passes over land, it loses its energy source: warm, moist air. If the hurricane doesn't travel over another source of warm, moist air to fuel it, it will gradually weaken.

When a hurricane makes landfall, high waves, severe flooding, and wind damage often accompany it. A hurricane's low pressure and high winds can raise the level of the water in the ocean below it by as much as 6 meters above normal sea level. The result is a **storm surge**, a "dome" of water that sweeps across the coast where the hurricane is traveling. Storm surges can cause great damage, destroying human-made structures as well as coastal ecosystems.

✓READING CHECK **Determine Conclusions** Why don't hurricanes form in oceans in northern latitudes of the world?

....

....

....

HANDS-ON LAB

☑**Investigate** Record and analyze historical hurricane data to predict future events.

223

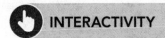

INTERACTIVITY

Determine the conditions that favor the formation of tornadoes.

VIDEO

Watch how tornadoes form.

Tornadoes

Thunderstorms can lead to something even more dangerous than heavy rains, flooding, or hail. Under certain conditions, they can also generate tornadoes. A **tornado** is an extremely fast spinning column of air extending from the base of a thunderstorm to Earth's surface. Tornadoes tend to be brief, intense, and destructive. While a tornado may touch the ground for 15 minutes or less and be only a few hundred meters across, its wind speed can exceed 300 km/h.

Most tornadoes develop in the late afternoon during spring and early summer, when the ground tends to be warmer than the air above it. The ground absorbs solar radiation more quickly than air so the ground warms faster than the air.

Tornadoes occur throughout the United States. However, the Great Plains have a weather pattern that spawns more tornadoes there than in other parts of the country. When a cold, dry air mass moving south from Canada encounters a warm, humid air mass moving north from the Gulf of Mexico, the colder, denser air pushes under the warmer air mass, forcing it to rise. Warm ground can "turbo-charge" this process by releasing some of the heat it absorbed from the sun. This extra heat forces the air above to rise even faster. An area of low pressure develops and rapidly draws surrounding air inward and up. This fast-moving air rotates as it rises and forms a funnel. If the funnel touches Earth's surface, it becomes a tornado.

Tornado damage comes from both strong winds and the flying debris those winds carry. Tornadoes can move large objects and scatter debris many miles away. The Fujita Scale, shown in **Figure 6**, allows meteorologists to categorize tornadoes based on the amount and type of damage they cause. Only about one percent of tornadoes is ranked as F4 or F5. In 2007, the original Fujita Scale was replaced by the Enhanced Fujita Scale to more closely align high wind speeds with the types of damage they typically cause to structures.

Tornado Damage

Figure 6 ✎ Use the image to rate the damage shown by circling a rating on the Fujita Scale.

Fujita Scale	Types of Damage
F0	Branches broken off trees
F1	Mobile homes overturned
F2	Trees uprooted
F3	Roofs torn off
F4	Houses leveled
F5	Houses carried away

Floods and Drought

Storms are not the only type of hazardous severe weather. Floods, droughts, and excessive heat can occur in many different areas in the United States.

Floods Flooding is a major danger during severe storms, such as the one shown in **Figure 7**. A **flood** is an overflowing of water in a normally dry area. Some floods occur when excess water from rain or melting snow overflows a stream or river. In urban areas, floods occur when the ground can't absorb any water because it is already saturated.

Dams and levees are used to control flooding near rivers. A dam is a barrier across a river that may redirect the flow of the river or store floodwaters so that they can be released slowly. An embankment built along a river to prevent flooding of the surrounding land is a levee.

Droughts and Excessive Heat Having too little water can also cause problems. A long period with little or no rainfall is known as a **drought**. Drought is caused by hot, dry weather systems that stay in one place for weeks or months at a time. Long-term droughts can lead to crop failures and wildfires. Streams, reservoirs, and wells dry up, causing shortages of water for homes, businesses, plants, and animals. People can help lessen the impacts of drought by conserving water.

The excessive heat caused by heat waves can also be harmful to people. Prolonged exposure to heat and the sun can cause skin damage, heat stroke, and dehydration. To prevent overexposure to the sun, wear protective clothing, sunglasses, and sunscreen, and avoid direct sunlight between the hours of 10 am and 2 pm.

Flood Damage
Figure 7 In 2012, as Sandy made landfall, the hurricane lost strength and became a post-tropical cyclone, causing heavy damage from flooding.

☑ **READING CHECK** **Cite Textual Evidence** What are two ways to help prevent floods?

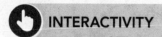

INTERACTIVITY

Examine the technologies used to predict and mitigate the effects of severe weather.

Storm Safety

When potentially dangerous storms are likely, weather announcements indicate where there is a storm "watch" and where there is a storm "warning." A watch means that conditions are right for producing severe weather, but the severe weather has not yet developed. A warning signifies that severe weather is approaching and people should take shelter. **Figure 8** shows the precautions people should take for each type of severe storm.

Severe Storm Safety

Figure 8 Different severe storms require different safety measures.

Tornado If you hear a tornado warning, go to a safe area quickly. Move to the middle of the ground floor. Stay away from windows and doors.

Winter Storm Winter storms can limit your vision and make it easy to get lost. Strong winds cool bodies rapidly. Stay or get indoors and keep a supply of water and food on hand in case of a power outage.

Thunderstorm Get and stay indoors. If in a car, it's safe to stay there. But if you are outside, find a low area away from trees, fences, and poles. If you are swimming or in a boat, get to shore and find shelter.

Hurricane Today, weather satellites can track and warn people well in advance of an approaching hurricane. You should be prepared to evacuate, or move away temporarily. If you hear a hurricane warning and are told to evacuate, leave the area immediately.

✓ **READING CHECK** **Determine Central Ideas** What safety precautions are common to all types of severe weather?

....

....

1. Identify What are four types of severe storms?

....

....

2. Patterns A certain severe storm causes much property damage from heavy rain and winds that travel in a straight line. What type of severe storm has these characteristics? Why don't the other types of storm apply to this description?

....

....

....

....

....

3. Apply Scientific Reasoning Why does the damage from floods last longer than the storms that produce them?

....

....

....

4. Draw Conclusions The circle graph shows the percentage of deaths from hurricane related causes from 1970 to 1999.

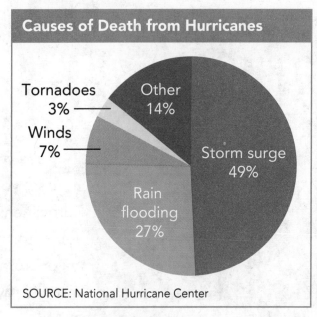

Causes of Death from Hurricanes

Tornadoes 3%
Other 14%
Winds 7%
Storm surge 49%
Rain flooding 27%

SOURCE: National Hurricane Center

Based on the facts in the lesson and these data, what do you think would be important for authorities to do to prepare for a hurricane?

....

....

....

....

....

Quest CHECK-IN

In this lesson, you studied how storms like thunderstorms, hurricanes, and tornadoes form. You also learned about the damage these storms can cause and how people can protect themselves from severe storms.

Summarize Choose a severe storm. What information about this storm would you include in a public service announcement about storm safety?

....

....

HANDS-ON LAB

The History of Hazardous Weather

Do the Hands-On lab to determine how examining past data help to prepare people for future weather hazards. Then analyze data about tornadoes in the United States.

SC.6.E.7.7, SC.6.E.7.8

THE CASE OF THE

Florida Hurricane

Have you ever lived through a hurricane? If so, you know how dangerous they can be. Hurricane winds range from 74 to nearly 200 miles per hour. Storm surges can be greater than 8 feet. These major storms can submerge whole neighborhoods and destroy houses.

During a hurricane, downed power lines result in widespread power outages, flooding can reach as high as the second floor of houses, and downed trees and telephone poles make roads dangerous or impassable. Roofs can be torn off buildings and hurled violently through the air, along with other movable property such as lawn chairs. The powerful storm can even cause some buildings to collapse.

Hurricanes and Florida

Hurricanes generate far out at sea. They may pick up strength and speed over warm water as they move toward the coast, or weaken in cold water before they reach land. Florida's exceptionally long coastline and tropical location make it a prime target for hurricanes. These two factors explain why Florida is hit by more major hurricanes than any other U.S. state.

In 2016, Hurricane Matthew did not hit Florida directly, but it dumped flooding rains on the state. Insurance claims for damage have thus far added up to more than $218 million.

There's no changing the fact that Florida lies in the path of many hurricanes. Officials in the state are working hard to find ways to lower the risks, including issuing new rules for storm-resistant structures and spending more money on disaster planning, so that communities will be better prepared for future storms.

Hurricane Matthew caused severe flooding and major property damage in Florida in 2016.

Use the map to answer questions 1–2.

1. Analyze Data How many times more likely is a hurricane to strike Broward County than Okaloosa County?

....

....

2. Construct Explanations How would you characterize the risk of a hurricane strike where you live? Use evidence from the map to support your explanation.

....

....

....

....

....

Total Number of Hurricane Strikes by Coastal County, 1900–2010

KEY
Total Strikes
0–2
3–4
5–6
7–9
10–12
13–14
15–16
17–19
20–25
26–32

Source: National Oceanic and Atmospheric Administration

3. Solve Problems Besides the solutions mentioned in the text, what do you think Floridians might do to address the continual threat of major hurricanes?

....

....

....

....

Lesson

(5) Climate Factors

Guiding Questions

- How do temperature, altitude, and land distribution affect regional climates?
- How does climate differ from weather?

Connections

Literacy Integrate With Visuals

 SC.6.E.7.2 Investigate and apply how the cycling of water between the atmosphere and hydrosphere has an effect on weather patterns and climate.
SC.6.E.7.6 Differentiate between weather and climate. (Also **SC.6.N.1.1** and **SC.6.N.2.3**)

Vocabulary

climate

Academic Vocabulary

describe

📱 VOCABULARY APP

Practice vocabulary on a mobile device.

 CONNECTION

Continue to gather information to help you on your Quest.

Connect It!

✏️ **Label the parts on the image that indicate what kind of temperature and precipitation is present in Antarctica.**

Make Generalizations From what you see in the image, how would you describe conditions in Antarctica?

....

Infer How do you think humans would adapt to this climate?

....

....

....

Factors That Affect Climate

No matter where you live, the weather changes every day. In some areas, the temperature might change just one degree from one day to the next. In other areas, a cold, rainy day might be followed by a warm, sunny one.

While weather describes the short-term conditions in an area, **climate** is the long-term weather pattern in an area. Specifically, climate refers to the average, year-after-year conditions of temperature, precipitation, wind, and clouds. So, while "it's hot" or "it's snowing" can describe the weather, you would need more information to describe the climate. For example, information about how much it rains or snows in a year **describes** the climate of an area.

The water cycle determines climate patterns. For example, year-round freezing temperatures in Antarctica prevent snow from melting and limit evaporation from the ocean. **Figure 1** shows that Antarctica has a cold, dry climate.

Another example is California's Mojave Desert, where the limited precipitation evaporates rapidly. The climate there is hot and dry. But, if you move west from the Mojave Desert toward California's coast, you would notice a cooler, more humid climate. Why does this happen?

Climate is affected by latitude, altitude, distance from large bodies of water, ocean currents, and global prevailing winds. These factors are not constant; they continuously change. If the factors change too drastically, an area's overall climate could change as well.

HANDS-ON LAB

Explore how moving north or south on Earth affects the climate of the region.

Academic Vocabulary

How might you describe your favorite food?

....

....

....

....

Temperature and Climate

Figure 1 Polar climates have certain patterns of temperature and precipitation, as shown in this image of Antarctica.

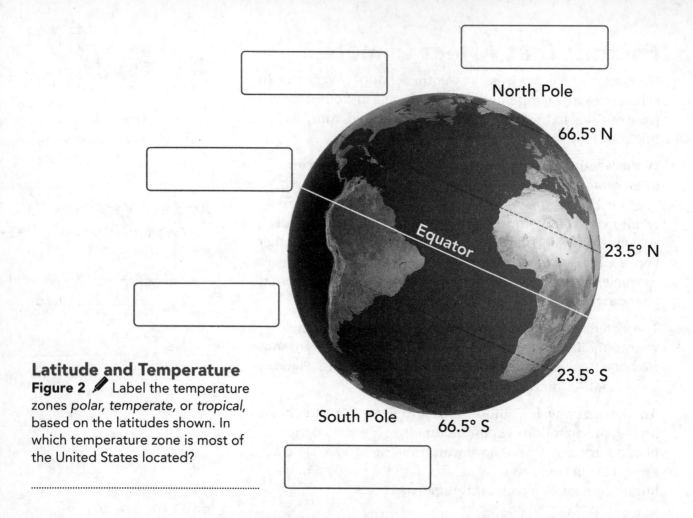

North Pole

66.5° N

Equator

23.5° N

23.5° S

South Pole

66.5° S

Latitude and Temperature

Figure 2 ✏ Label the temperature zones *polar*, *temperate*, or *tropical*, based on the latitudes shown. In which temperature zone is most of the United States located?

....

Literacy Connection

Integrate With Visuals As you look at **Figure 2**, think about why this image was included in this book. Underline the portion of the text that relates to the image. How does the image add to the information you gained by reading the text? How does it support what you have read?

Latitude People who live in the northern United States tend to have snowy winters, while people in the south have mild, warm winters. This is because areas closer to the equator have warmer climates than areas farther from it. The sun's rays hit Earth's surface more directly at the equator than at the poles. At the poles, the same amount of solar radiation hits at a greater angle, which brings less warmth. Based on latitude, Earth's surface is divided into three types of temperature zones, as shown in **(Figure 2)**.

The width of the tropical zone is the result of Earth's 23.5° tilt on its axis. The polar zones extend from about 66.5° to 90°N and 66.5° to 90°S latitudes. Between them are the temperate zones. In summer, the sun's rays strike the temperate zones quite directly. In winter, the sun's rays strike at a lower angle.

Altitude In the case of high mountains, altitude is a more important climate factor than latitude. Near Earth's surface, temperature decreases about 6.5°C for every 1-kilometer increase in altitude. Thus, many mountainous areas have cooler climates than the lower areas around them.

Distance from Large Bodies of Water The

ocean and other large bodies of water, such as lakes, can affect the weather and climate of nearby land by moderating local air temperatures. Water heats up and cools down about five times more slowly than land. As a result, the air above water heats up and cools down more slowly than air over land. When winds blow across oceans onto land, they moderate temperatures in coastal areas, bringing mild winters and cool summers. The centers of most continents, however, are too far from the ocean to be warmed or cooled by it. These areas have continental climates, with colder winters and warmer summers.

Ocean Currents Marine climates are strongly influ-

enced by the temperature of nearby ocean currents—streams of water within the ocean that move in regular patterns caused by different amounts of solar energy striking Earth at different latitudes. As shown in **Figure 3**, most warm ocean currents move toward the poles. Conversely, cold water currents tend to move toward the equator. Cold currents affect climate by carrying cold water from the polar zones toward the equator, cooling local air masses.

☑ READING CHECK **Determine Conclusions** How doe, the North Atlantic Drift most likely affect the climate in Europe?

📓 Write About It
Describe the relationship between weather on the continents and weather at sea.

Major Ocean Currents
Figure 3 Major currents circulate warm and cold ocean water between the poles and the equator. Compare and contrast the major ocean currents north and south of the equator.

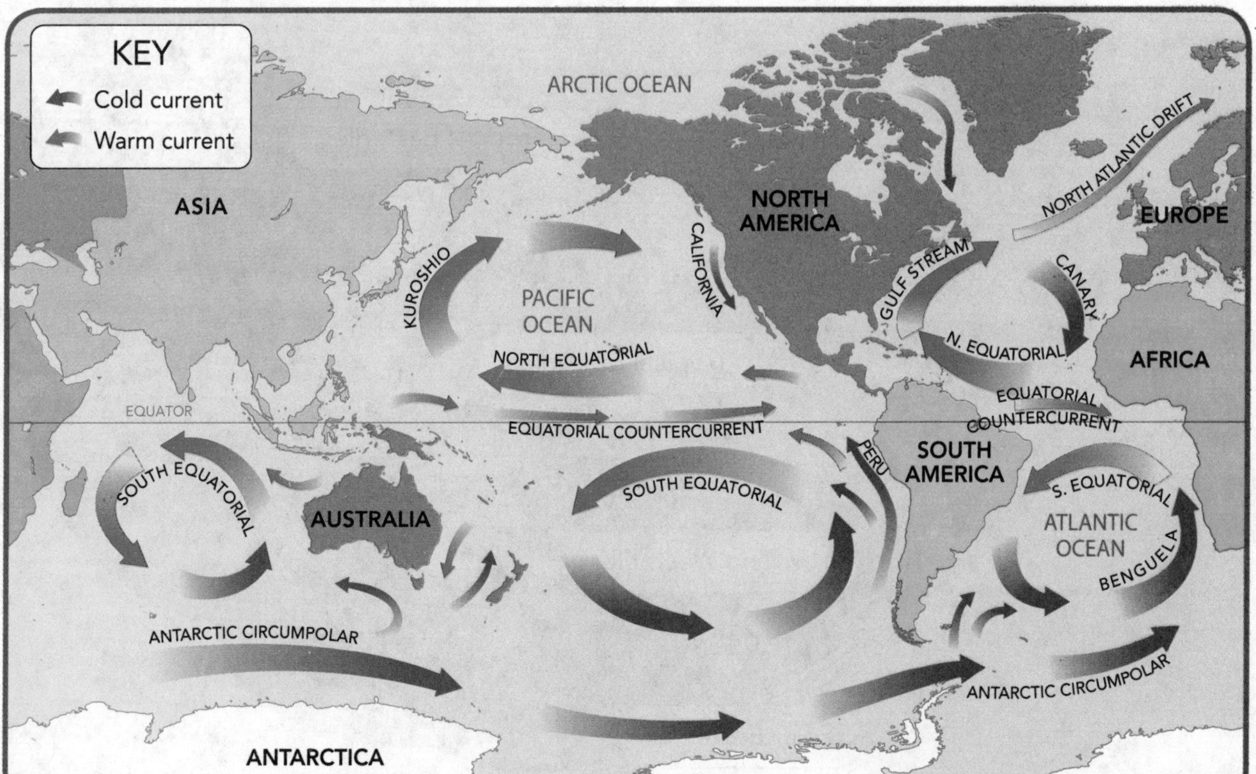

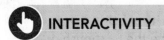
Factors That Affect Precipitation

The amount of precipitation a particular area experiences from month to month and year to year can vary greatly. By analyzing the amount of precipitation an area has received over many years, meteorologists determine the average yearly precipitation for that area. The main factors that affect the amount of precipitation an area receives are prevailing winds, presence of mountains, and seasonal winds.

Prevailing Winds Prevailing winds are winds that usually blow in one direction over large distances on Earth. As shown in **Figure 4,** these winds are organized into belts that can move air masses with different temperatures and humidities over long distances. The amount of water vapor an air mass carries affects how much rain or snow it can produce.

Prevailing Winds

Figure 4 ✏ Circle the name of the wind belt that most affects Europe.

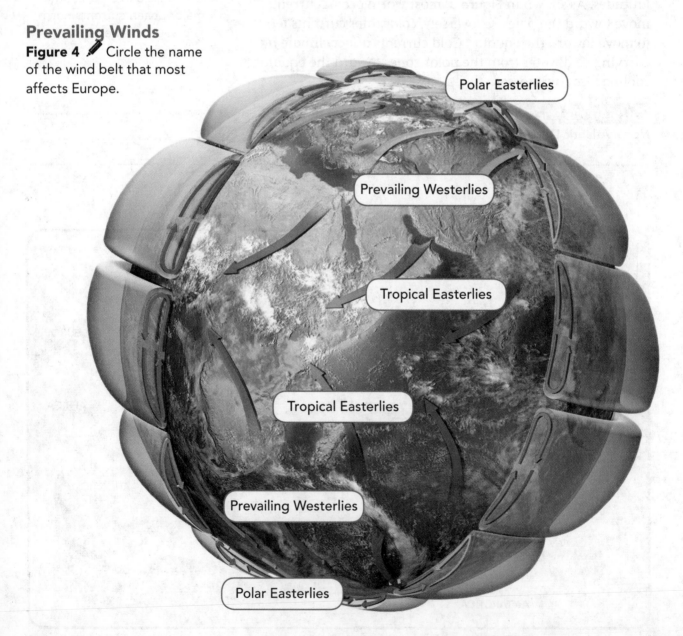

Polar Easterlies

Prevailing Westerlies

Tropical Easterlies

Tropical Easterlies

Prevailing Westerlies

Polar Easterlies

1. Warm, moist air is carried from the Pacific Ocean by the prevailing westerlies.

2. Somewhat drier air continues to move eastward, rising along with the slope of the land.

3. Now dry air continues to move east after passing the mountains.

Mountain Ranges The presence of a mountain range, like the one in **Figure 5,** can affect the type and location of precipitation any air masses may produce as they pass over the area. Humid air masses blown in from the ocean are forced to rise as they encounter coastal mountains, producing clouds and precipitation on the side of the mountain facing the wind. After passing over the mountains, the air mass is drier, having lost much of its water vapor. This leaves the side of the mountain facing away from the wind in a rain shadow, where little precipitation falls.

Seasonal Winds A seasonal change in wind patterns and precipitation, called a monsoon, occurs in some parts of the world. Monsoons are caused by different rates of heating and cooling between the ocean and nearby land. During the summer in southern Asia, when the land gradually gets warmer than the ocean, warm humid winds constantly blow in from the ocean, producing heavy rains. In winter, the opposite occurs as the land becomes colder than the ocean. Cool, dry winds constantly blow out to sea from the land.

Mountains and Precipitation

Figure 5 🖊 This image shows what happens when a mountain range is in the path of a prevailing wind. Draw rain and snow where they are most likely to occur. Add a redwood tree and a cactus in the locations that you think favor the growth of these plants.

✅ **READING CHECK** **Integrate With Visuals** If the area shown in **Figure 5** were located in a region where monsoons occur, would the figure represent a summer monsoon or a winter monsoon? Explain.

....

....

....

Major Climates

Figure 6 ✏️ The locations of major climate regions covering Earth's surface are influenced by many factors. Draw a circle around the area on the map where you live. What type of climate exists where you live?

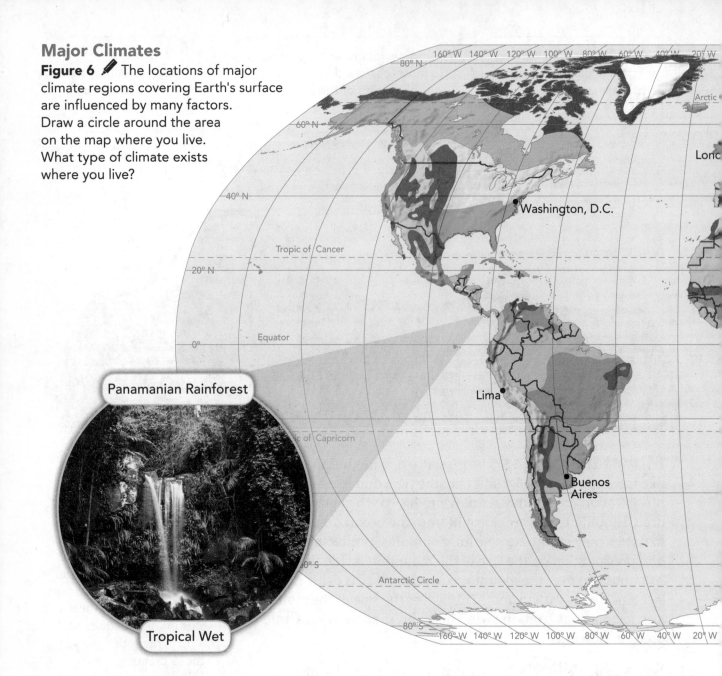

Washington, D.C.

Lima

Buenos Aires

Panamanian Rainforest

Tropical Wet

HANDS-ON LAB

✏️**Investigate** Observe some of the factors that help to distinguish among climate regions.

World Climates

Imagine winning a vacation to the Australian Outback! The Outback is a region near the central area of Australia. What type of clothes should you take on the trip? The best way to find out is to learn more about your destination's climate.

Scientists classify climates by taking into account an area's average temperature, average annual precipitation, and the vegetation found growing there. Recall that these characteristics are greatly influenced by local factors including prevailing and seasonal winds, the presence of major land features, and nearness to large bodies of water and ocean currents. As shown in **Figure 6,** the major climate regions of Earth each have their own smaller subdivisions.

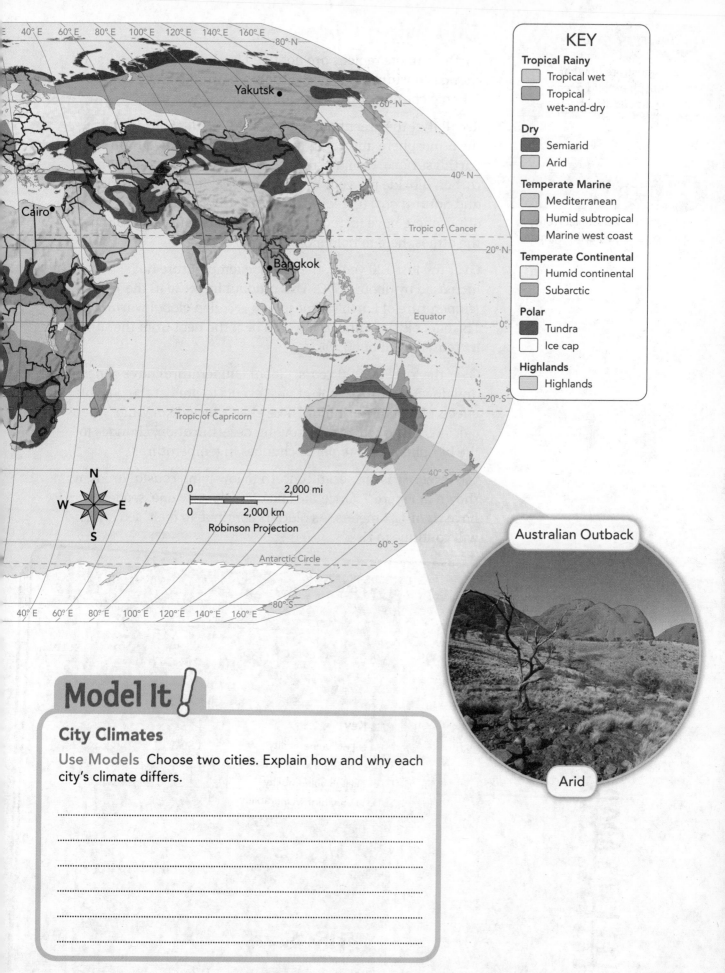

KEY

Tropical Rainy
- Tropical wet
- Tropical wet-and-dry

Dry
- Semiarid
- Arid

Temperate Marine
- Mediterranean
- Humid subtropical
- Marine west coast

Temperate Continental
- Humid continental
- Subarctic

Polar
- Tundra
- Ice cap

Highlands
- Highlands

Yakutsk

Cairo

Bangkok

Tropic of Cancer

Equator

Tropic of Capricorn

Antarctic Circle

N W E S

0   2,000 mi
0   2,000 km
Robinson Projection

Australian Outback

Arid

Model It

City Climates

Use Models Choose two cities. Explain how and why each city's climate differs.

....

....

....

....

....

....

INTERACTIVITY

Demonstrate how the atmosphere and ocean circulations affect climate.

VIDEO

Watch how ocean currents help to regulate the climate.

Changing Climates

Earth's climate regions are not fixed in position. Local climates change constantly due to changes in natural climate factors. Climate change also occurs due to human activity.

Recall that the greenhouse effect is the result of gases in the atmosphere absorbing thermal energy radiated from Earth's surface. Humans release billions of tons of additional carbon dioxide per year by burning fossil fuels such as coal and natural gas. Increased levels of carbon dioxide in the atmosphere have increased the greenhouse effect, enabling the atmosphere to hold more thermal energy.

Over the last 120 years, the average temperature has increased by about 0.7°C. This gradual increase in the temperature of Earth's atmosphere is called global warming. The effect is the same as it would be if the heat from the sun increased by about 0.5%.

Over the last 800,000 years, global temperatures have gone up and down. Scientists look at past events to predict the possible effects of global warming. These effects include melting glaciers, rising sea levels, drought, desertification, changes to the biosphere, and regional changes in temperature.

Sea level rise is of special concern to low-lying coastal areas, as shown in **Figure 7**. Since the end of the last ice age, sea levels have risen 122 meters. As glaciers continue to melt, sea levels will continue to rise.

Sea Level Rise
Figure 7 This satellite image shows how rising sea levels may affect the eastern United States.

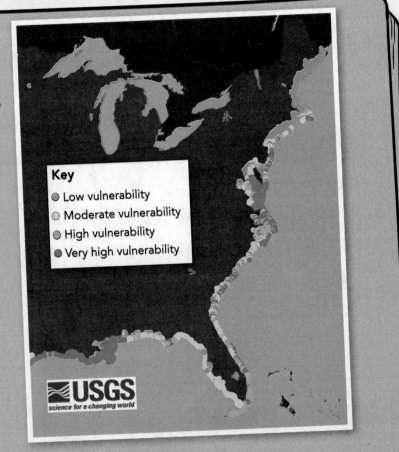

Key
● Low vulnerability
○ Moderate vulnerability
● High vulnerability
● Very high vulnerability

USGS
science for a changing world

SC.6.E.7.2, SC.6.E.7.6

1. Compare and Contrast What is the difference between weather and climate?

....

....

....

....

2. Apply Concepts Suppose climate change leads to a rapid warming of the climate in a particular area with mountains. Predict two effects on a species adapted to the climate at a middle elevation in the mountains.

....

....

....

....

....

....

Use Figure 3 to answer Question 3.

3. Apply Scientific Reasoning The south equatorial current follows the flow of winds above it and normally carries moisture to cause rain in Australia. But during El Niño events, the eastern Pacific becomes warmer, and the winds driving the south equatorial current slow or reverse direction. Evaluate and explain the effects of El Niño on rainfall patterns.

....

....

....

....

4. Apply Concepts How do climate factors affect temperature patterns where you live?

....

....

....

....

....

Use Figure 4 to answer Question 5.

5. Interpret Diagrams Recall that rising air masses cool and lose their moisture, while falling air masses tend to warm and absorb moisture. Explain why equatorial Africa has a tropical wet climate, and northern Africa has an arid climate.

....

....

....

....

....

....

....

....

6. Apply Concepts What could happen to climate in Europe if the Gulf Stream weakened due to climate change?

Gulf Stream

....

....

....

....

....

....

....

239

1 Water in the Atmosphere

SC.6.E.7.2

1. Which is not a type of precipitation?
   A. snow   B. hail
   C. cloud droplets   D. rain

2. **Draw Conclusions** The diagram shows how much water vapor can be held in air.

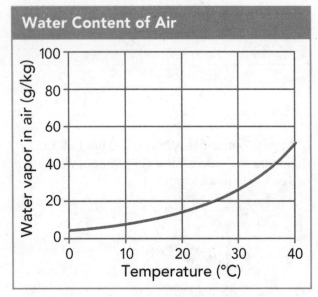

Water Content of Air

The table shows temperatures and water vapor content on two different days at the same location.

	Temp °C	Water Content (g/kg)
Day 1	20	10
Day 2	35	20

Identify which day feels more humid and explain.

....
....
....
....

2 Air Masses

SC.6.E.7.2, SC.6.E.7.3

The graph shows changes in air temperature, air pressure, and precipitation. **Use the graph to answer Questions 3 and 4.**

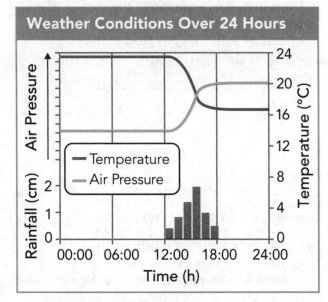

Weather Conditions Over 24 Hours

3. **Draw Conclusions** Explain the weather during this time period in terms of air masses and fronts.

....
....
....
....
....

4. **Apply Concepts** Based on the graph, describe two other effects you would expect.

....
....
....
....

5. What type of air mass is most likely to form over the Atlantic Ocean near the equator?

....

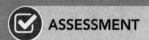
3 Predicting Weather Changes

SC.6.E.7.2, SC.6.E.7.3

Use Figure 4 in Lesson 3 to answer Questions 6 and 7.

6. Interpret Diagrams In the symbol for a weather front, the triangles or semicircles face the area the front is moving toward. Describe the area(s) on the map that have warm temperatures and explain your choice(s).

....

....

....

7. Construct Explanations What reason(s) could there be for the lack of precipitation around the north–south cold front and the large area of precipitation around the stationary front in the northeast?

....

....

....

....

....

....

....

4 Severe Weather and Floods

SC.6.E.7.7, SC.6.E.7.8

8. Which of the following are **not** used to prevent flooding during storms?
   A. dams   B. levees
   C. breakwaters   D. sandbags

9. Draw Conclusions Much of Florida is less than 6 m above sea level. The maximum elevation on the Florida peninsula is 95 m. Explain ways that Florida is particularly at risk from hurricane damage.

....

....

....

....

5 Climate Factors

SC.6.E.7.2, SC.6.E.7.6

Use Figures 3, 4, and 6 in Lesson 5 to answer Question 10.

10. Construct Explanations Apply what you know about global wind and ocean current patterns to explain the arid outback of Australia. It extends to the western coast, but not to the eastern coast, which has more rainfall.

....

....

....

....

....

....

11. Compare and Contrast Use an example to describe the difference between weather and climate.

....

....

....

....

Circle the letter of the best answer.

The diagram shows the typical weather and cycling of water around a lake fed by a mountain stream. **Use the diagram to answer questions 1–4.**

❶ Describe the process indicated by the upward arrows.

A Water evaporates from the lake and trees into the air to form clouds.

B Water vapor rises by transpiration from the land into the warmer air.

C Water changes to vapor by transpiration and evaporation and rises in warm air.

D Water vapor moves by evaporation and transpiration from the lake to the clouds.

❷ Suppose you are caught outside during a thunderstorm near this lake. Which of the following actions is most likely to protect you from harm?

F Get under the largest nearby tree and stay next to its trunk.

G Get into the water of the lake, staying very near the shoreline.

H Get in a rowboat and quickly move close to the center of the lake.

I Move away from the water and trees to a low area and crouch down.

❸ In the winter, areas to the east of this lake are often affected by lake-effect snow. This occurs most often when the jet stream dips to the south of the lake, allowing a shift in the prevailing winds such that a westerly wind blows over the lake. Under which additional condition is lake-effect snow most likely to occur?

A when the lake water is warmer than the surrounding land

B when the waves on the lake create a rough surface over which the wind blows

C when the lake water is colder than the surrounding land

D only after the lake surface has frozen over with ice

❹ Near the top of the picture is a cloud. Which combination of factors is necessary to produce this cloud?

F water vapor in the air, warm air temperature and solar energy

G water vapor in the air, cool air temperature, and small electrical charges in the air

H water vapor in the air, cool air temperature, and small particles in the air

I water vapor in the air, a warm air mass, and small particles in the air

The table shows the average number of tornadoes each year by land area in each state. **Use this table to answer Questions 5 and 6.**

	No./year	No./year–1000 mi²
Texas	155	0.59
Kansas	96	1.17
Florida	66	1.23
Oklahoma	62	0.90
Illinois	54	0.97

5 Based on the table, which statement about tornadoes in these states is most accurate?

A Encountering a tornado is most likely in Florida.

B Encountering a tornado is most likely in Texas.

C Encountering a tornado is least likely in Illinois

D Encountering a tornado in Kansas is more likely than in Florida.

6 What additional information would you need to compare the estimated risk of human deaths and injuries from tornadoes for these states?

F the number of cities in each state

G the number of houses in each state

H the population size of each state

I the length of tornado season in each state

7 Which statement refers to weather rather than climate?

A This area usually has a relative humidity lower than 50 percent.

B A thunderstorm is expected today.

C Precipitation amounts have increased over the last several years.

D The temperature is usually around 24°C (75°F).

Quest FINDINGS

Complete the Quest!

Create your PSA to help people understand, predict, prepare for, and avoid the dangers of severe weather.

Apply Concepts Severe storms can harm people and damage property. What climate and weather factors do meteorologists track to help people stay informed about severe weather events? Explain.

....
....
....
....
....
....
....
....
....
....
....
....
....

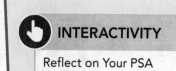 **INTERACTIVITY**

Reflect on Your PSA

SC.6.E.7.2, SC.6.N.1.1, SC.6.N.1.4

Water From Trees

How can you **gather evidence** that **plants** are part of the **water cycle**?

Background

A local horticultural society that opposes the construction of a new mall in the community has enlisted your help. The group members believe that cutting down thousands of trees will have a negative impact on the environment. In this lab, you will design an investigation to collect evidence that trees play an important role in the water cycle.

Materials

(per group)

- balance scale
- 3 plastic sandwich bags
- 3 small pebbles
- 3 twist ties

Plan Your Investigation

HANDS-ON LAB

ⓘ**Demonstrate** Go online for a downloadable worksheet of this lab.

1. You will use the materials provided by your teacher to design and conduct an investigation to identify the mass of water released by several plant leaves outside over a 7-day period.

2. Consider the following questions before you begin planning your investigation:

   - How can you use the bag, pebble, and twist tie to collect water from several leaves of a tree?

   - How many trials will you conduct?

   - What data will you collect?

   - How can you determine the mass of water released by the plant leaf after 7 days?

3. In the space provided, write out a procedure that identifies the steps you will follow to conduct your investigation. Include a sketch of your setup.

4. Create a data table in the space provided to record the data you collect.

5. After receiving your teacher's approval for your plan, conduct your investigation.

Procedure and Sketch

Data Table

Analyze and Interpret Data

1. **Make Observations** What did you observe in the plastic bags after 7 days? Where did the water you observed come from?

   ....

   ....

   ....

2. **Calculate** A large, mature tree can contain as many as 200,000 leaves. Using the data you collected, calculate the mass of water that might transpire from a mature tree in one day.

   ....

   ....

3. **Evaluate Your Plan** Review the data table from another group's investigation. How might your group modify your data table?

   ....

   ....

   ....

4. **Construct Arguments** In the space provided, sketch a diagram of Earth's water cycle. Use arrows and labels to indicate water's movement through the cycle. Based on your evidence, include a tree in your diagram to show the role that trees and other plants play in the water cycle.

Earth's Surface Systems

SC.6.E.6.1 Describe and give examples of ways in which Earth's surface is built up and torn down by physical and chemical weathering, erosion, and deposition. (Also **SC.6.N.1.1** and **SC.6.N.3.4**)

How did this rock get its strange shape?

HANDS-ON LAB

uConnect Explore how the height and width of a hill affects mass movement.

GO ONLINE
to access your
digital course

 VIDEO

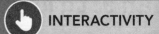 INTERACTIVITY

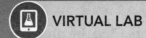 VIRTUAL LAB

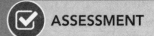 ASSESSMENT

 eTEXT

 APP

The Essential Question

What processes change Earth's surface?

Known as Thor's Hammer, this towering column of rock is a favorite sight at Bryce Canyon National Park in Utah. Hoodoos, or the tall, sedimentary rock spires, are commonly found in high plateau areas and regions of the northern Great Plains, but they are most abundant in Bryce Canyon. How do you think this feature formed?

....

....

....

Quest KICKOFF

How can I design and build an artificial island?

One way to expand a city surrounded by water is to make more land. In New York City, the area of lower Manhattan known as Battery Park City was created by civil engineers using soil and rock excavated during the construction of new skyscrapers. But what factors do engineers need to consider when they create new land in water? In this problem-based Quest activity, you will design an artificial island that can withstand nature's forces and that has minimal environmental impact.

👆 **INTERACTIVITY**

Ingenious Island

SC.6.E.6.1 Describe and give examples of ways in which Earth's surface is built up and torn down by physical and chemical weathering, erosion, and deposition. (Also **SC.6.N.1.1** and **SC.6.N.3.4**)

NBC LEARN ▶ VIDEO

After watching the Quest Kickoff video about how coastal engineers study and reduce coastal erosion, complete the 3-2-1 activity.

3 ways that water changes land

....

....

....

2 ways that wind changes land

....

....

1 way that those changes could be prevented or minimized

....

Quest CHECK-IN

IN LESSON 1

How does weathering affect various materials? Consider the benefits and drawbacks of using different materials for an artificial island.

HANDS-ON LAB

Breaking It Down

Quest CHECK-IN

IN LESSON 2

What criteria and constraints need to be considered when designing your island model to resist erosion over periods of time? Design and build your island model.

HANDS-ON LAB

Ingenious Island: Part I

 INTERACTIVITY

Changing Landscapes

Quest CHECK-IN

IN LESSON 3

How resistant is your island model to erosion? Test the effects of the agents of erosion on your model and make improvements.

HANDS-ON LAB

Ingenious Island: Part II

Beachfront properties line one of the "branches" of the Palm Jumeirah in the United Arab Emirates. The palm-shaped artificial island extends into the Persian Gulf off the coast of Dubai. It provides miles of additional shoreline for homes and elaborate hotels.

Quest CHECK-IN

IN LESSON 4
How can wave erosion impact the location of your artificial island? Adjust your design as needed to account for wave erosion.

👆 **INTERACTIVITY**

Breaking Waves

Quest FINDINGS

Complete the Quest!

Present your island model and explain how your design decisions relate to the forces that change Earth's surface.

👆 **INTERACTIVITY**

Reflect on Your Ingenious Island

251

Weathering and Soil

Guiding Questions

- How does erosion change Earth's surface?
- How does weathering change Earth's surface?
- How does soil form?

Connections

Literacy Write Explanatory Texts

Math Reason Quantitatively

🏴 **SC.6.E.6.1** Describe and give examples of ways in which Earth's surface is built up and torn down by physical and chemical weathering, erosion, and deposition. (Also **SC.6.N.1.5** and **SC.6.N.3.4**)

Vocabulary

uniformitarianism
erosion
mechanical
   weathering
chemical
   weathering
soil
humus

Academic Vocabulary

principle
component

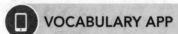

📱 **VOCABULARY APP**

Practice vocabulary on a mobile device.

Quest CONNECTION

Think about what criteria need to be considered when designing an island to resist erosion.

Connect It !

✏️ **The Wave is a stunning dip in Earth's surface. Draw an arrow showing where the material originally covering the Wave would have begun.**

Construct Explanations What processes have broken apart and carried off the many layers of solid rock that covered the Wave for millions of years?

....

....

Breaking Down Earth's Surface

Even the hardest rocks wear down over time on Earth's surface. Natural processes, such as the one that produced the Wave in **Figure 1**, break down rocks and carry the pieces away. Geologists make inferences about what processes shaped Earth's surface in the past based on the **principle** of **uniformitarianism** (yoon uh form uh TAYR ee un iz um). This principle states that the geologic processes that operate today also operated in the past. Scientists infer that ancient landforms and features formed through the same processes they observe today and will continue to do so in the future.

The processes of weathering and **erosion** (ee ROH zhun) work together to change Earth's surface by wearing down and carrying away rock particles. The process of weathering breaks down rock and other substances. Heat, cold, water, ice, and gases all contribute to weathering. Erosion involves the removal of rock particles by wind, water, ice, or gravity.

Weathering and erosion work continuously to reshape Earth's surface. The same processes that wear down mountains also cause bicycles to rust, paint to peel, and sidewalks to crack. Weathering and erosion can take millions of years to break down and wear away huge mountains, or they can take seconds to carry rock away in an avalanche. These processes started changing Earth's surface billions of years ago and they continue to do so.

Academic Vocabulary
Describe another principle you follow in science or in your everyday life.

....

....

....

Determine Meaning
How has weathering or erosion affected you? In your science notebook, describe an example of weathering or erosion you observed and any impact it had on you or your community.

Riding the Rock Wave
Figure 1 Known as the Wave, this sandstone dip in Earth's surface in Northern Arizona was buried beneath solid rock for millions of years.

Mechanical Weathering

Figure 2 Label each photo with an agent of mechanical weathering.

Explain Phenomena How might more than one agent of mechanical weathering operate in the same place?

....

....

....

....

Weathering Earth's Surface

The type of weathering in which rock is physically broken into smaller pieces is called **mechanical weathering**. A second type of weathering, called chemical weathering, also breaks down rock. **Chemical weathering** is the process that breaks down rock through chemical changes.

Mechanical Weathering Rocks that are cracked or split in layers have undergone mechanical weathering. Mechanical weathering usually happens gradually, over very long periods of time. Mechanical weathering, as part of erosion, can eventually wear away whole mountains.

The natural agents of mechanical weathering include freezing and thawing, release of pressure, plant growth, actions of animals, and abrasion, as shown in **Figure 2**. Abrasion (uh BRAY zhun) refers to the wearing away of rock by rock particles carried by water, ice, wind, or gravity. Human activities, such as mining and farming, also cause mechanical weathering.

Through mechanical weathering, Earth systems interact and shape the surface. For example, the geosphere (rocks) interacts with the hydrosphere (water, ice) during frost wedging. Frost wedging occurs when water seeps into cracks in rocks and expands as it freezes. Wedges of ice in rocks widen and deepen cracks. When the ice melts, water seeps deeper into the cracks. With repeated freezing and thawing, the cracks slowly expand until pieces of rock break off.

Chemical Weathering
Chemical weathering often produces new minerals as it breaks down rock. For example, granite is made up of several minerals, including feldspars. Chemical weathering causes the feldspar to eventually change to clay minerals.

Water, oxygen, carbon dioxide, living organisms, and acid rain cause chemical weathering. Water weathers some rock by dissolving it. Water also carries other substances, including oxygen, carbon dioxide, and other chemicals, that dissolve or break down rock.

The oxygen and carbon dioxide gases in the atmosphere cause chemical weathering. Rust forms when iron combines with oxygen in the presence of water. Rusting makes rock soft and crumbly and gives it a red or brown color. When carbon dioxide dissolves in water, carbonic acid forms. This weak acid easily weathers certain types of rock, such as marble and limestone.

As a plant's roots grow, they produce weak acids that gradually dissolve rock. Lichens—plantlike organisms that grow on rocks—also produce weak acids.

Humans escalate chemical weathering by burning fossil fuels. This pollutes the air and results in rainwater that is more strongly acidic. Acid rain causes very rapid chemical weathering of rock.

✓ READING CHECK **Summarize Text** How are the agents of weathering similar and different?

....

....

Literacy Connection
Write Explanatory Texts
An ancient marble statue is moved from a rural location to a highly polluted city. Explain how the move might affect the statue and why you think so.

....

....

....

....

....

....

....

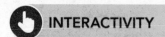
Rate of Weathering

In historic cemeteries, slate tombstones from the 1700s are less weathered than marble tombstones from the 1800s. Why? Some kinds of rocks weather more rapidly than others. The rate at which weathering occurs is determined by the type of rock and the climate.

Type of Rock Rocks wear down slowly if they are made of minerals that do not dissolve easily. Rocks weather faster if they are made of minerals that dissolve easily.

Some rocks weather more easily because they are permeable. A permeable (PUR mee uh bul) material is full of tiny air spaces. The spaces increase the surface area. As water seeps through the spaces in the rock, it carries chemicals that dissolve the rock and removes material broken down by weathering.

Climate Climate is the average weather conditions in an area. Weathering occurs faster in wet climates. Rainfall causes chemical changes. Freezing and thawing cause mechanical changes in cold and wet climates.

Chemical reactions occur faster at higher temperatures. That is why chemical weathering occurs more quickly where the climate is both hot and wet. Human activities, such as those that produce acid rain, also increase the rate of weathering.

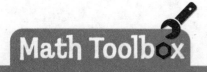

Math Toolbox

Comparing Weathered Limestone

The data table shows how much rock was broken down by weathering for two identical pieces of limestone in two different locations.

1. **Construct Graphs** ✏ Use the data to make a double-line graph. Decide how to make each line look different. Be sure to provide a title and label the axes and each graph line.

2. **Reason Quantitatively** As time increases, the limestone thickness (increases/decreases).

3. **Evaluate Data** Limestone A weathered at a (slower/faster) rate than Limestone B.

Weathering Rates of Limestone

Time (years)	Thickness of Limestone Lost (mm)	
	Limestone A	Limestone B
200	1.75	0.80
400	3.50	1.60
600	5.25	2.40
800	7.00	3.20
1,000	8.75	4.00

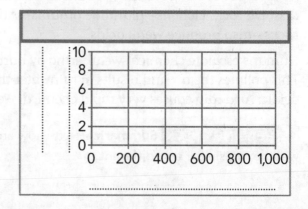

Gravel	Sand	Silt	Clay
2 mm & larger	Less than 2 mm	Less than 0.05 mm	Less than 0.002 mm

Source: Michigan Technological University

Forming Soil

Have you ever wondered how plants grow on rocks? Plants can grow only when soil begins to form in the cracks. **Soil** is the loose, weathered material on Earth's surface in which plants grow.

Soil Composition Soil is a mixture of rock particles, minerals, decayed organic material, water, and air. The main **components** of soil come from bedrock. Bedrock is the solid layer of rock beneath the soil. Once bedrock is exposed to air, water, and living things, it gradually weathers into smaller and smaller particles.

The particles of rock in soil are classified by size as gravel, sand, silt, and clay. **Figure 3** shows the relative sizes of these particles. A soil's texture depends on the size of the soil particles.

The decayed organic material in soil is called humus. **Humus** (HYOO mus) is a dark-colored substance that forms as plant and animal remains decay. Humus helps to create spaces in soil that are then filled by air and water. It contains nutrients that plants need.

☑ READING CHECK **Write Explanatory Texts** Explain how you might determine the rate of weathering on a sample of rock.

....

....

....

....

Soil Particle Size

Figure 3 ✏ The rock particles shown here have been enlarged. On the graph, mark the size of a 1.5-mm particle with an X.

Classify Explain how you would classify that size particle and why.

....

....

....

Academic Vocabulary

What are the similarities between components of a computer and the components of soil?

....

....

....

....

 **INTERACTIVITY**

Learn how minerals affect the colors of sand.

Soil Formation

Soil forms as rock is broken down by weathering and mixes with other materials on the surface. Soil forms constantly wherever bedrock weathers. Soil formation continues over a long period of time, taking hundreds to thousands of years. The same process that forms soil today was also taking place billions of years ago and will continue to form soil in the future.

Gradually, soil develops layers called horizons. A soil horizon is a layer of soil that differs in color, texture, and composition from the layers above or below it. **Figure 4** shows the sequence in which soil horizons form.

Soil and Organisms

Recall that organisms are part of Earth's biosphere. Many organisms live in soil and interact with the geosphere. Some soil organisms aid in the formation of humus, which makes soil rich in the nutrients that plants need. Other soil organisms mix the soil and make spaces in it for air and water.

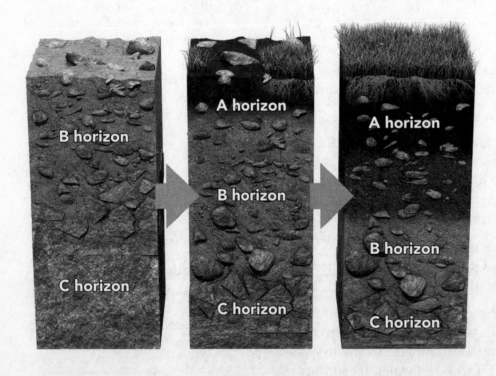

A horizon
The A horizon is made up of topsoil, a crumbly, dark brown soil that is a mixture of humus, clay, and minerals. Topsoil forms as plants add organic material to the soil, and plant roots weather pieces of rock.

B horizon
The B horizon, often called subsoil, usually consists of clay and other particles of rock, but little humus. It forms as rainwater washes these materials down from the A horizon.

C horizon
The C horizon forms as bedrock begins to weather. The rock breaks up into small particles.

Soil Horizons

Figure 4 Soil horizons form in three main steps.

1. **Interpret Diagrams** ✏ Underline the soil horizon that contains the most organic matter.

2. **Evaluate Quantity** In what climates would you expect soil to form fastest? Why?

....

....

Forming Humus Dead leaves, roots, and other plant materials contribute most of the organic remains that form humus. Humus forms in a process called decomposition carried out by a combination of decomposers including fungi, bacteria, worms, and other organisms. Decomposers break down the remains of dead organisms into smaller pieces through the process of chemical digestion. This material then mixes with the soil as nutrient-rich humus where it can be used by living plants.

Mixing the Soil Earthworms and burrowing mammals mix humus with air and other materials in soil, as shown in **Figure 5**. As earthworms eat their way through the soil, they carry humus down to the subsoil and from the subsoil up to the surface. These organisms increase the soil's fertility by dispersing organic matter throughout the soil. Mammals such as mice, moles, and prairie dogs break up hard, compacted soil and mix humus with it. Animal wastes contribute nutrients to the soil as well.

☑ READING CHECK **Integrate With Visuals** Review the information and illustrations in **Figure 4**. How is weathering related to soil formation?

....

....

....

Organisms Impact Soil
Figure 5 Earthworms and chipmunks break up hard, compacted soil, making it easier for air and water to enter the soil.

1. **Synthesize Information** Besides breaking up and mixing soil, the (earthworm/chipmunk) is also a decomposer.

2. **Apply Concepts** As these organisms change the soil, which Earth systems are interacting?

....

....

Model It ✏

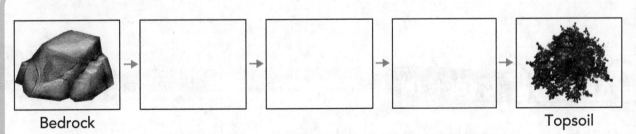

Bedrock .... Topsoil

From Rock to Soil

Figure 6 The illustrations show bedrock and topsoil rich in humus.

1. **Develop Models** ✏ In the empty boxes, draw the processes that help to change the bedrock into soil. Label the processes in each drawing. Include at least two processes that involve organisms.

2. **Use Models** The topsoil represents the (A/B/C) horizon.

☑ LESSON 1 Check

1. Describe How does erosion affect Earth's surface?

....

....

....

....

2. Cause and Effect A geologist studies an area of cracked and split rock in a cold region. What processes most likely caused the rock's appearance?

....

....

....

....

....

3. Infer A family noticed that the decorative rocks supporting their patio have begun to turn red. What has most likely led to this discoloration and why is it a problem?

....

....

....

....

....

4. Apply Concepts A community group wants to buy a statue for the city. What factors should they take into consideration when choosing the type of rock and location for the statue? Support your answers with evidence.

....

....

....

....

....

....

....

....

5. Draw Conclusions Drought can affect soil health. How might an extended drought impact soil formation? Support your answer with evidence.

....

....

....

....

....

....

....

....

....

Quest CHECK-IN

In this lesson, you learned how weathering and erosion change Earth's surface. You also discovered how soil forms.

Use Models How can modeling the effects of weathering on different materials help you to design your island?

....

....

....

....

HANDS-ON LAB

Breaking It Down

Investigate what constraints need to be considered when designing an island to resist long-term erosion.

GROUND SHIFTING ADVANCES:
Maps Help Predict

INTERACTIVITY

Learn about the causes of landslides and predict where they might occur.

Do you know what happens after heavy rains or earthquakes in California? There are landslides. Engineers look for patterns to determine how and where they can happen.

The Challenge: To protect highways and towns from landslides.

Evaluating hazards is one way to prepare for natural disasters. In the early 1970s, the California Geological Survey (CGS) began drawing up "Geology for Planning" maps. Its goal was to create maps showing areas all over the state where natural hazards, such as wildfires and landslides, were most likely to occur. Engineers and city planners could then use the maps to prepare for, or possibly prevent, natural disasters.

Landslides destroy roadways, cut people off from access to vital services, and disrupt local economies.

In 1997, the Caltrans Highway Corridor Mapping project began. Caltrans stands for California Department of Transportation. Caltrans engineers set out to map all known sites of landslides, as well as unstable slopes along the major interstate highways. Most of the landslide sites were along highways that wind through California's mountains. Using these maps, engineers have installed sensitive monitoring equipment to help predict future landslides.

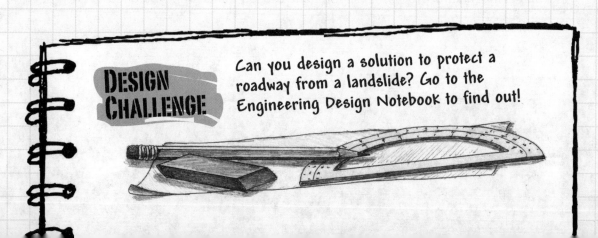

DESIGN CHALLENGE

Can you design a solution to protect a roadway from a landslide? Go to the Engineering Design Notebook to find out!

Erosion and Deposition

Guiding Questions

- What processes change Earth's surface?
- How does mass movement change Earth's surface?
- How does wind change Earth's surface?

Connections

Literacy Integrate With Visuals

Math Analyze Quantitative Relationships

 SC.6.E.6.1 Describe and give examples of ways in which Earth's surface is built up and torn down by physical and chemical weathering, erosion, and deposition. (Also **SC.6.N.3.4**)

Vocabulary

sediment
deposition
mass movement
deflation
sand dune
loess

Academic Vocabulary

similar
significant

 VOCABULARY APP

Practice vocabulary on a mobile device.

Quest CONNECTION

As you design and build a model of your island, consider the effects of erosion and deposition.

Connect It !

✏️ **Circle the change shown in the photo, then draw an arrow to show the direction of the rocks' movement.**

Interpret Photos How has Earth's surface changed in this photo?

....

....

Predict What natural processes do you think caused the change you observe?

....

....

Changing Earth's Surface

Have you ever watched water carry away bits of gravel and soil during a rainstorm? If so, you observed erosion. Recall that erosion is a process that moves weathered rock from its original location. Gravity, water, ice, and wind are all agents of erosion.

The process of erosion moves material called **sediment**. Sediment may consist of pieces of rock or soil, or the remains of plants and animals.

Deposition occurs where the agents of erosion deposit, or lay down, sediment. Like erosion, deposition changes the shape of Earth's surface. You may have watched an ant carry away bits of soil and then put the soil down in a different location to build an ant hill. The ant's activity is **similar** to erosion and deposition, which involves picking up, carrying away, and putting down sediment in a different place.

Weathering, erosion, transportation, and deposition act together in a continuous cycle that wears down and builds up Earth's surface. As erosion wears down a mountain in one place, deposition builds up a new landform in another place. Some changes happen over a large area, while others occur in a small space. Some happen slowly over thousands or millions of years, and others take only a few minutes or seconds, such as the rockslide shown in **Figure 1**. No matter how large or fast the changes, the cycle of erosion and deposition is continuous. The same changes that shaped Earth's surface in the past still shape it today and will continue to shape it in the future.

Academic Vocabulary
Using two things you can observe right now, write a sentence describing how they are similar.

....

....

....

....

Literacy Connection
Integrate With Visuals
In the third paragraph of the text, underline a statement that is supported by evidence in the photograph.

Moving Rock
Figure 1 The sudden change in the appearance of this hillside was caused by the natural movement of rock.

263

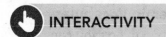
Mass Movement

If you place a ball at the top of a hill, with a slight push the ball will roll down the hill. Gravity pulls the ball downward. Gravity is also the force that moves rock and other materials downhill.

Gravity causes **mass movement**, one of several processes that move sediment downhill. Mass movement can be rapid or slow. Erosion and deposition both take place during a mass movement event. The different types of mass movement include landslides, mudflows, slumps, and creep (**Figure 2**).

A mass movement may be caused by a natural disaster, such as a flood, earthquake, or hurricane. Natural disasters can dramatically and suddenly change Earth's surface. Scientists make maps of past mass movements in a region to better understand their hazards. Such maps help scientists to identify patterns and predict where future mass movement is likely to occur in order to prevent human casualties.

Mass Movement

Figure 2 Different types of mass movement have different characteristics.

1. **Develop Models** ✏️
   Draw arrows on each image of mass movement to show the direction that material moves.

2. **Identify Patterns** What pattern(s) can you identify among the types of mass movement?

....

....

☑ READING CHECK **Integrate With Visuals** Read and think about the information relating to different kinds of mass movement. Which type of mass movement do you think is least dangerous? Why?

....

....

Landslides

A landslide occurs when rock and soil slide quickly down a steep slope. Some landslides contain huge masses of rock, while others contain only small amounts of rock and soil. Often caused by earthquakes, landslides occur where road builders have cut highways through hills or mountains, leaving behind unstable slopes.

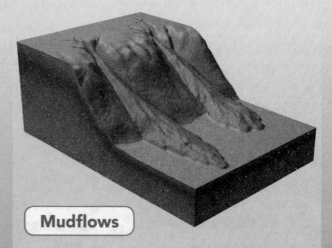

Mudflows

A mudflow is the rapid downhill movement of a mixture of water, rock, and soil. Mudflows often occur after heavy rains in a normally dry area. In clay-rich soils with a high water content, mudflows may occur even on very gentle slopes. Under certain conditions, clay-rich soil suddenly behaves as a liquid and begins to flow.

Major Landslides and Mudflows

Landslides and mudflows are a problem in all 50 states and all around the world. Annually in the United States, landslides cause $1 billion to $2 billion in damage and about 25 deaths. But some catastrophic mass movements in other countries have killed more than 100,000 people.

1. Use Proportional Relationships What proportion of the landslides were caused by earthquakes?

....

2. Analyze Quantitative Relationships Which process caused the most landslides? Which caused the fewest landslides?

....

Major Landslides and Mudflows of the 20th Century

Year	Location	Cause
1919	Java, Indonesia	volcanic eruption
1920	Ningxia, China	earthquake
1933	Sichuan, China	earthquake
1949	Tadzhikistan	earthquake
1958	Japan	heavy rains
1970	Peru	earthquake
1980	Washington, USA	earthquakes
1983	Utah, USA	heavy rain and snowmelt
1985	Colombia	volcano
1998	Central America	hurricane rains

Slumps

In a slump, a mass of rock and soil suddenly slips down a slope. Unlike a landslide, the material in a slump moves down in one large mass. It looks as if someone pulled the bottom out from under part of the slope. A slump often occurs when water soaks the bottom of clay-rich soil.

Creep

Creep is the very slow downhill movement of rock and soil. It can even occur on gentle slopes. Creep often results from the freezing and thawing of water in cracked layers of rock beneath the soil. Even though it occurs slowly, you can see the effects of creep in vertical objects such as telephone poles and tree trunks. Creep may tilt these objects at unusual angles.

Academic Vocabulary

Describe a significant change in weather from the winter to the summer.

....

....

....

Erosion and Deposition by Wind

Recall that wind, or moving air, is an agent of erosion and deposition. Through these processes, wind wears down and builds up Earth's surface.

Wind Erosion Wind can be a **significant** agent in shaping the land in areas where there are few plants to hold the soil in place. In a sandstorm, strong winds pick up large amounts of sediment and loose soil and transport it to new locations.

Deflation Wind causes erosion mainly by **deflation**, the process by which wind removes surface materials. You can see the process of deflation in **Figure 3**. When wind blows over the land, it picks up the smallest particles of sediment, such as clay and silt. Stronger, faster winds pick up larger particles. Slightly larger particles, such as sand, might skip or bounce for a short distance. Strong winds can roll even larger and heavier sediment particles. In deserts, deflation can create an area called desert pavement where smaller sediments are blown away, and larger rock fragments are left behind.

Abrasion Wind, water, and ice carry particles that rub or scrape against exposed rock. As particles move against the rock, friction wears away the rock by the process of abrasion.

Wind Erosion and Deflation

Figure 3 Wind causes deflation by moving surface particles in three ways.

1. **Patterns** 🖊 In each circle, draw the size of particles that would be moved by the wind.

2. **Explain** How is the height and distance of movement above the ground related to the size of the sediment particles?

....

....

....

3. **Interpret Diagrams** Complete each sentence to the right with one of the following words: Fine, Medium, Large.

.... particles are carried through the air.

.... particles skip or bounce.

.... particles slide or roll.

Wind Deposition All the sediment picked up by wind eventually falls to the ground. This happens when the wind slows down or encounters an obstacle. Wind deposition may form sand dunes and loess deposits.

Sand Dunes When wind meets an obstacle, such as a clump of grass, the result is usually a deposit of windblown sand called a **sand dune**. **Figure 4** shows how wind direction can form different dunes. The shape and size of sand dunes is determined by the direction of the wind, the amount of sand, and the presence of plants. This same process changed Earth's surface billions of years ago, just as it does today. You can predict how wind deposition will affect the surface in the future. You can see sand dunes on beaches and in deserts where wind-blown sediment builds up. Sand dunes also move over time because the sand shifts with the wind from one side of the dune to the other. Sometimes plants begin growing on a dune, and the roots help to anchor the dune in one place.

Loess Deposits The wind drops sediment that is finer than sand but coarser than clay far from its source. This fine, wind-deposited sediment is **loess** (LOH es). There are large loess deposits in central China and in states such as Nebraska, South Dakota, Iowa, Missouri, and Illinois. Loess helps to form soil rich in nutrients. Many areas with thick loess deposits are valuable farmlands.

☑ READING CHECK **Cite Textual Evidence** What factors affect wind erosion and deposition?

....

....

Question It!

Moving Sand Dunes

Sand dunes keep drifting and covering a nearby, busy parking lot.

Define the Problem   State the problem that needs to be solved in the form of a question.

....

....

Develop Possible Solutions Describe two possible solutions to the problem. Explain why each would solve the problem.

....

....

....

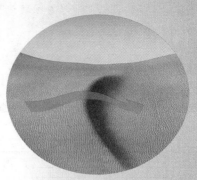

Crescent-shaped dune

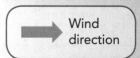

Wind direction

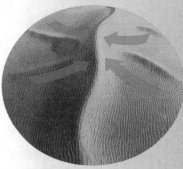

Star-shaped dunes

Dune Formation
Figure 4 Sand dunes form and change shape as the wind deposits sand.

1. **Predict** 🖊 Draw a line to show how the ridge of the crescent-shaped dune will likely shift over time.

2. **Explain** Why do these dunes have different shapes?

....

....

....

🖐 **INTERACTIVITY**

Explore fast and slow changes to Earth's surface.

1. **Identify** Which kinds of mass movement would most likely occur after a heavy rain?

2. **Infer** How is physical weathering related to mass movements?

3. **Patterns** A crescent-shaped sand dune forms in a desert. What processes might have occurred to create this surface change?

4. **Evaluate Questions** To narrow down the location for a new development, a construction company gets several plots of land assessed. They study the soil type, shape of the land, and vegetation. How would you evaluate their assessment? Explain how to improve it.

5. **Interpret Data** Hill X experiences a slump after being hit by a hurricane. Hill Y in the same town experiences the same storm and has a steeper slope, but does not have a mass movement. Why did Hill X experience the mass movement, while Hill Y did not? Explain your answer.

Quest CHECK-INS

In this lesson, you learned how gravity causes erosion and deposition. You also learned how wind causes erosion and deposition.

Refine Your Solution What are some ways that the effects of erosion can be mitigated in your design for the artificial island?

HANDS-ON LAB

Ingenious Island, Part I

👆 INTERACTIVITY

Changing Landscapes

Do the hands-on lab to test your island's resistance to erosion by surface water.

Go online to explore how landscapes can be changed.

CAREERS

Civil Engineer

Civil Engineers SAVE THE DAY!

Who put the civil in civilization? Engineers! Civil engineers are responsible for all the works that benefit the citizens of a society. After a natural disaster, civil engineers get involved in reconstruction efforts.

Think of the networks and systems we rely on every day—roadways, train tracks, cell phone towers, the electrical grid, and gas lines. Consider the cities built on filled-in swamp or a town built over rough terrain. Think of all the bridges connecting two sides of a river—even one as wide as the Mississippi. Civil engineers and the construction workers they guided made all of this possible.

Whether planning a new road or bridge, civil engineers must take into account the forces that change Earth's surface. Water and wind erosion, for example, have serious effects on roadways and can cause costly damage. A civil engineer's job is to determine how to build the road in a way that minimizes nature's potentially damaging effects.

If you want to be a civil engineer, you'll need to study science and math. You'll also need to develop your imagination, because solutions require creativity as well as analytical thinking.

▶ VIDEO

Watch what's involved in being a civil engineer.

MY CAREER

Type "civil engineer" into an online search engine to learn more about this career.

Civil engineers survey and measure the surface of Earth. The data they collect are used to plan construction projects such as this bridge.

3 Water Erosion

Guiding Questions

- How does moving water change Earth's surface?
- What landforms form from water erosion and deposition?
- How does groundwater change Earth?

Connection

Literacy Cite Textual Evidence

🔁 **SC.6.E.6.1** Describe and give examples of ways in which Earth's surface is built up and torn down by physical and chemical weathering, erosion, and deposition. (Also **SC.6.N.3.4**)

Vocabulary

runoff
stream
tributary
flood plain
delta
alluvial fan
groundwater

Academic Vocabulary

develop
suggest

 VOCABULARY APP

Practice vocabulary on a mobile device.

Quest CONNECTION

Think about how other types of erosion might impact your island design.

Connect It !

🖊 **Draw a line showing where Niagara Falls may have been in the past.**

Construct Explanations How do you think Niagara Falls formed?

....

....

....

Apply Scientific Reasoning What do you think this waterfall and all other waterfalls have in common?

....

How Water Causes Erosion

Erosion by water doesn't start with a giant waterfall, such as the one in **Figure 1**. It begins with a little splash of rain. Some rainfall sinks into the ground, where it is absorbed by plant roots. Some water evaporates, while the rest of the water runs off over the land surface. Moving water of the hydrosphere is the primary agent of the erosion that shaped Earth's land surface, the geosphere, for billions of years. It continues to shape the surface today in small and large ways.

Runoff As water moves over the land, it picks up and carries sediment. This moving water is called **runoff**. When runoff flows over the land, it may cause a type of erosion called sheet erosion, where thin layers of soil are removed. The amount of runoff in an area depends on five main factors. The first factor is the amount of rain an area gets. A heavy or lengthy rainfall can add water to the surface more quickly than the surface can absorb it. A second factor is vegetation. Grasses, shrubs, and trees reduce runoff by absorbing water and holding soil in place. A third factor is the type of soil. Different types of soils absorb different amounts of water. A fourth factor is the shape of the land. Runoff is more likely to occur on steeply sloped land than on flatter land. Finally, a fifth factor is how people use land. For example, pavement does not absorb water. All the rain that falls on it becomes runoff. Runoff also increases when trees or crops are cut down, because this removes vegetation from the land.

Factors that reduce runoff also reduce erosion. Even though deserts have little rainfall, they often have high runoff and erosion because they have few plants and thin, sandy soil. In wet areas, such as rain forests and wetlands, runoff and erosion may be low because there are more plants to protect the soil.

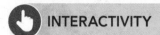
INTERACTIVITY

Locate evidence of water erosion and determine why it happened.

Literacy Connection

Cite Textual Evidence As you read the second paragraph, number the factors that affect runoff.

Taking the Plunge
Figure 1 The powerful Niagara River plunges more than 50 meters from the highest point of Niagara Falls. Here, the hydrosphere (river) interacts with the geosphere (land) and shapes Earth's surface.

HANDS-ON LAB

Investigate Trace the paths raindrops can follow after hitting the ground.

Stream Formation Gravity causes runoff and the sediment it carries to flow downhill. As runoff moves across the land, it flows together to form rills, gullies, and streams, as shown in **Figure 2**.

Rills and Gullies As runoff travels, it forms tiny grooves in the soil called rills. Many rills flow into one another to form a gully. A gully is a large groove, or channel, in the soil that carries runoff after a rainstorm. As water flows through gullies, it picks up and moves sediment with it, thus enlarging the gullies through erosion.

Streams and Rivers Gullies join to form a stream. A **stream** is a channel along which water is continually flowing down a slope. Unlike gullies, streams rarely dry up. Small streams are also known as creeks or brooks. As streams flow together, they form larger bodies of flowing water called rivers.

Tributaries A **tributary** is a stream or river that flows into a larger river. For example, the Missouri and Ohio rivers are tributaries of the Mississippi River. A drainage basin, or watershed, is the area from which a river and its tributaries collect their water.

☑ READING CHECK **Integrate With Visuals** Review the information in paragraph 2 and in **Figure 2**. How does the amount of water change as it moves from rills and gullies to streams?

....

....

Stream Formation

Figure 2 🖊 In the diagram, shade only the arrows that indicate the direction of runoff flow that causes erosion.

Reason Quantitatively How will the depth of the channel likely change with further erosion?

....

....

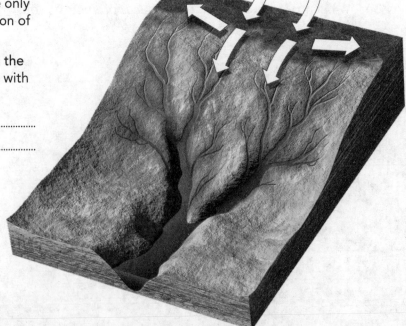

Waterfalls
Figure 3 Waterfalls form where rivers erode hard and soft rock layers at different rates.

1. Interpret Diagrams The rock at the top of the waterfall erodes at a (slower/faster) rate than the rock below it.

2. Predict How do you think erosion will change this waterfall in the next 100 years?

....

....

....

....

....

Water Erosion and Deposition Change Earth's Surface

Some landforms result from erosion by rivers and streams, while others result from deposition. Still other landforms are created from a combination of these processes. Erosion by water removes particles on Earth's surface, while deposition by water builds it up.

Water Erosion Many rivers begin on steep mountain slopes as flowing rain water or melted snow. This running water starts out fast-flowing and generally follows a straight, narrow course. The steep slopes along the river erode rapidly, resulting in a deep, V-shaped valley. As a river flows to the sea, it forms other features such as waterfalls, flood plains, meanders, and oxbow lakes.

Waterfalls Waterfalls, as shown in **Figure 3,** erode soft rock, leaving a ledge made up of hard, slowly eroding rock. Eventually a waterfall develops along the ledge where the softer rock has worn away. Rushing water and sediment can cause further erosion at the base of the waterfall. Rough water rapids also occur where a river tumbles over hard rock, wearing away the supporting rock base and leaving the rock above it unsupported.

Flood Plains Lower down on its course, a river usually flows over more gently sloping land. The river spreads out and erodes the land along its side, forming a wide river valley. The flat, wide area of land along a river is a **flood plain**. During a flood or a rainy season, a river overflows its banks and flows onto the flood plain. As the flood water retreats, it deposits sediment. This gradually makes the soil of a flood plain rich in nutrients.

What things did you develop
in science class this year?
Name two examples.

....

....

....

▶ **VIDEO**

Explore landforms caused
by water erosion.

Meanders A river often **develops** meanders where it flows
through easily eroded rock or sediment. A meander is a loop-like
bend in the course of a river. A meandering river erodes
sediment from the outer bank and deposits the sediment on the
inner bank farther downstream. The water flows faster in the
deeper, outer section of each bend, causing more erosion. Over
time, a meander becomes more curved.

Flood plains also follow the meander as sediment erodes more
of the land to the side of the river. Here, the river's channel is
often deep and wide. For example, the southern stretch of the
Mississippi River meanders on a wide, gently sloping flood plain.

Oxbow Lakes Sometimes a meandering river forms a feature
called an oxbow lake. An oxbow lake occurs when a meander
develops such a large loop that the bends of the river join
together. Sediment deposits block the ends of the bends, cutting
off the river flow. Oxbow lakes are the remains of the river's
former bend, seen in **Figure 4**.

☑ READING CHECK **Cite Textual Evidence** What evidence
supports the idea that a floodplain is formed by erosion and
deposition?

....

....

....

Model It !

Oxbow Lakes

Figure 4 A meander may gradually form an oxbow lake.

Develop Models ✎ Draw steps 2 and 4 to show how an oxbow lake forms. Then describe step 4.

1. A small obstacle
creates a slight
bend in the
river.

2. As water erodes the
outer edge, the bend
becomes bigger,
forming a meander.
Deposition occurs
along the inside bend
of the river.

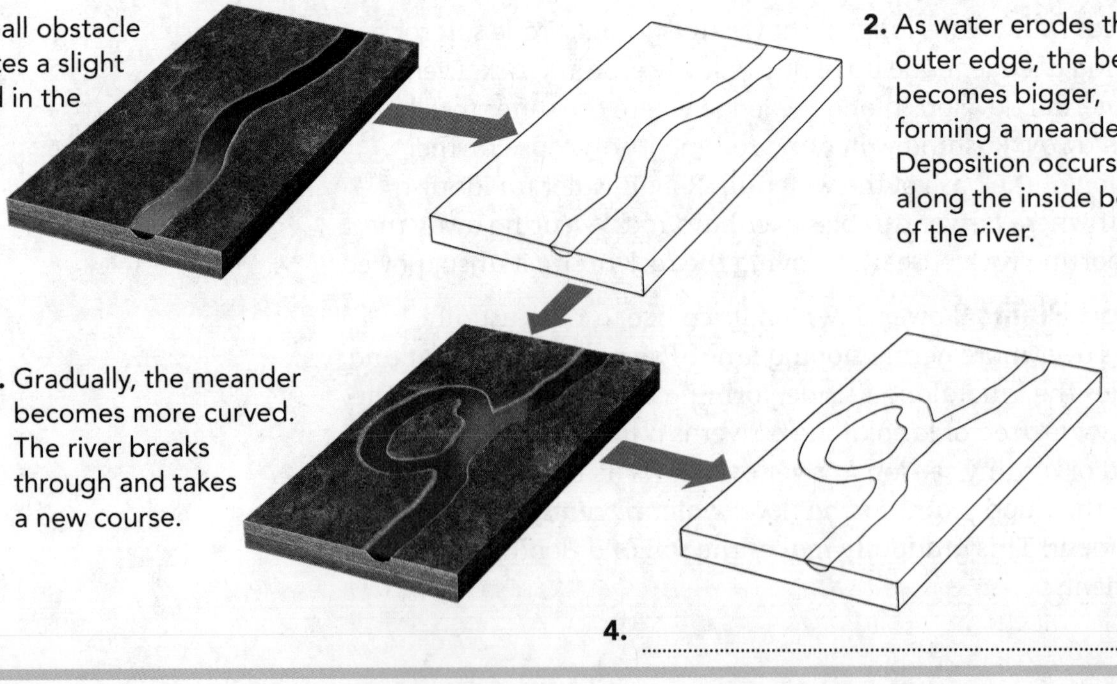

3. Gradually, the meander
becomes more curved.
The river breaks
through and takes
a new course.

4. ....

Delta and Alluvial Fan

Figure 5 ✎ Draw arrows to show the direction in which water carries sediment to each landform.

Interpret Photos Record your observations about deltas and alluvial fans.

....

....

....

....

....

....

....

Water Deposition

Any time moving water slows, it deposits some of the sediment it carries. First, larger rocks stop rolling and sliding as fast-moving water starts to slow down. Then, finer and finer particles fall to the river's bed as the water flows even more slowly. In this way, water deposition builds up Earth's surface and produces landforms such as deltas and alluvial fans.

Deltas Eventually, a river flows into a body of water, such as an ocean or a lake. Because the river water no longer flows downhill, the water slows down. At this point, the sediment in the water drops to the bottom. Sediment deposited where a river flows into an ocean or lake builds up a landform called a **delta**. Some deltas are arc-shaped, while others are triangular. The delta of the Mississippi River, shown in **Figure 5**, is an example of a type of delta called a "bird's foot" delta.

Alluvial Fans When a stream flows out of a steep, narrow mountain valley, it suddenly becomes wider and shallower. The water slows down and deposits sediments in an **alluvial fan**. An alluvial fan is a wide, sloping deposit of sediment formed where a stream leaves a mountain range. As its name **suggests**, this deposit is shaped like a fan.

Academic Vocabulary

Suggest means "to mention as a possibility." Use *suggest* in a sentence.

....

....

....

....

275

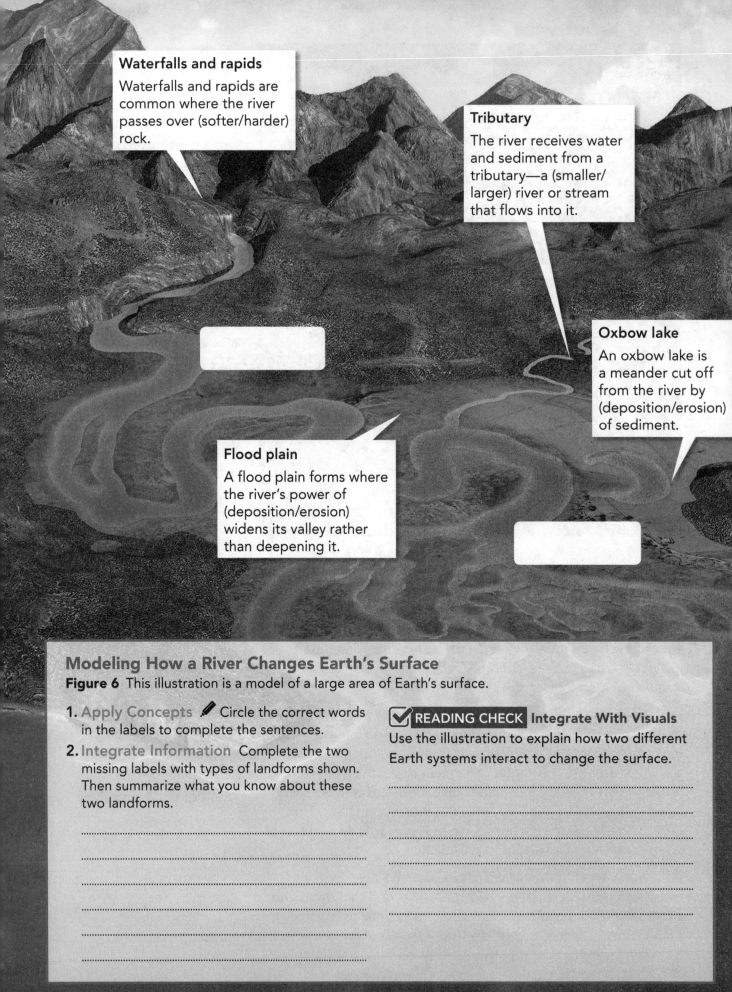

Waterfalls and rapids
Waterfalls and rapids are common where the river passes over (softer/harder) rock.

Tributary
The river receives water and sediment from a tributary—a (smaller/larger) river or stream that flows into it.

Oxbow lake
An oxbow lake is a meander cut off from the river by (deposition/erosion) of sediment.

Flood plain
A flood plain forms where the river's power of (deposition/erosion) widens its valley rather than deepening it.

Modeling How a River Changes Earth's Surface

Figure 6 This illustration is a model of a large area of Earth's surface.

1. **Apply Concepts** ✏ Circle the correct words in the labels to complete the sentences.

2. **Integrate Information** Complete the two missing labels with types of landforms shown. Then summarize what you know about these two landforms.

....

....

....

....

....

....

☑ **READING CHECK** **Integrate With Visuals**
Use the illustration to explain how two different Earth systems interact to change the surface.

....

....

....

....

....

....

....

Groundwater Changes Earth's Surface

When rain falls and snow melts, some water soaks into the ground. It trickles into cracks and spaces in layers of soil and rock. **Groundwater** is the term geologists use for this underground water. Like moving water, groundwater changes the shape of Earth's surface.

Groundwater Erosion Groundwater causes erosion by chemical weathering. In the atmosphere, rain water combines with carbon dioxide to form a weak acid called carbonic acid, which can break down limestone. Groundwater may also become more acidic as it flows through leaf debris at the surface. When groundwater flows into cracks in limestone, some of the limestone dissolves and gets carried away. This process gradually hollows out pockets in the rock. Over time, large underground holes, called caves or caverns, develop.

Groundwater Deposition The action of carbonic acid on limestone can also result in deposition. Water containing carbonic acid and calcium drips from a cave's roof. Carbon dioxide escapes from the solution, leaving behind a deposit of calcite. A deposit that hangs like an icicle from the roof of a cave is known as a stalactite (stuh LAK tyt). On the floor of the cave, a cone-shaped stalagmite (stuh LAG myt) builds up as water drops from the cave roof (**Figure 7**).

 **Write About It** How does groundwater form caves? In your science notebook, write entries for a tourist brochure for a cave, explaining to visitors how the cave and its features formed through erosion and deposition.

👆 **INTERACTIVITY**

Explore erosion caused by groundwater.

Groundwater Erosion and Deposition
Figure 7 ✏ On the photo, draw a line from each label to the formation it names.

Synthesize Information How do deposition and erosion shape caves? Outline your ideas in the table.

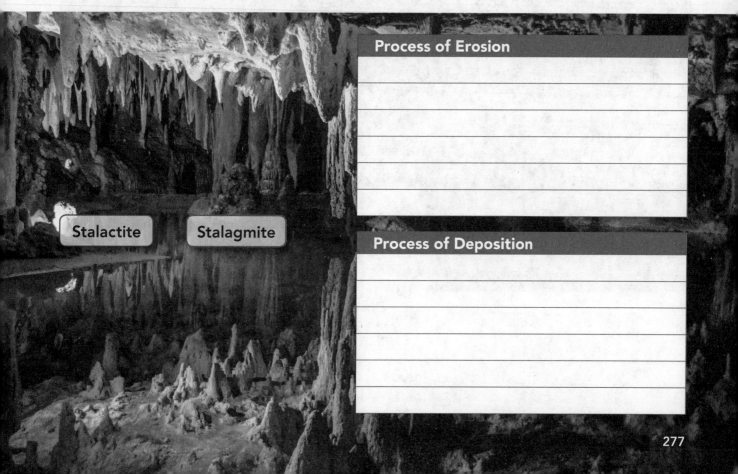

Stalactite

Stalagmite

Process of Erosion

Process of Deposition

INTERACTIVITY

Explore the impact of water on Earth's surface.

Karst Topography

Figure 8 This sinkhole formed in a day in Winter Park, Florida, in 1981. What was the cause of the sinkhole?

....

1. **Interpret Diagrams** ✏️ Circle the state that has the most karst topography.

2. **Interpret Diagrams** Identify two states that have very little karst topography.

....

....

Karst Topography In rainy regions such as Florida where there is a layer of limestone near the surface, groundwater erosion can significantly change the shape of Earth's surface. Deep valleys and caverns commonly form. If the roof of a cave collapses because of limestone erosion, the result is a depression called a sinkhole. This type of landscape is called karst topography.

The formation of karst topography happens over small to large areas and over short to very long time periods. Groundwater erosion starts with a single drop of water that dissolves a microscopic amount of limestone in seconds. After 100 years, groundwater might deposit 1 or 2 cm of calcite on the roof of a cave. Erosion might take thousands to millions of years to form a deep valley or huge cave system hundreds of kilometers long. The roof of a cave may very slowly erode over hundreds of years, but collapse within minutes to form a small or large sinkhole, as shown in **Figure 8**.

☑ READING CHECK **Summarize** How does groundwater cause karst topography?

....

....

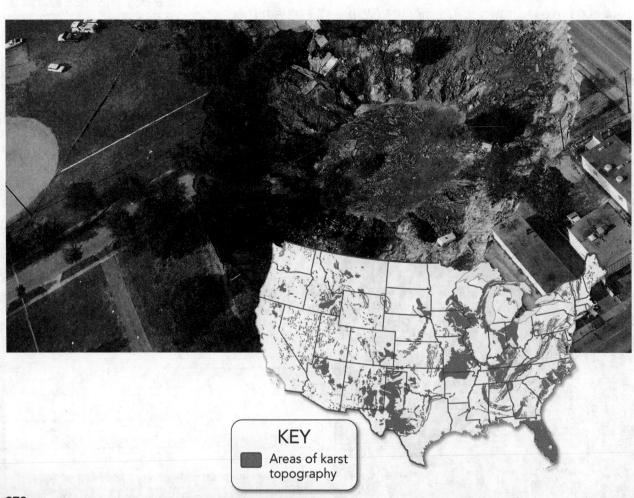

KEY

■ Areas of karst topography

1. **Identify** What are two features that result from deposition by groundwater?

....

....

2. **Classify** Which surface change is an example of erosion and deposition occurring simultaneously? Explain your answer.

....

....

....

....

3. **Predict** The mountain slope a river is flowing down has soft rock on top of a layer of harder rock. Which landform is likely to form over time? Support your answer.

....

....

....

....

....

....

4. **Predict** A river flowing slowly across gently sloping land with a load of sediment reaches the ocean. What landform will eventually develop? Explain.

....

....

....

....

....

5. **Construct a Solution** Suppose you are a landscape contractor, and your client's sloping property is experiencing erosion during heavy rains. The soil is a clay mix and it is exposed. Develop a plan for your client. What steps will best reduce erosion on the property?

....

....

....

....

Quest CHECK-IN

In this lesson, you learned how water on Earth's surface causes erosion and deposition. You also found out how groundwater causes erosion and deposition.

Evaluate Your Solution Why is it important to take different types of erosion and deposition into account when designing an artificial island?

....

....

....

....

....

HANDS-ON LAB

Ingenious Island: Part II

Investigate how you can use a model to test the effects of the agents of erosion on your artificial island.

1

Water table

Sand and clay

Cavity

Limestone

2

3

When a cavity forms in limestone below the ground, a sinkhole can form when the ground eventually collapses into the cavity.

Buyer Beware!

It may sound like something out of a science fiction movie, but Florida is home to monsters that can destroy a roadway or swallow an entire house in a single gulp. They're known as sinkholes.

Geologic Hazards

Sinkholes come in all sizes—from an area the size of a small carpet and 30 centimeters deep to an area spreading over hundreds of acres and several hundreds of meters deep. The size of a sinkhole depends on the surrounding land features. Collapse sinkholes, for example, tend to happen in regions with clay sediments on top of limestone bedrock. As their name suggests, collapse sinkholes form quickly. The ceiling of an underground cavity suddenly gives way, and everything on the surface above that cavity collapses down into it.

In addition to the natural processes that form sinkholes, such as heavy rainfall or extreme drought, human activities can have an impact. As we turn more of the countryside into housing developments, more people are living in areas prone to sinkholes. As we develop land, we use more water. Overuse of the groundwater, digging new water wells, and creating artificial ponds can all increase the chances of sinkhole formation.

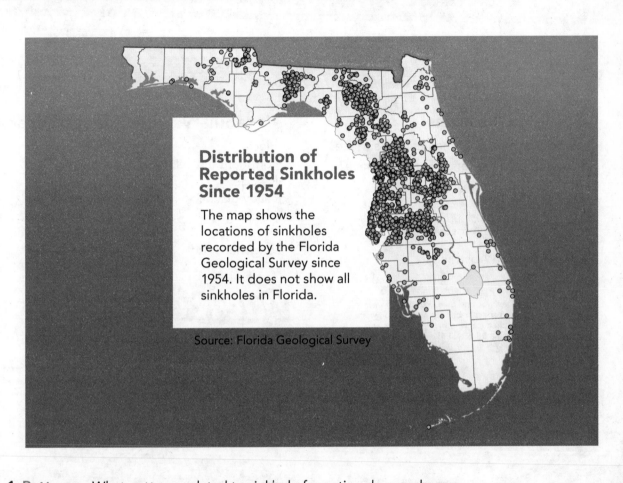

Distribution of Reported Sinkholes Since 1954

The map shows the locations of sinkholes recorded by the Florida Geological Survey since 1954. It does not show all sinkholes in Florida.

Source: Florida Geological Survey

1. **Patterns**   What patterns related to sinkhole formation do you observe in the map? What might account for this pattern?

....

....

....

2. **Interpret Diagrams**   Based on the diagram, why do you think that the overuse of groundwater can cause a sinkhole to form?

....

....

....

3. **Form an Opinion**   How might communities prevent the damage and destruction caused by sinkholes?

....

....

....

④ Glacial and Wave Erosion

Guiding Questions

- How do glaciers change Earth's surface?
- How do waves change Earth's surface?

Connections

Literacy Write Informative Texts

Math Reason Abstractly

🏵 **SC.6.E.6.1** Describe and give examples of ways in which Earth's surface is built up and torn down by physical and chemical weathering, erosion, and deposition. (Also **SC.6.N.3.4**)

Vocabulary

glacier
continental glacier
ice age
valley glacier
plucking
till
longshore drift

Academic Vocabulary

interaction
impact

📱 **VOCABULARY APP**

Practice vocabulary on a mobile device.

Quest CONNECTION

Consider how wave erosion impacts the location of your island.

Connect It!

🖊 **Look closely at the image of the glacier. Draw an arrow showing the direction in which the glacier is flowing.**

Apply Scientific Reasoning How do you think this giant mass of ice changes Earth's surface?

....

....

Glaciers Change Earth's Surface

If you were to fly over Alaska, you would see snowcapped mountains and evergreen forests. Between the mountains and the Gulf of Alaska, you would also see a thick, winding mass of ice. This river of ice in **Figure 1** is a glacier. Geologists define a **glacier** (GLAY shur) as any large mass of ice that moves slowly over land.

Glaciers occur in the coldest places on Earth. That's because they can form only in an area where more snow falls than melts. Layers of snow pile on top of more layers of snow. Over time, the weight of the layers presses the particles of snow so tightly together that they form a solid block of ice.

Glaciers are part of the cryosphere (KRI oh sfear), which includes all the frozen water on Earth. As glaciers move slowly over land, the cryosphere interacts with the rocky upper layer of the geosphere that is known as the lithosphere. This **interaction** changes Earth's surface through weathering, erosion, and deposition. When the ice of the cryosphere melts, it becomes part of the hydrosphere.

HANDS-ON LAB

Examine how glaciers move across Earth's surface.

Academic Vocabulary

Describe an interaction you observed and one you took part in. Be sure to identify the people and things involved in the interaction.

....

....

....

....

....

Giant Bulldozer of Ice

Figure 1 Like a slow-moving bulldozer, Alaska's Bering Glacier, the largest glacier in North America, plows across Earth's surface.

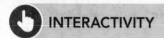

INTERACTIVITY

Learn about the effects of glaciers.

Continental Glaciers

A **continental glacier** is a glacier that covers much of a continent or large island. It can spread out over millions of square kilometers and flow in all directions. Today, continental glaciers cover about 10 percent of Earth's land, including Antarctica and most of Greenland.

During **ice ages**, continental glaciers covered larger parts of Earth's surface. The glaciers gradually advanced and retreated several times, changing the shape of Earth's surface each time.

Valley Glaciers

A **valley glacier** is a long, narrow glacier that forms when snow and ice build up in a mountain valley. High mountains keep these glaciers from spreading out in all directions, and gravity pulls the glacier downhill. Valley glaciers usually move slowly down valleys that have already been cut by rivers. Sometimes a valley glacier can experience a surge, or a quick slide, and move about 6 kilometers in one year. Alaska's Bering Glacier, shown in **Figure 1**, is a valley glacier.

Math Toolbox

Comparing Glacier Thickness

The graph shows the cumulative mass balance of a set of glaciers observed by scientists from 1945 to 2015. The cumulative mass balance is the total amount of ice the glaciers have gained or lost since 1945. The curve is always negative, so the glaciers have lost ice since 1945. The slope of the curve (how steep it is) shows how fast or slow the glaciers are losing ice.

1. **Reason Abstractly** What does a flat slope indicate? What does a steep slope indicate?

....

....

....

....

2. **Interpret Graphs** According to the data, the reference glaciers have melted and lost ice in every decade. In which decade did the glaciers lose ice slowest? In which decade did they lose ice quickest?

....

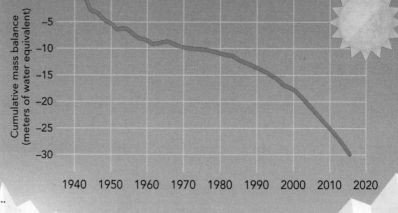

Average Cumulative Mass Balance of "Reference" Glaciers Worldwide, 1945–2015

Source: World Glacier Monitoring Service, 2016

Glacial Erosion

The movement of a glacier slowly changes the land beneath it. The two processes by which glaciers erode the land are plucking and abrasion.

As a glacier flows over the land, it picks up rocks in a process called **plucking**. The weight of the ice breaks rocks into fragments that freeze to the bottom of the glacier. Then the rock fragments get carried with the glacier, as shown in **Figure 2**. Plucking leaves behind a jagged landscape.

Many rocks remain embedded on the bottom and sides of the glacier, and the glacier drags them across the land much like sandpaper in a process called abrasion. Land is worn away and deep gouges and scratches form in the bedrock.

For most glaciers, advancing, retreating, and eroding the land are very slow events. It can take years for scientists to observe any change in a glacier or its effects. Sometimes, however, glaciers move unusually fast. In 2012, scientists determined that a glacier in Greenland advanced up to 46 meters per day, faster than any other glacier recorded.

Although glaciers move and work slowly, they are a major force of erosion. They can take years to carve tiny scratches in bedrock. They can also carve out huge valleys hundreds of kilometers long over thousands of years. Through slow movement and erosion, glaciers dramatically change the shape of large areas of Earth's surface.

Glacial Erosion

Figure 2 Glaciers wear down Earth's surface by plucking and abrasion.

1. Interpret Diagrams 🖉 Draw an arrow in the diagram to show the direction in which the ice is moving. Draw an X where you think abrasion is occurring. Draw a circle where plucking is happening.

2. Explain Phenomena In your own words, describe the glacial erosion taking place in the diagram.

....
....
....
....
....
....
....
....

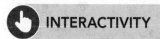

INTERACTIVITY

Examine water's effect on glaciers.

Glacial Deposition

A glacier carries large amounts of rock and soil as it erodes the land in its path. As the glacier melts, it deposits the sediment it eroded from the land, creating various landforms, detailed in **Figure 3**. These landforms remain for thousands of years after the glacier has melted. The mixture of sediments that a glacier deposits directly on the surface is called **till**, which includes clay, silt, sand, gravel, boulders, and even rock ground so finely it is called rock flour.

Moraine The till deposited at the edges of a glacier forms a ridge called a moraine. Lateral moraines are deposits of sediment along the sides of a glacier. A terminal moraine is the ridge of till that is dropped at the farthest point reached by a glacier.

Landforms of Glacial Erosion and Deposition

Figure 3 Glacial erosion and deposition wear down and build up Earth's surface, producing landforms.

Classify ✏ In the model of a landscape shaped by glaciers, identify the features of erosion and deposition. In the circles, write *E* for erosion and *D* for deposition.

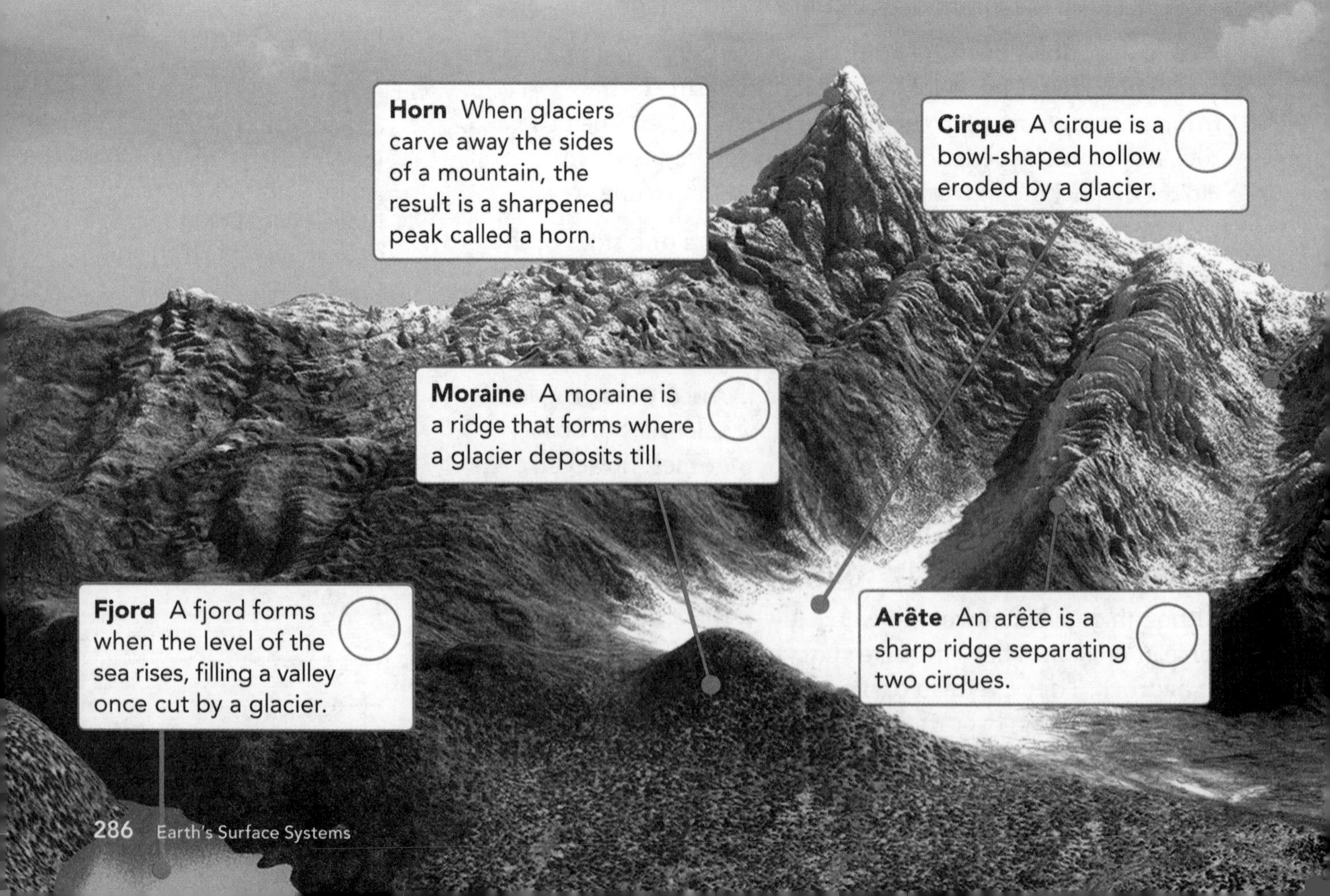

Horn When glaciers carve away the sides of a mountain, the result is a sharpened peak called a horn.

Cirque A cirque is a bowl-shaped hollow eroded by a glacier.

Moraine A moraine is a ridge that forms where a glacier deposits till.

Fjord A fjord forms when the level of the sea rises, filling a valley once cut by a glacier.

Arête An arête is a sharp ridge separating two cirques.

Kettle Retreating, or melting, glaciers also create features called kettles. A kettle is a steep-sided depression that forms when a chunk of ice is left in glacial till. When the ice melts, the kettle remains. The continental glacier of the last ice age left behind many kettles. Kettles often fill with water, forming small ponds or lakes called kettle lakes. Such lakes are common in areas such as Wisconsin that were once covered with glaciers.

☑ READING CHECK **Write Informative Texts** What are the effects of glacial deposition?

....

....

....

....

Model It

U-Shaped valley A flowing glacier scoops out a U-shaped valley. ◯

Kettle lake A kettle lake forms when a depression left in till by melting ice fills with water. ◯

Develop Models 🖊 In the space provided, draw part of the same landscape to show what the surface looked like before glacial erosion and deposition.

Waves Change Earth's Surface

Like glaciers, waves change Earth's surface. The energy in most waves comes from the wind. Stronger winds cause larger waves. The friction between the wave and the ocean floor slows the wave. Then the water breaks powerfully on the shore. This forward-moving water provides the force that changes the land along the shoreline.

Wave Erosion Waves shape the coast through weathering and erosion by breaking down rock and moving sand and other sediments. Large waves can hit rocks along the shore with great force, or **impact**. Over time, waves can enlarge small cracks in rocks and cause pieces of rock to break off. Waves also break apart rocks by abrasion. As a wave approaches shallow water, it picks up and carries sediment, including sand and gravel. When the wave hits land, the sediment wears away rock like sandpaper slowly wearing away wood.

Waves approaching the shore gradually change direction as different parts of the waves drag on the bottom, as shown in **Figure 4**. The energy of these waves is concentrated on headlands. A headland is a part of the shore that extends into the ocean. Gradually, soft rock erodes, leaving behind the harder rock that is resistant to wave erosion. But over time, waves erode the headlands and even out the shoreline.

Academic Vocabulary

How might you use the word *impact* in everyday life? Write a sentence using the word.

....

....

....

....

....

Headland Erosion

Figure 4 Wave erosion wears away rock to form headlands.

1. Interpret Diagrams ✏ Shade in the arrows that indicate where waves concentrate the greatest amount of energy.

2. Predict ✏ Draw a line to show how continued erosion will change the shoreline.

3. Use Models How does this model help you understand a system or process of change?

....

....

....

....

....

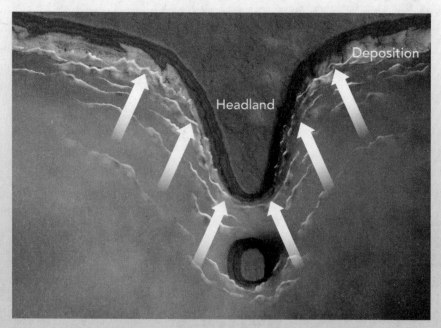

Deposition

Headland

Landforms Formed by Wave Erosion

When an ax strikes the base of a tree trunk, the cut gets bigger and deeper with each strike. Similarly, when ocean waves hit a steep, rocky coast, they erode the base of the land. Waves erode the softer rock first. Over time, the waves may erode a hollow notch in the rock called a sea cave. Eventually, waves may erode the base of a cliff so much that the cliff collapses. The rubble is washed out by wave action and the result is a wave-cut platform at the cliff's base, which is all that remains of the eroded cliff. A sea arch is another feature of wave erosion that forms when waves erode a layer of softer rock that underlies a layer of harder rock. If an arch collapses, a pillar of rock called a sea stack may result.

Wave erosion changes Earth's surface at different rates. Sometimes it changes the land quickly. During a single powerful storm with strong winds that form high-energy waves, part of a cliff or sea stack may crumble. Waves may pick up and carry away large amounts of sediment along a shore. In general, waves erode rock slowly, cutting cliffs and headlands back centimeters to meters in a year. Waves may take hundreds to thousands of years to wear away headlands and even out shorelines.

☑ **READING CHECK** **Write Explanatory Texts** Reread the text. Then explain how you think a sea cave might become a sea arch.

....

....

Landforms Formed by Wave Erosion

Figure 5 ✎ Identify and label the landforms in the photo.

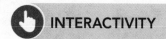
Wave Deposition Deposition occurs when waves lose energy and slow down, causing the water to drop the sediment it carries. Waves change the shape of a coast when they deposit sediment and form landforms.

Landforms Formed by Wave Deposition A beach is an area of wave-washed sediment along a coast. The sediment deposited on beaches is usually sand. Some beaches are made of coral or seashell fragments piled up by wave action. Florida has many such beaches.

Waves usually hit the beach at an angle, creating a current that runs parallel to the coastline. As waves repeatedly hit the beach, some of the sediment gets carried along the beach with the current, in a process called **longshore drift**.

Longshore drift also builds up sandbars and creates barrier islands. Sandbars are long ridges of sand parallel to the shore. A spit is an extended part of a beach that is connected by one end to the mainland. A barrier island forms when waves pile up large amounts of sand above sea level, forming a long, narrow island parallel to the coast. Barrier islands are found in Florida and numerous other places along the Atlantic coast of the United States. Barrier islands are constantly changing from wave erosion and deposition that occur during hurricanes and other storms.

☑ READING CHECK **Translate Information** Use the information in the text and **Figure 6** to determine how the coastline might change if large amounts of sand built up higher than sea level as a result of storm deposition.

Landforms Formed by Wave Deposition

Figure 6 ✏ On the diagram, draw arrows and label them to show the direction of longshore drift and the flow of sediment from the river to the sea.

Beach

Spit

Sandbar

☑LESSON 4 Check

SC.6.E.6.1

1. **Identify** What are three landforms formed by wave deposition?

....

....

....

....

....

2. **Cause and Effect** How do glaciers and waves cause Earth's surface to wear down?

....

....

....

....

....

....

....

3. **Apply Concepts** A glacier slowly traveled along an area of land. It eventually stopped and began to melt. Which landforms did this glacier's movement most likely cause through deposition?

....

....

....

....

....

....

....

4. **Develop Models** ✏ The soft rock of a cliffside is eroded by wave action. Waves continue to hit the remaining piece of land. Create and label a diagram to show how wave action might have changed this shore area 20 or more years in the future.

Quest CHECK-IN

In this lesson, you discovered how erosion and deposition by glaciers change Earth's surface. You also learned how erosion and deposition by waves change Earth's surface.

Evaluate Your Solution Why is it important to consider the effects of wave erosion and deposition when designing an artificial island?

....

....

....

👆 **INTERACTIVITY**

Breaking Waves

Go online to examine how wave erosion might impact the location of your island, and adjust your design as needed.

1 Weathering and Soil

SC.6.E.6.1

1. A rock is worn and cracked from sediments carried by the wind, animal actions, acid rain, and ice wedging. Which of the following is an example of chemical weathering?
A. sediments carried by the wind
B. animal actions
C. acid rain
D. ice wedging

2. Limestone is broken into pieces by the actions of animals. What effect would this have on the rate of chemical weathering of the limestone?
A. It would not affect the rate of chemical weathering.
B. It would stop chemical weathering from occurring.
C. It would decrease the rate of chemical weathering by reducing the amount of the limestone exposed.
D. It would increase the rate of chemical weathering by providing more surface area.

3. Classify A statue splits after repeated freezing and thawing. What type of weathering caused this change? Why?

....
....
....

4. Integrate Information How does weathering help to create soil horizons? Cite evidence.

....
....
....
....
....
....

2 Erosion and Deposition

SC.6.E.6.1

5. Which change occurs as a result of wind slowing down?
A. abrasion
B. deposition
C. deflation
D. mass movement

6. Which of the following statements describes a factor that leads to loess deposits?
A. The wind changes direction.
B. The wind carries sandy sediment.
C. The wind carries fine sediment.
D. Plant roots act as an anchor.

7. Which type of mass movement occurs rapidly when a single mass of soil and rock suddenly slips downhill?
A. creep
B. landslide
C. mudslide
D. slump

8. Predict What would most likely occur if an earthquake occurred near a dry, steep slope? Why?

....
....
....
....

9. Construct Explanations Over time, fence posts on a slope have tilted. Trees in the area are also beginning to tilt. What is this process called? What processes are causing it to occur in this area?

....
....
....
....

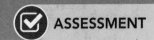
3 Water Erosion

SC.6.E.6.1

10. Erosion and deposition work together to shape Earth's surface. Which of the following statements **best** describes deposition?
    A. A river flows into an ocean slows and drops sediment.
    B. Rushing water beats against the rocks at the base of a waterfall.
    C. A rushing river spreads out and forms a wide river valley.
    D. Sediment is carried away from the outer bank of a river.

11. Which of the following processes causes sinkholes to form?
    A. erosion of sediment by runoff
    B. deposition of sediment by a river
    C. deposition of calcite by groundwater
    D. erosion of limestone by groundwater

12. Which of the following statements describes the formation of an alluvial fan?
    A. Runoff forms grooves in the soil.
    B. A stream flows into a larger river.
    C. Sediment is deposited as water rushes out of a mountain valley.
    D. Sediment blocks a meander from the flow of a river.

13. Analyze Data Examine the data table. Which area is more likely to experience water erosion? Why?

	Area A	Area B
Average annual rainfall	75 cm	88 cm
Vegetation	Sparse grasses	Grass, trees, shrubs
Soil type	Sandy soil	Humus-rich soil
Land shape	Steep hills	Gradual slope

....
....
....

4 Glacial and Wave Erosion

SC.6.E.6.1

14. During abrasion, glaciers wear away Earth's surface by dragging embedded rocks. Which of the following actions is **most** similar to glacial abrasion?
    A. Truck tires make deep tracks on a muddy trail.
    B. A piece of sandpaper is used to remove paint.
    C. A hose is used to spray leaves off of a patio.
    D. Ants carry sediment to a new location to build a hill.

15. Which of the following statements describes the formation of a sea stack?
    A. A river carries sediment to the ocean.
    B. A rock cliff breaks apart from powerful waves.
    C. Ocean waves slowly erode large rocks.
    D. Waves wear away part of the shore that extends into the ocean.

16. Which of the following actions lead to long-shore drift?
    A. wave action wearing away layers of soft rock
    B. the collapse of the base of a sea stack
    C. the formation of a barrier island
    D. sediments are carried by a current along the beach

17. Cite Evidence A scientist is studying terminal moraines and till deposits in a valley. What conclusion will the scientist **most likely** make about what caused these landforms? Give evidence.

....
....
....
....
....

Circle the letter of the best answer.

On a trip through the desert you observe land-forms of different shapes and sizes. As you get out of the car to take a closer look at one interesting landform, the wind picks up and starts to blow sand and dust into your face. **Use the picture to answer Questions 1 and 2.**

1 What is the most likely major cause of the landform in this picture?

A Deposition occurred when sediments carried by winds were built up.

B Abrasion occurred when particles carried by the wind scraped away rock.

C Mechanical weathering occurred when plant roots grew into cracks in the rocks and broke it apart.

D Mechanical weathering occurred when freezing and thawing cycles broke the rock.

2 How did the type of rocks in this structure **most likely** affect its shape?

F The types of rocks and that make up this structure have weathered at different rates.

G Some of the types of rock have had more chemical weathering from organisms than others.

H Some of the rock making up the structure has been more affected by freeze-thaw cycles.

I Rocks in different areas of the structure have been exposed to different weather conditions.

3 A town plans to clear a patch of forest to make a road wider. What possible changes should the town take into account?

A increased erosion caused by runoff

B decreased deposition caused by runoff

C increased deposition caused by groundwater

D decreased erosion caused by wind

4 Which of the following will **most likely** affect a structure built on a floodplain?

F erosion by wind

G erosion by a river

H erosion by organisms

I erosion by groundwater

5 Erosion and deposition are often discussed together. Which statement **most** accurately describes their difference?

A Erosion wears material away, and deposition moves the material.

B Erosion moves weathered material, and deposition resettles it.

C Erosion wears material away, and deposition resettles it.

D Erosion and deposition are not different; both describe moving weathered material.

6 A town built a new housing development on a previously empty lot. Many of the new owners complain about water and soil damage to their houses and yards. Which of the following conclusions can you make about the area chosen for this housing development?

F The development has humus-rich soil, and it is located near a grassy meadow.

G The development has sandy soil, and it is located at the top of a steep slope.

H The development has rocky soil, and it is located near a wide river valley.

I The development has clay-rich soil, and it is located at the bottom of a gradual slope.

A developer wants to build houses on flat land along the Little St. Marys River. She knows the river eventually drains into the Atlantic Ocean, and that the river's soil is made up of sand and clay. She needs to assess the land before making her final decision. **Use the image to answer Questions 7 and 8.**

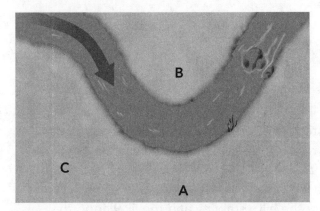

7 The developer is thinking of choosing Location A. Which of the following factors is **most** important for the developer to take into account before building the houses in Location A?

A the rate of weathering in the rocks and soil along the river

B the direction the river is flowinge

C the increased chance of a mass movement

D the rate of deposition of sediments

8 Suppose the developer chooses Location B. What problem would she **most likely** face over time?

F As the river picks up and deposits more sediment, Location B could become a delta.

G As rocks erode in the rivers path, Location B could experience increased flooding due to rapids.

H Location B could experience increased flooding as the river formed an alluvial floodplain.

I The meander could form an oxbow, and Location B would be on the other side of the river.

Complete the Quest!

Reflect on how changes to Earth's surface will impact an artificial island. Then prepare and deliver an oral or written presentation explaining your island design and your model.

Analyze Systems What are three things you learned about the processes that shape Earth's surface that helped you to design your artificial island?

....

....

....

....

....

....

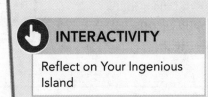 **INTERACTIVITY**

Reflect on Your Ingenious Island

Materials on a Slope

How can you use a **model** to determine the likelihood of **mass movement**?

Background

Geoscience processes such as rapid mass movement result in large amounts of sediment moving down hillsides.

In this investigation, you will work as part of a landslide monitoring team. You will develop and use a model to explore the relationship between the height and width of a hill. You will gain understanding about how these factors affect the hill's stability and the likelihood that mass movement will occur.

Safety

Be sure to follow all safety guidelines provided by your teacher. The Safety Appendix of your textbook provides more details about the safety icons.

Materials

(per group)

- tray (about 15 cm × 45 cm × 60 cm)
- several sheets of white paper
- masking tape
- cardboard tube
- spoon or paper cup

- dry sand (500 mL) in container
- wooden skewer
- metric ruler
- pencil or crayon
- graph paper

Landslides are destructive events that not only damage roadways and buildings, but also result in the loss of life.

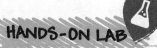

HANDS-ON LAB

иDemonstrate Go online for a downloadable worksheet of this lab.

Plan Your Investigation

☐ Use the metric ruler to mark off centimeters across the length of the paper. Take the tray provided by your teacher and use the paper to cover its interior surface. Secure the paper with tape. In the middle of the tray, stand the cardboard tube upright. Use a spoon or cup to fill the tube with sand.

☐ When the tube is nearly full, slowly and steadily pull the tube straight up so that the sand falls out of the bottom and forms a cone-shaped hill. Use different quantities of sand and observe the shapes and sizes of the sand hills created.

☐ Using the materials provided by your teacher, design an investigation to explore the relationship between the height and width of a sand hill. Determine how many sand hills you will create in your investigation.

☐ Then use the space provided to outline your procedure. Have your teacher review and approve your procedure, and then conduct your investigation. Create a data table to record your data about the heights and widths of the sand hills your group models.

Design Your Procedure

Data Table

Analyze and Interpret Data

1. Analyze Data Study your data table. What patterns do you notice in your data?

....

....

2. Use Evidence What do your data suggest about the relationship between the height and width of a sand hill?

....

....

....

3. Identify Limitations What are the advantages of using the sand hill model in this investigation? What are the limitations of using the model?

....

....

....

....

....

....

4. Use Models How is your sand hill model similar to and different from a natural hill that undergoes mass movement?

....

....

....

....

5. Construct Explanations How could you apply the results of your investigation to help assess the likelihood of and forecast future mass movement events such as landslides? Use evidence from your investigation to support your explanation.

....

....

....

....

TOPIC 7

Living Things in the Biosphere

SC.6.L.14.A All living things share certain characteristics.
SC.6.L.14.D Life is maintained by various physiological functions essential for growth, reproduction, and homeostasis.
SC.6.L.14.6 Compare and contrast types of infectious agents that may infect the human body, including viruses, bacteria, parasites, and fungi.
SC.6.L.15.1 Analyze and describe how and why organisms are classified according to shared characteristics with emphasis on the Linnaean system combined with the concept of Domains. (Also **SC.6.N.1.1** and **SC.6.N.2.2**)

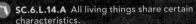

HANDS-ON LAB

uConnect Expand your knowledge of what might be an animal.

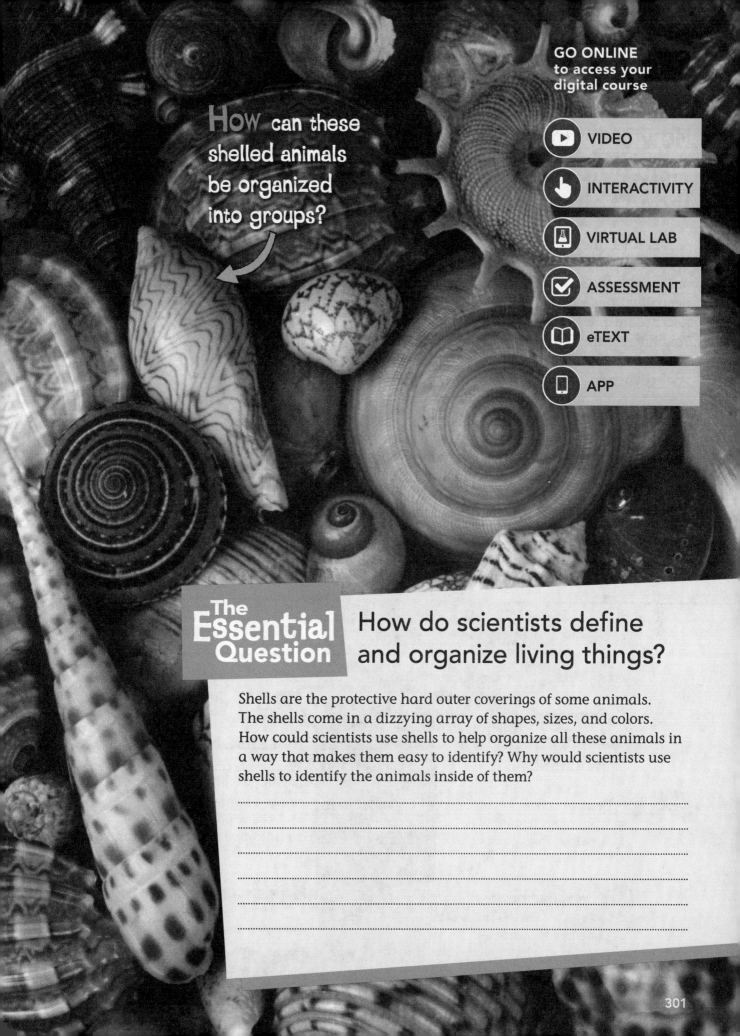

How can these shelled animals be organized into groups?

GO ONLINE
to access your
digital course

▶ VIDEO

👆 INTERACTIVITY

🧪 VIRTUAL LAB

☑ ASSESSMENT

📖 eTEXT

📱 APP

The Essential Question

How do scientists define and organize living things?

Shells are the protective hard outer coverings of some animals. The shells come in a dizzying array of shapes, sizes, and colors. How could scientists use shells to help organize all these animals in a way that makes them easy to identify? Why would scientists use shells to identify the animals inside of them?

....
....
....
....
....
....

Quest KICKOFF

How can you design a field guide to organize living things?

A 2011 scientific study estimates that there are around 8.7 million, plus or minus 1.3 million, species on our planet. Guess how many species have actually been identified! About two million. To identify these new organisms, taxonomists look at characteristics. Taxonomy is the branch of science that classifies organisms. In this problem-based Quest activity, you will design a field guide to help people identify the different organisms they may see at a nature center. By applying what you learn in each lesson, digital activity, or hands-on lab, you will gather key Quest information. With this information, you will develop your field guide in the Findings activity.

INTERACTIVITY

Sort Out Those Organisms

SC.6.L.15.1 Analyze and describe how and why organisms are classified according to shared characteristics with emphasis on the Linnaean system combined with the concept of Domains. (Also **SC.6.N.1.5** and **SC.6.N.2.3**)

NBC LEARN ▶ **VIDEO**

After watching the Quest Kickoff video about discovering and categorizing organisms, choose two organisms that you observe in your daily life. Complete the Venn diagram by describing what makes them similar and different.

Quest CHECK-IN

IN LESSON 1

What do all living things have in common? Analyze specimens to determine whether they are living or nonliving.

👆 **INTERACTIVITY**

Under the Microscope

Quest CHECK-IN

IN LESSON 2

What characteristics do biologists consider when grouping organisms? Model a scientific classification system using seeds.

🧪 **HANDS-ON LAB**

Classifying Seeds

This plant can be identified by making detailed observations about its characteristics and comparing those observations to descriptions in a field guide.

Quest CHECK-INS

IN LESSON 3

What distinguishes unicellular and multicellular organisms? Classify organisms based on their characteristics as unicellular or multicellular.

👆 **INTERACTIVITIES**

- Discovering Rainforest Organisms
- Multicellular Rainforest Organisms

Quest FINDINGS

Complete the Quest!

Identify the criteria and constraints for your field guide. Then create a field guide that will help people identify different organisms in a local nature center.

👆 **INTERACTIVITY**

Create Your Field Guide

① Living Things

Guiding Questions

- What evidence is there that all living things are made of cells?
- Where do living things come from?
- What do living things need to stay alive, grow, and reproduce?

Connection

Literacy Gather Information

 SC.6.L.14.A All living things share certain characteristics.
SC.6.L.14.D Life is maintained by various physiological functions essential for growth, reproduction, and homeostasis. (Also **SC.6.N.1.3** and **SC.6.N.2.2**)

Vocabulary

organism
cell
unicellular
multicellular
stimulus
response
spontaneous
 generation
homeostasis

Academic Vocabulary

characteristics

 VOCABULARY APP

Practice vocabulary on a mobile device.

Quest CONNECTION

Consider how the characteristics of living things are important when creating a field guide.

Connect It !

✎ **Circle the things in the image that appear to be living.**

Conduct Research Suppose you scraped off some of the pale green stuff from the tree bark. How would you know whether it was alive or not? What observations would you note? What tests could you do to see whether it's alive?

....

....

....

Characteristics of Living Things

An **organism** is any living thing. It could be a horse, a tree, a mushroom, strep bacteria, or the lichens (LIE kins) in **Figure 1**. Some organisms are familiar and obviously alive. No one wonders whether a dog is an organism. Other organisms are a little harder to distinguish from nonliving things. Lichens, for example, can be very hard and gray. They don't seem to grow much from year to year. How can we separate living from nonliving things? The answer is that all organisms share several important **characteristics**:

- All organisms are made of cells.
- All organisms contain similar chemicals and use energy.
- All organisms respond to their surroundings.
- All organisms grow, develop, and reproduce.

HANDS-ON LAB

Explore what makes a living thing alive.

Academic Vocabulary

A *characteristic* is a feature that helps to identify something. How would you describe the characteristics of a good movie or book?

....

....

....

....

....

Still Life with Lichens
Figure 1 Lichens blend in with the trees.

Characteristics of Living Things

Figure 2 All living things share certain characteristics.

Determine Conclusions What is the one characteristic that all living things and only living things have in common?

....

....

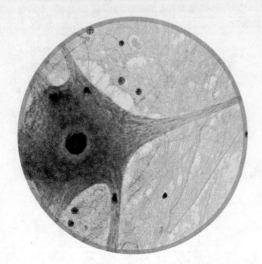

Cellular Organization
All living things are made of smaller living units called cells. **Cells** are the basic unit of structure and function in living things. In a single-celled or **unicellular** organism, one cell carries out the functions necessary to stay alive. Organisms consisting of many cells are **multicellular**. You are a multicellular organism with trillions of cells specialized to do certain tasks. The nerve cell shown here sends electrical signals throughout your body. It may signal you to let go of something hot or to take a step. In a multicellular organism, all cells work together to keep the organism alive.

The Chemicals of Life
All substances, including living cells, are made of chemicals. The most common chemical in cells is water, which is essential for life. Other chemicals, called carbohydrates (kahr boh HY drayts) provide the cell with energy. Proteins and lipids are chemicals used in building cells, much as wood and bricks are used to build schools. Finally, nucleic (noo KLEE ik) acids provide chemical instructions that tell cells how to carry out the functions of life. You've probably heard of DNA, deoxyribonucleic acid, but did you know what it looks like? The nucleic acid DNA directs the actions of every cell in your body.

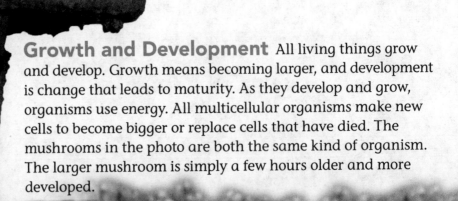

Growth and Development
All living things grow and develop. Growth means becoming larger, and development is change that leads to maturity. As they develop and grow, organisms use energy. All multicellular organisms make new cells to become bigger or replace cells that have died. The mushrooms in the photo are both the same kind of organism. The larger mushroom is simply a few hours older and more developed.

Response to Surroundings

Have you ever touched the palm of a baby's hand? If so, you may have observed the baby's fingers curl to grip your fingertip. The baby's grip is a natural reflex. Like a baby's curling fingers, all organisms react to changes in their surroundings. Any change or signal in the environment that can make an organism react in some way is called a **stimulus** (plural *stimuli*). Stimuli include changes in light, sound, flavors, or odors. An organism reacts to a stimulus with a **response**—an action or a change in behavior. Responding to stimuli helps the baby and all other organisms to survive and function.

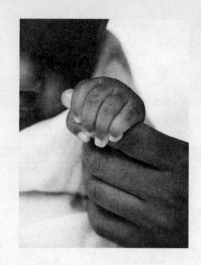

Reproduction

Organisms reproduce to create offspring that are similar to the parent or parents. Some organisms reproduce asexually, creating an identical offspring with only one parent. One example is the young hydra (HY druh) budding off the parent hydra in the image. Mammals, birds, and most plants reproduce sexually. In sexual reproduction, two parents combine their DNA to create an offspring with a mix of both parents' characteristics.

Energy Use

All organisms need energy to power their cells. Within an organism's cells, chemical reactions break down materials to get energy. Some organisms, called producers, can get energy from sunlight in a process known as photosynthesis, while other producers use different chemicals in their environment to make energy. Other organisms, called consumers, get energy by eating other living things. The shrew pictured here must eat more than its own weight in food every day. A shrew can starve to death if it goes five hours without eating!

HANDS-ON LAB

Investigate Identify structures found in the cells of living things.

Life Produces More Life

Every spring, wildflowers seem to pop up out of the ground from nowhere. Do the plants sprout directly from rocks and soil? No, we know that the new plants are reproduced from older plants. Four hundred years ago, however, people believed that life could appear from nonliving material. For example, when people saw flies swarming around spoiled meat, they concluded that the meat produced the flies. The mistaken idea that living things arise from nonliving sources is called **spontaneous generation**. It took hundreds of years and many experiments to convince people that spontaneous generation does not occur.

Redi's Experiment In the 1600s, an Italian doctor named Francesco Redi helped to prove spontaneous generation wrong. Redi investigated the source of the maggots that develop into adult flies on rotting meat. Redi performed a controlled experiment so he was certain about the cause of the results. In a controlled experiment, a scientist carries out two or more tests that are identical in every way except one. As shown in **Figure 3**, Redi set up two jars in the same location with meat in them. Then Redi changed just one variable in his experiment and watched to see what would happen.

Redi's Experiment

Figure 3 Redi showed that meat did not cause the spontaneous generation of flies.

Relate Text to Visuals 🖉 Read the steps below. Then sketch steps 2 and 3.

Step 1 Redi placed meat in two identical jars. He covered one jar with a cloth that let in air, the control in the experiment.

Step 2 After a few days, Redi saw maggots (young flies) on the decaying meat in the open jar.

Step 3 Redi reasoned that flies had laid eggs on the meat in the open jar. The eggs hatched into maggots.

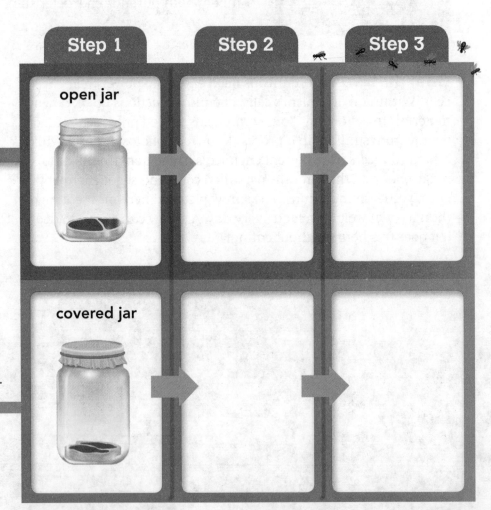

Pasteur's Experiment Even after Redi's experiment, many people continued to believe in spontaneous generation. Almost 200 years after Redi's experiment, French chemist Louis Pasteur (pah STUHR) decided to put spontaneous generation to the test. In his experiment, Pasteur used a control group. A control group is exposed to the same factors as the experimental group, except that it is not exposed to the variable being tested. **Figure 4** shows the experiment that convinced the scientific community that spontaneous generation was just a myth.

✓ READING CHECK **Gather Information** How did both the Redi and Pasteur experiments prove there was no such thing as spontaneous generation?

....

....

....

Pasteur's Experiment

Figure 4 Pasteur carefully controlled his experiment.

1. Relate Text to Visuals ✏ Draw and label the flasks in steps 2 and 3. Label the control and experimental flasks.

2. Draw Conclusions What did the bacterial growth in Step 3 confirm for Pasteur?

....

....

....

Step 1	Step 2	Step 3
Pasteur put clear broth into flasks with curved necks. The necks let in air but kept out bacteria. He boiled the broth in the flasks to kill all bacteria present. 	The boiled broth remained clear. Pasteur then set some of the flasks aside, just as they were.	The broth in these flasks remained clear. Pasteur concluded that bacteria could not arise from the broth.
....	Pasteur broke the curved necks off the other flasks. Bacteria from the outside air were able to enter these flasks.	The broth in the broken flasks became cloudy, showing bacterial growth.

Though it may seem surprising, pine trees, worms, and all other organisms have the same basic needs as you do. All living things must satisfy their basic needs for water, food, living space, and homeostasis.

Water All living things depend on water for their survival. In fact, some organisms can live only for a few days without water. All cells need water to carry out their daily functions. Many substances dissolve easily in water. Once food or other chemicals are dissolved, they are easily transported around the body of an organism. About half of human blood is made of water. Our blood carries dissolved food, waste, and other chemicals to and from cells. Also, many chemical reactions that take place in cells require water.

Food All living things consume food for energy. Some organisms, such as plants, capture the sun's energy and use it to make food through the process of photosynthesis. Producers are organisms that make their own food. Producers are also called autotrophs (AW toh trohfs). *Auto-* means "self" and *-troph* means "feeder." Autotrophs use the sun's energy to convert water and a gas into food.

Every organism that can't make its own food must eat other organisms. Consumers are organisms that cannot make their own food. Consumers are also called heterotrophs (HET uh roh trohfs). *Hetero-* means "other," so combined with *-troph* it means "one that feeds on others." A heterotroph may eat autotrophs, other heterotrophs, or break down dead organisms to get energy. **Figure 5** shows an interaction between autotrophs and heterotrophs.

Autotrophs and Heterotrophs

Figure 5 Every organism has to eat!

Apply Concepts ✏ Write whether each organism is an autotroph or a heterotroph in the space provided.

Crocodile

Plan It!

Can a Person Be an Autotroph?

Shelby and Michaela are learning about organisms. Shelby says she is sometimes an autotroph because she makes her own food after school, a bowl of cut fruit.

Explain Phenomena How can Michaela prove to Shelby that she is not an autotroph? What could she do to help Shelby investigate what an autotroph is?

....

....

....

Space All organisms need a place to live—a place to get food and water and find shelter. Whether an organism lives in the savanna, as shown in **Figure 5**, or the desert, its surroundings must provide what it needs to survive. Because there is a limited amount of space on Earth, some organisms compete for space. Trees in a forest, for example, compete with other trees for sunlight. Below ground, their roots compete for water and minerals. If an organism loses its living space, it must move to a new place or it may die.

✔️ **READING CHECK** **Cite Textual Evidence** Why do living things need water, food, and space to live?

....

....

....

Tick

Zebra

Grass

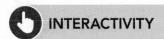

INTERACTIVITY

Examine why an object that has a few characteristics of living things is not living.

Homeostasis When you go outside on a freezing cold day, does your body temperature fall below freezing as well? Of course not! Your body is able to keep the temperature of your insides steady even when outside conditions change. Shivering, moving to a warmer place, and putting on more clothes all help you to stay warm. The maintenance of stable internal conditions is called **homeostasis** (hoh mee oh STAY sis). All organisms maintain homeostasis to stay alive.

Organisms have many different methods for maintaining homeostasis. The methods depend on the challenges faced by the organism. Consider the marine iguana, pictured in **Figure 6**. Marine iguanas feed underwater in the ocean and swallow a lot of salty water. To maintain homeostasis, the iguanas need a way to get rid of the extra salt. In a human, extra salt would be removed in sweat, tears, or urine. The iguana has a different way of maintaining homeostasis. Iguanas produce very salty liquid that comes out near their noses. Frequent sneezing clears the salty liquid away. Homeostasis is maintained!

READING CHECK **Determine Central Ideas** The paws of the arctic fox are covered in thick fur. How does this help the fox maintain homeostasis?

....

....

....

....

Salty Sneezes

Figure 6 As they eat underwater plants, marine iguanas maintain homeostasis by sneezing out salty liquid.

Apply Concepts Which basic need is an iguana meeting by feeding on underwater plants?

....

....

1. **Apply Concepts** Name two autotrophs and two heterotrophs that live near your home.

....

....

2. **Use Models** ✏ Draw a diagram showing all the things that an organism needs to survive. Label the drawing to show how the organism can meet its needs right where it lives.

3. **Synthesize** How would you state the one question answered by both Redi's and Pasteur's experiments?

....

....

....

4. **Construct an Explanation** Research Louis Pasteur's invention of pasteurization or his experiments in fermentation or vaccination. Summarize his accomplishment in writing, or sketch thumbnails for a slide show, relating it to his experiment in this lesson.

Quest CHECK-IN

In this lesson, you learned about the characteristics of living things and where living things come from. You also learned about what living things need to grow, stay alive, and reproduce.

Evaluate Your Plan What are your plans for your field guide? How will you use the characteristics of living things to identify and categorize different organisms?

....

....

....

....

 INTERACTIVITY

Under the Microscope

Go online to observe different objects and determine whether they are living or nonliving.

The TOUGH and *Tiny* TARDIGRADE

Imagine being shrunk to the size of the period at the end of this sentence and getting plopped down in a bed of moss. You just might run into a tardigrade as big as you. Sort of cute, right? No wonder they're nicknamed the water bear.

rehydration

dehydration

All living things need water, a safe temperature range, and the right pressure to sustain functioning cells. But one microscopic organism called a tardigrade defies all those rules. Tardigrades survive the most extreme conditions on Earth.

How do they do it? Tardigrades dehydrate themselves. They shed 95 percent of the water in their bodies. Life comes to a nearly complete halt in the dried-out tardigrade. Studies suggest that tardigrades produce proteins and sugars that help to protect their cells while they are dehydrated. Add water and the tardigrade rehydrates and bounces back to life. Scientists study tardigrades to learn more about the activities inside cells that enable animals to develop and survive.

Extreme Temperatures

Tardigrades have been found in conditions ranging from polar waters to bubbling hot springs. In one lab experiment, they even survived at an unimaginable –272°C (–458°F). And they withstood temperatures well over boiling, too.

Intense Pressure

If you stood in the very deepest part of the ocean, the pressure would crush you flat. But tardigrades? They can withstand *six times* that pressure. In the vacuum of space where there's almost no pressure, your insides would start to expand until your body exploded like a balloon. But tardigrades toured outer space for ten days and came back to Earth unharmed.

Radiation

In high doses, radiation damages cells and destroys DNA. Humans can withstand only very small doses (measured in Grays, or Gy), but tardigrades can survive 5,000 Gy or more. With their ability to protect their cells from these extremes, you'd think tardigrades would live in the wildest places on Earth. But they prefer to live in the water, or in damp places, such as among wet leaves and in moist soil.

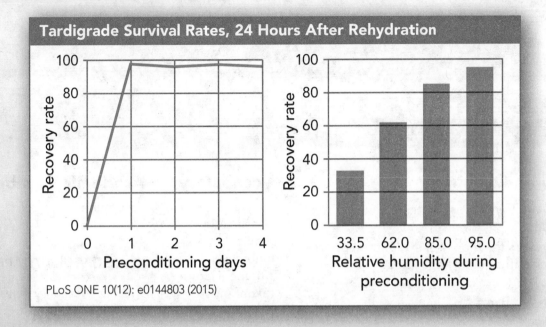

Tardigrade Survival Rates, 24 Hours After Rehydration

PLoS ONE 10(12): e0144803 (2015)

Tardigrades are exposed to different amounts of humidity (or moisture) before dehydrating. This is called preconditioning. The graphs show results from an experiment that tested whether preconditioning was necessary. The bar graph above shows the results of changing the amount of humidity in the air during preconditioning. The recovery rate is the percent of tardigrades who survive the transition from dehydration to rehydration.

1. **Analyze Properties** When you think of the common characteristics that all living things share, which one stands out the most in this experiment?

....

2. **Evaluate Data** What does the bar graph above suggest about the effects of relative humidity during preconditioning?

....

....

3. **Predict** What do you think the data would look like if the relative humidity were 45 percent?

....

....

....

4. **Synthesize Information** Why might humidity be helpful to a tardigrade?

....

....

....

Classification Systems

Guiding Questions

- How are living things classified into groups?
- How does the theory of evolution support the classification of organisms?

Connections

Literacy Assess Sources

Math Write an Expression

 SC.6.L.15.1 Analyze and describe how and why organisms are classified according to shared characteristics with emphasis on the Linnaean system combined with the concept of Domains. (Also **SC.6.N.2.1** and **SC.6.N.2.2**)

Vocabulary

species
classification
genus
binomial
   nomenclature
taxonomy
domain
evolution
convergent
   evolution

Academic Vocabulary

determine

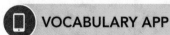 **VOCABULARY APP**

Practice vocabulary on a mobile device.

Quest CONNECTION

Think about how a classification system might be used to organize different organisms in your field guide.

Connect It !

✎ **Draw arrows and label parts of the organism that help you to identify it.**

Make Observations What kind of living thing do you think this is?

....

....

....

Classifying Organisms

It is estimated that there are approximately 8.7 million species of organisms on the planet, with thousands more discovered each day. A **species** is a group of similar organisms that can mate with each other and produce offspring that can also mate and reproduce. Biologists place similar organisms into groups based on characteristics they have in common. **Classification** is the process of grouping things based on their similarities. To classify the organism in **Figure 1**, you'd first need to know about its characteristics. Then you could figure out which group it belonged to.

Linnaean Naming System
In the 1730s, biologist Carolus Linnaeus arranged organisms in groups based on their observable features. Then he gave each organism a two-part scientific name. The first word in the name is the organism's **genus**, a group of similar, closely-related organisms. The second word is the species and might describe where the organism lives or its appearance. This system in which each organism is given a unique, two-part scientific name that indicates its genus and species is known as **binomial nomenclature**. Today, scientists still use this naming system that classifies organisms according to their shared characteristics.

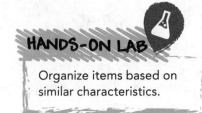

HANDS-ON LAB

Organize items based on similar characteristics.

Write About It Pick a favorite animal or plant. What is it that you find most interesting? In your science notebook, describe its characteristics.

Animal, Vegetable, or Mineral?
Figure 1 Some organisms are much harder to classify than others!

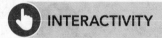
Literacy Connection

Assess Sources Books become outdated and the Internet is full of incorrect information. If you need an accurate answer to a scientific question, where would you look? Whom could you ask for help?

....

....

....

....

....

Taxonomy The scientific study of how organisms are classified is called **taxonomy** (tak SAHN uh mee). Scientists use taxonomy to identify the name of an unknown organism or to name a newly discovered organism. For example, if you look closely at the characteristics of the organism in **Figure 1**, you might classify it as a sea slug. It would then be simple to look up sea slugs and find out that they are animals related to slugs and snails. All sea slugs have sensitive tentacles that they use to smell, taste, and feel their way around. They eat other animals by scraping away their flesh. Sea slugs can even gain the ability to sting by eating stinging animals!

Domains In classification of organisms, the broadest level of organization is the **domain**. There are three domains: Eukarya, Archaea, and Bacteria. Eukarya (yoo KA ree uh) includes the familiar kingdoms of plants, animals, and fungi, and a less familiar kingdom, Protista, which has much simpler organisms. Members of Domain Eukarya are called eukaryotes. Eukaryotes have nuclei containing DNA. Domain Archaea (ahr KEE uh) contains a group of one-celled organisms with no nuclei in their cells. Members of Domain Bacteria, like Archaea, have only one cell and no nucleus, but bacteria have different structures and chemical processes from those of Archaea. **Figure 2** shows the levels of classification for Domain Eukarya.

✓ **READING CHECK** **Determine Central Ideas** What do scientists use to determine how organisms are classified in each level? Explain your answer.

....

....

....

Model It

So Many Levels of Classification!

There are ways to memorize a long list of terms so that you can remember them months or even years later. A mnemonic (nee MON ic) can help you memorize a list of terms in order. To create one type of mnemonic, you compose a sentence from words that start with the first letter of each term in the list. One popular mnemonic for levels of classification is: "Dear King Philip Come Over For Good Spaghetti." In the space, devise your own mnemonic to help you remember the levels of classification.

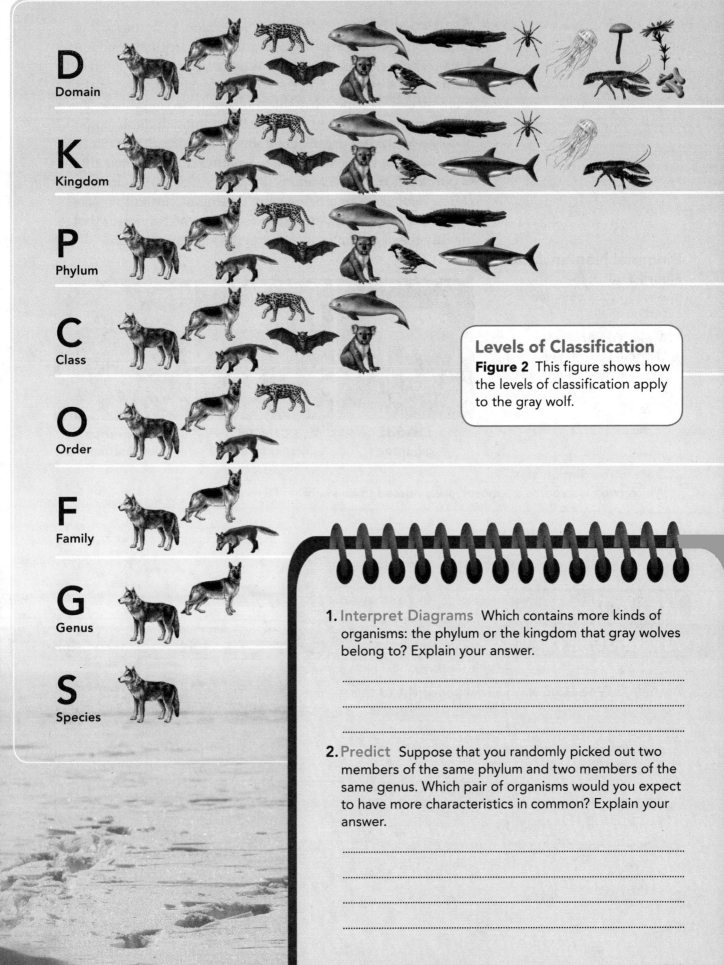

D Domain

K Kingdom

P Phylum

C Class

O Order

F Family

G Genus

S Species

Levels of Classification
Figure 2 This figure shows how the levels of classification apply to the gray wolf.

1. **Interpret Diagrams** Which contains more kinds of organisms: the phylum or the kingdom that gray wolves belong to? Explain your answer.

....

....

....

2. **Predict** Suppose that you randomly picked out two members of the same phylum and two members of the same genus. Which pair of organisms would you expect to have more characteristics in common? Explain your answer.

....

....

....

....

Binomial Nomenclature As explained at the start of this lesson, the first word in an organism's scientific name is its genus. The genus (plural *genera*) is a classification grouping of similar, closely related organisms. Each genus contains one or more species. The more classification levels two organisms share, the more characteristics they have in common and the more closely related they are. **Figure 3** shows a giant puffball mushroom found in the genus *Calvatia*. Another closely related kind of puffball is also in *Calvatia*. Still other puffballs that are not as closely related are in other genera. The giant puffball's species name, *gigantea*, describes its size. Together, the two words that identify the genus and species form the scientific name.

Binomial Nomenclature

Figure 3 All of these mushrooms are commonly called puffballs.

1. Make Observations
List some characteristics that all three mushrooms share.

....

....

....

| Calvatia gigantea | Calvatia craniiformis | Lycoperdon echinatum |

2. Determine Similarities
Which two mushrooms are most closely related to one another? Explain.

....

....

Math Toolbox

Aristotle and Classification

Aristotle, a Greek scholar who lived from 384 to 322 BCE, created the classification system shown in the table.

1. Write an Expression 🖊 Use variables to write an expression to find the percentage of animals that swim. Then, complete the table.

....

....

2. Classify How did Aristotle organize the animals?

....

....

Animals with blood that...	Percentage of animals
fly 	22%
walk, run, or hop 	46%
swim	

Scientific Names A complete scientific name is written in italics. The first letter in the first word is capitalized. You will notice that most scientific names use Latin. Linnaeus used Latin in his naming system because it was the common language used by all scientists. **Figure 4** shows how using different common names for the same organism can get confusing. Scientists also use taxonomic keys, as shown in **Figure 5**, to help name and identify organisms.

☑ **READING CHECK** **Determine Meaning** How are scientific names written?

....

....

Using a Taxonomic Key

Figure 5 While on a hike, you find an organism with eight legs, two body regions, claw-like pincers, and no tail. Use the key.

1. **Interpret Diagrams** How many different organisms can be identified using this key?

....

2. **Analyze Properties** Use the taxonomic key to identify the organism you observed on your hike.

....

Confusing Common Names

Figure 4 Is this a firefly, a lightning bug, a glowworm, or a golden sparkler? Different names are used in different parts of the country. Luckily, this insect has only one scientific name, *Photinus pyralis*.

Predict What characteristic of the insect do you think scientists used to give it the species name *pyralis*?

....

....

Taxonomic Key			
Step		Characteristics	Organism
1	1a.	Has 8 legs	Go to Step 2.
	1b.	Has more than 8 legs	Go to Step 3.
2	2a.	Has one oval-shaped body region	Go to Step 4.
	2b.	Has two body regions	Go to Step 5.
3	3a.	Has one pair of legs on each body segment	Centipede
	3b.	Has two pairs of legs on each body segment	Millipede
4	4a.	Is less than 1 millimeter long	Mite
	4b.	Is more than 1 millimeter long	Tick
5	5a.	Has clawlike pincers	Go to Step 6.
	5b.	Has no clawlike pincers	Spider
6	6a.	Has a long tail with a stinger	Scorpion
	6b.	Has no tail or stinger	Pseudoscorpion

HANDS-ON LAB

Use a taxonomic key to identify an unknown pest.

HANDS-ON LAB

Investigate Create a taxonomic key to classify different tree leaves.

Evolution and Classification

When Linnaeus was alive, people thought that species never changed. This point of view changed when Charles Darwin developed a new idea in the 1830s. Darwin was an Englishman. He sailed around the world for five years observing nature and collecting samples of fossils and animals. During the voyage, he was fascinated by the relationships between modern species and ancient types, as shown in **Figure 6**. Darwin was one of the first scientists to understand **evolution**, or the process of change over time. He concluded that all modern species developed from earlier kinds of life through natural selection. Natural selection is the idea that some individuals are better adapted to their environment than others. The better-adapted individuals are more likely to survive and reproduce than other members of the same species.

Common Ancestry Evolution by natural selection is the organizing principle of life science. Evidence from thousands of scientific investigations supports the idea of evolution. As understanding of evolution increased, biologists changed how they classify species. Scientists now understand that certain organisms may be similar because they share a common ancestor and an evolutionary history. The more similar the two groups are, in fact, the more recent their common ancestor.

5.2 million years ago (mya)

Pakicetus, land-dwelling, four-footed mammal

4.8 mya

Ambulocetus, "walking whale," mammal lived both on land and in water

4.1 mya

Dorudon, "spear tooth," water-dwelling mammal

2.2 mya

Evolution of the Dolphin

Figure 6 Darwin compared ancient and modern species to develop his theory of evolution by natural selection. Skeletons of dolphin ancestors show how the species evolved.

Form a Hypothesis Why do you think the ancient ancestor of the dolphin became a water-dwelling animal?

....

....

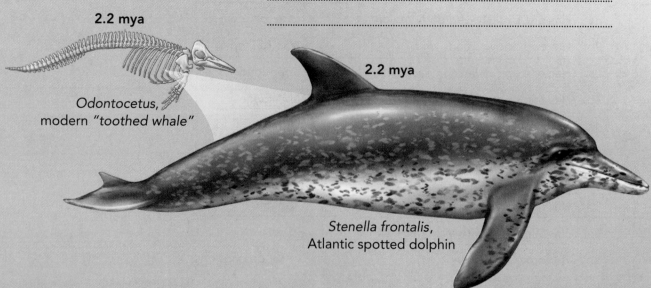

Odontocetus, modern "toothed whale"

2.2 mya

Stenella frontalis, Atlantic spotted dolphin

Convergent Evolution

Figure 7 These three organisms evolved a similar characteristic over time.

1. Identify ✎ Circle the characteristic that the three organisms share.

2. Form a Hypothesis Why did the same characteristic evolve?

....

....

....

....

Evolutionary Relationships

Scientists **determine** the evolutionary history of a species by comparing the structures of organisms. Scientists also compare the genetic information contained in the DNA of organisms' cells. Sometimes, unrelated organisms that live in similar environments evolve similar characteristics, as shown in **Figure 7**. Sharing common characteristics, however, does not necessarily mean that organisms are closely related. The process by which unrelated organisms evolve similar characteristics is called **convergent evolution**. When scientists discovered convergent evolution, they had to change the placement of organisms within the classification system. Because scientific research leads to discovery and new knowledge, scientists sometimes reclassify organisms to account for new evidence. In this sense, the system of classification also evolves.

☑ READING CHECK Assess Sources Suggest one reliable source of information about Charles Darwin. What makes this source reliable?

....

....

....

Academic Vocabulary

To determine is to find out an answer by doing research. When have you determined the answer to an important question?

....

....

....

....

☑ LESSON 2 Check

1. Draw Conclusions What can you conclude about two organisms that can mate and produce fertile offspring?

....

2. Classify Use the chart. Which two species are most closely related? How do you know? Which species is most distantly related to the other three? Explain.

Some Types of Trees				
Common Name	**Kingdom**	**Family**	**Genus**	**Species**
Bird cherry	Plants	Rosaceae	*Prunus*	*avium*
Flowering cherry	Plants	Rosaceae	*Prunus*	*serrula*
Smooth-leaved elm	Plants	Ulmaceae	*Ultima*	*minor*
Whitebeam	Plants	Rosaceae	*Sorbus*	*aria*

....

....

....

....

....

....

3. Determine Similarities How are evolution and classification related?

....

....

....

4. Identify Limitations Review the taxonomic key in **Figure 5**. If the hike had been near the ocean, would the key have been as accurate? Support your explanation with evidence.

....

....

....

....

....

....

5. Ask Questions A friend claims her pet ferret is descended from the wild polecat. You want to learn more about this ferret ancestor. An online search shows several different kinds of polecats. How could you figure out which one is the ferret ancestor?

....

....

....

....

....

Quest CHECK-IN

In this lesson, you learned how scientists classify living things based on shared characteristics.

Identify Limitations What are some limitations of using a classification system to categorize living things?

....

....

....

HANDS-ON LAB

Classifying Seeds

Go online for a downloadable worksheet of this lab. Model a scientific classification system using seeds. Then brainstorm ideas for how you might use classification in your field guide.

324 Living Things in the Biosphere

SC.6.L.15.1, SC.6.N.2.2

Classification:
What's a Panda?

What's in a name? In the Linnaean classification system, an animal's name tells what species it is. And with millions of species on Earth, this naming system comes in handy.

The naming system is based on observable physical characteristics—an animal's coloration, number of legs, the shape of its wings, and so on. But with today's technology, scientists can now classify animals from the inside out, by using their DNA.

DNA has helped scientists to figure out pandas, which have posed quite a puzzle. *Giant* pandas share a lot of physical traits with bears—their shape, size, shaggy fur, and lumbering movement. But smaller *red* pandas have more in common with raccoons. So what exactly is a "panda"?

Recent DNA studies show that giant pandas and red pandas are not closely related after all. Giant pandas share more DNA with bears and have been classified in the bear family (*Ursidae*). Red pandas, however, didn't make the cut. They're not bears, and, currently, they're not raccoons either. For now, they are classified in their own family, *Ailuridae*. But with further DNA evidence, this could change. Until then, the red panda is an animal unto itself.

MY DISCOVERY

Is a red panda a raccoon? The evidence points in different directions, and scientists are still debating. Read up on these animals and see what you think.

The red panda has a bushy, ringed tail, much like a raccoon's.

Are giant pandas really bears? DNA evidence reveals the answer.

325

Viruses, Bacteria, Protists, and Fungi

Guiding Questions

- What are all living things made of?
- What are the characteristics of viruses, bacteria, protists, and fungi?
- How do viruses, bacteria, protists, and fungi interact with nature and people?

Connections

Literacy Cite Textual Evidence

Math Analyze Relationships

 SC.6.L.14.6 Compare and contrast types of infectious agents that may infect the human body, including viruses, bacteria, fungi, and parasites. (Also **SC.6.N.1.5** and **SC.6.N.2.2**)

Vocabulary

virus
host
vaccine
bacteria
protist
parasite

Academic Vocabulary

resistant

 VOCABULARY APP

Practice vocabulary on a mobile device.

Quest CONNECTION

Think about how you could compare and contrast unicellular and multicellular organisms. How could this information help you to design a better field guide?

Connect It !

🖊 **Write a checkmark on one individual of each kind of living thing you see.**

Make Observations Describe the different types of organisms you see.

....

....

Reason Why might it be unwise to drink water straight from a pond?

....

....

Microorganisms

When people think of organisms, they picture plants or animals. Yet many of the organisms we come in contact with every day are so small that you need a microscope to see them. These microorganisms are vital for the survival of all plants and animals. **Figure 1** shows some amazing microbes living in a single drop of pond water.

Protists are classified in Domain Eukarya and are simpler than the plants, animals, and fungi they are grouped with. However, organisms in Domains Archaea and Bacteria are less complex than protists. Archaea and bacteria are unicellular microorganisms that do not have a nucleus. These microorganisms are classified in different domains because of their different characteristics.

Many archaea live in extreme conditions and make food from chemicals. You might find archaea in hot springs, very salty water, or deep underground. Archaea is a great example of how science is always changing. The domain Archaea was only proposed by taxonomists in 1977!

Bacteria have different structures and chemical processes than archaea do. Some bacteria are autotrophs, meaning they can make their own food. Other bacteria are heterotrophs who must find their food. Still other types of bacteria are decomposers that absorb nutrients from decaying organisms. Bacteria are found in soil, water, and air. In fact, bacteria are found everywhere, even inside you.

☑ READING CHECK **Determine Central Ideas** If you had a powerful microscope, how could you determine whether a cell was from a eukaryote?

....

....

....

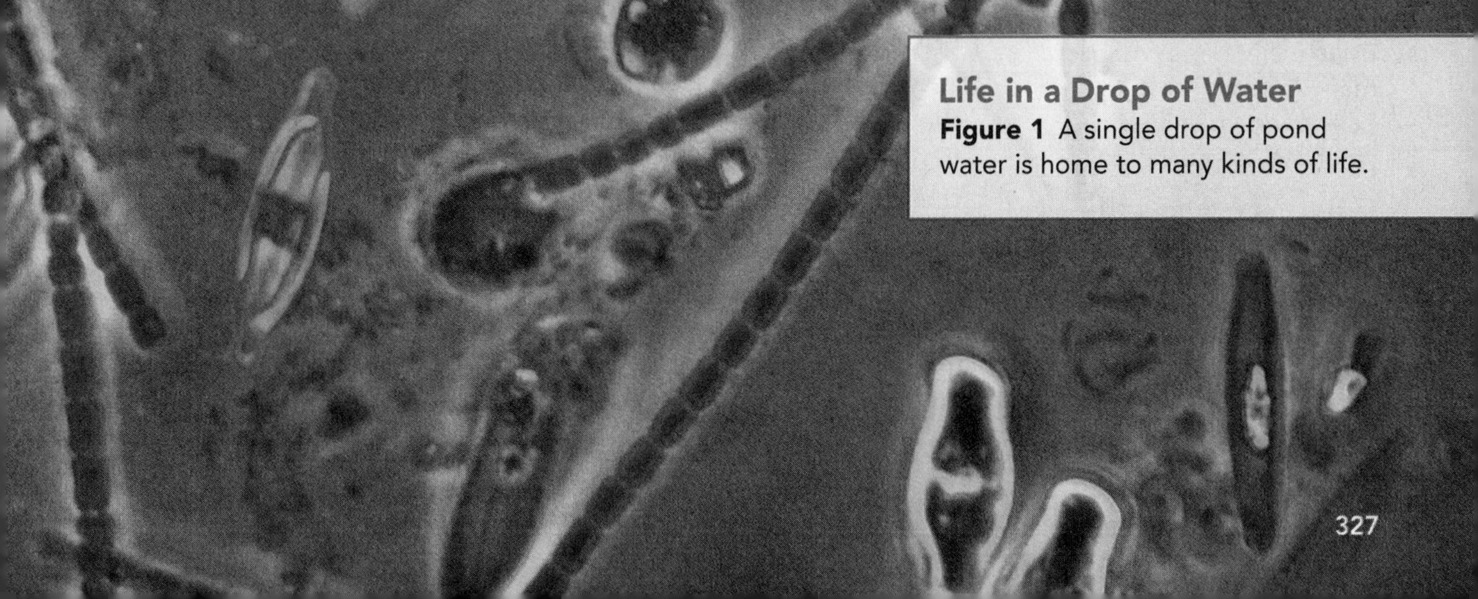

Life in a Drop of Water
Figure 1 A single drop of pond water is home to many kinds of life.

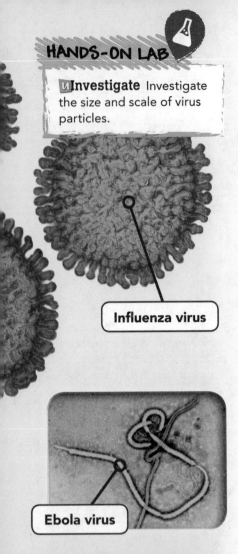

Influenza virus

Ebola virus

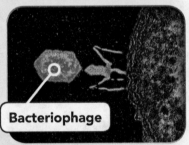

Bacteriophage

Viral Variety

Figure 2 Viruses come in many shapes. These images have been magnified and colorized to show details.

Determine Similarities

✎ Circle the virus that most closely resembles a cell. Explain your choice.

....

....

Viruses

You may have noticed that viruses were not included in the domains of living things. That's because viruses are not alive. A **virus** is a tiny, nonliving particle that enters and then reproduces inside a living cell. They lack most of the characteristics of living things. Some viruses may look like cells, but they are not cells. Viruses cannot reproduce on their own. Instead, they cause the cells they enter to reproduce more viruses. Viruses do not use food for energy or to grow. They also do not respond to their surroundings or produce wastes.

Shapes and Names Viruses can be round or shaped like bricks, threads, or bullets. Some viruses even have complex, robot-like shapes, as shown in **Figure 2**. Viruses are so small that they are measured in units called nanometers (nm), or one billionth of a meter. The common cold virus is 75 nm in diameter. The diameter of a red blood cell—7,500 nm—is much larger. Scientists name some viruses after the disease they cause or after the area where they were discovered.

Reproduction A virus is very small and simple. All viruses contain genetic material with a protein coating. The genetic material contains chemical instructions for making more copies of the virus. To reproduce, a virus attaches itself to a host cell, as shown in **Figure 3**. A **host** is an organism that provides a source of energy or a suitable environment for a virus to live. The virus either enters the cell or injects its genetic material into the host cell. Inside the host cell, the virus's genetic material takes over and forces the cell to make more copies of the virus! Finally, the host cell bursts open, releasing many new viruses which then infect other healthy cells, repeating the process.

Disease Many copies of a virus attacking your cells at once may cause a disease. Some viral diseases are mild, such as the common cold. Other viral diseases can produce serious illnesses. Viruses spread quickly and attack the cells of nearly every kind of organism. Fortunately, scientists have developed vaccines to prevent many dangerous viral diseases. A **vaccine** is a substance used in vaccination that consists of pathogens, such as viruses, that have been weakened or killed but can still trigger the body to produce chemicals that destroy the pathogens. **Figure 4** shows the vaccination process.

☑ **READING CHECK** **Distinguish Facts** What makes viruses so dangerous and vaccines so important?

....

....

Virus Invasion!

Figure 3 A cell invaded by a virus becomes a kind of zombie. All the cell's energy goes into making more and more new viruses.

Draw Conclusions Which came first: viruses or living organisms? Explain.

....

....

....

The virus that causes a disease is isolated. The virus is then damaged by heat, and a vaccine is prepared from it.

VIRUS

HOST CELL

Step 1 Virus injects genetic material into host cell.

After being injected with a vaccine, the body prepares defenses against the virus.

The body can now resist infection by the disease-causing virus.

Step 2 Cell makes copies of virus.

Step 3 Cell bursts, releasing many new copies of virus.

Vaccine Protection

Figure 4 Vaccinations can prevent measles and other viral diseases.

Construct Explanations Why is it important to use a weakened virus in a vaccine?

....

....

....

Math Toolbox

A Viral Epidemic

When a virus sickens many people at the same time within a limited geographic area, the outbreak is called an epidemic. During the 2014–2015 Ebola epidemic in West Africa, people began to get sick faster and faster beginning in May. There were about 375 new Ebola cases at the beginning of June. By July first, there were about 750 new cases.

1. **Analyze Relationships** Explain the relationship between the number of cases reported and time.

....

2. **Write an Expression** Find the number of new cases expected by September. Use an expression to plot the number of new cases for both September and October on the graph. Then finish drawing the line.

....

....

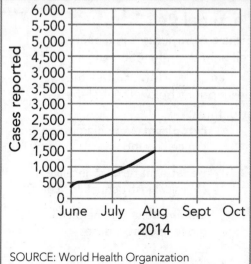

Ebola Cases in West Africa, 2014

SOURCE: World Health Organization

329

Bacteria Shapes

Figure 5 The shape of a bacteria helps a scientist to identify it.

Apply Concepts Label the shape of each bacteria.

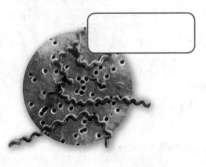

Bacteria

If life were a movie, bacteria would be both villains and heroes. Bacteria would also make up most of the supporting cast. Bacteria make up the great majority of organisms on Earth. Bacteria are very small; millions can fit into the period at the end of this sentence. The smallest bacteria are about the size of the largest viruses. Most bacteria are one of three basic shapes: ball, rod, or spiral. You can see some of these shapes in **Figure 5**. The shape of the cell helps scientists identify the type of bacteria.

Infectious Bacteria You have probably heard of *E. coli,* *Streptococcus* ("strep throat"), and *Staphylococcus* ("staph"). They are types of infectious, or disease–causing, bacteria. Someone can become infected when the bacteria enter the person's body. The bacteria then grow and multiply quite quickly. Because these bacteria give off toxins (dangerous chemicals that damage surrounding cells and tissues), they can cause serious infections. Luckily, fewer than one percent of bacteria are actually infectious.

Bacterial Cell Structures **Bacteria** are single-celled organisms, also known as prokaryotes, that lack a nucleus. Each cell is a separate living organism that performs all the functions needed for life. **Figure 6** shows the structure of a typical bacterial cell. Bacteria have cell walls that protect them from attacks and keep them from drying out. Inside the cell wall is a cell membrane. The cell membrane controls what substances pass into and out of the cell. Some bacteria have structures attached to the cell wall that help them move around. Flagella whip around like propellers to drive some bacteria toward their food.

Model It !

Bacterial Cell Structures

Figure 6 Structures in a bacterial cell help them function and survive.

Develop Models 🖉 Use the descriptions below to label the structures.

> **cytoplasm** everything inside the cell membrane
>
> **genetic material** string-like chemical instructions for cell
>
> **pili** tiny hairs that help cell move and reproduce
>
> **ribosomes** round structures where proteins are made

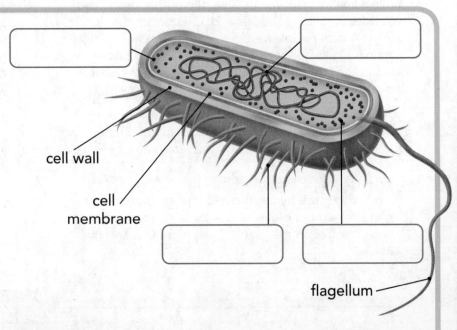

cell wall

cell membrane

flagellum

Obtaining Food Some bacteria make their own food from sunlight, like plants do. Other bacteria create food from chemicals. Chemicals from underwater volcanoes feed the bacteria in **Figure 7**. A third group of bacteria take in food through their cell walls. Food for these bacteria could be milk, sugar, meat, or dead cells. Your digestive system is a good home for bacteria! Some bacteria use the energy from food to make poisonous chemicals called toxins. Toxins cause the pain and sickness you feel when you get food poisoning.

Survival Bacteria cannot move fast. They cannot escape intense heat or hunt for food. In harsh conditions, some bacteria survive by sheltering in place. A thick-walled shell forms around genetic material and cytoplasm, forming a tough endospore. The endospore can grow back into a full cell when conditions improve.

Bacterial Reproduction Bacteria also keep ahead of predators by reproducing rapidly. Even if predators eat some individual bacteria, there are always more. Bacterial reproduction is shown in **Figure 8**. Most bacteria reproduce asexually by growing and then dividing into two identical cells. Asexual reproduction in bacteria is called binary fission.

Bacteria can also pass genetic material to a neighboring bacteria through conjugation. Conjugation occurs when two bacteria cells come together and exchange genetic material. Conjugation does not produce more bacteria, but it does allow genetic information to spread. For example, one bacterial cell could be **resistant** to antibiotics. The antibiotic-resistant cell could pass the resistance on to other bacteria by conjugation. Soon, the whole bacteria population can become resistant and the antibiotic will stop working.

INTERACTIVITY

Observe and compare different unicellular organisms.

Undersea Mystery
Figure 7 These "rocks" are layers of bacteria that have grown up around the mouth of the seafloor volcano.

Academic Vocabulary

Resistant means able to work against or hold off an opposing force. When have you been resistant?

....

....

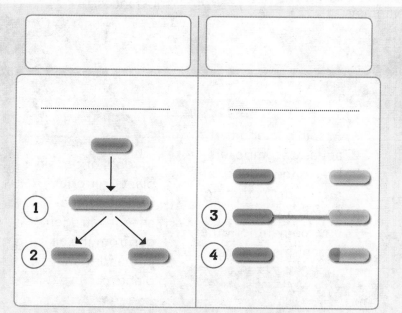

Bacterial Reproduction
Figure 8 🖊 Label the diagram with these terms: asexual reproduction, binary fission, conjugation, and transfer of genetic material. Then, match the number in the diagram to the step it describes below.

_____ Cells separate; one now has some genetic information from the other cell.

_____ Cell splits into two identical cells.

_____ Cell grows larger before dividing.

_____ One cell passes some of its genetic information to another cell.

331

Cite Textual Evidence
Would you classify bacteria as harmful or helpful? Explain.

....
....
....
....
....

The Many Roles of Bacteria

Figure 9 🖊 Bacteria do other things besides make people sick. They have many important roles in nature and human life. There are many ways we interact with bacteria. Circle or highlight one or more examples of harmful bacteria.

☑ READING CHECK **Cite Textural Evidence** According to what you have read, how do bacteria protect their genetic material and cytoplasm during harsh conditions?

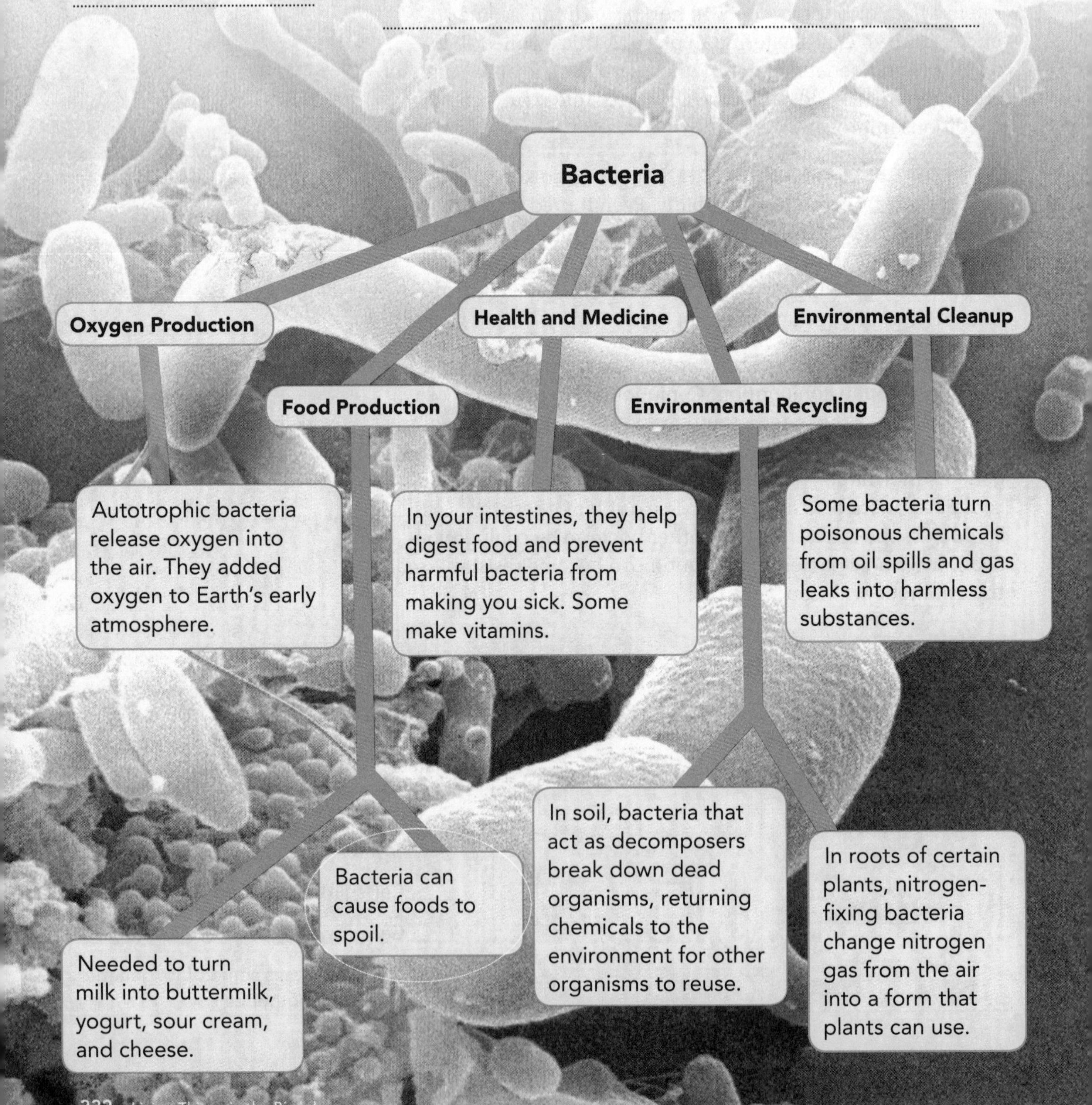

....
....
....

Bacteria

Oxygen Production

Health and Medicine

Environmental Cleanup

Food Production

Environmental Recycling

Autotrophic bacteria release oxygen into the air. They added oxygen to Earth's early atmosphere.

In your intestines, they help digest food and prevent harmful bacteria from making you sick. Some make vitamins.

Some bacteria turn poisonous chemicals from oil spills and gas leaks into harmless substances.

Bacteria can cause foods to spoil.

In soil, bacteria that act as decomposers break down dead organisms, returning chemicals to the environment for other organisms to reuse.

In roots of certain plants, nitrogen-fixing bacteria change nitrogen gas from the air into a form that plants can use.

Needed to turn milk into buttermilk, yogurt, sour cream, and cheese.

Protists

Protists are eukaryotic organisms that cannot be classified as animals, plants, or fungi. **Figure 10** shows that protists have a wide range of characteristics. All protists live in moist environments and are common where humans interact. Most protists are harmless, but some can cause illness or disease. Most harmful protists are **parasites**, organisms that benefit from living with, on, or in a host. Drinking water contaminated with these protists can cause fever, diarrhea, and abdominal pain. For example, a person can become ill after drinking water containing the protist *Giardia*. The protist attaches itself to the small intestine, where it takes in nutrients and prevents those nutrients from entering the human. The person gets ill from the disease giardiasis. Another parasitic protist travels with a mosquito. When a mosquito that is carrying the protist *Plasmodium* bites a human, the protist infects the red blood cells, causing malaria.

✓ READING CHECK **Cite Textual Evidence** Tasha and Marco examine a cell through a microscope. Tasha suggests that the cell is a protist. Marco thinks it might be a bacterium. What evidence would prove Tasha right?

....

....

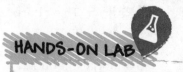

HANDS-ON LAB

✐**Investigate** Discover unicellular and multicellular organisms in pond water.

Diversity of Protists

Figure 10 Protists are classified in Domain Eukarya and Kingdom Protista. The three separate types are shown in the table below.

Identify Use information in the chart to identify the three photos of protists below. Write the name of each type of protist in the space provided.

	Animal-like Protists	**Plant-like Protists**	**Fungi-like Protists**
Food	Heterotrophs	Autotrophs; some also heterotrophs	Heterotrophs
Features	Unicellular	Unicellular or multicellular	Unicellular, but often live in colonies
Movement	Free-swimming	Free-swimming or attached	Move during some part of life cycle
Reproduction	Asexual and sexual	Sexual and asexual	Asexual
Examples	Amoebas: surround and trap food particles Giardia: common parasite, has eight flagella	Red algae: seaweeds people eat, known as nori Dinoflagellates: glow in the dark	Slime molds: brightly colored, grow in garden beds Water molds: attack plants, such as crops

Fungi

What's the largest organism ever to exist on Earth? Good guesses would be a dinosaur, a blue whale, or a giant tree. These are wrong. The biggest living thing is a honey fungus colony growing under a forest in Oregon. The colony is larger than a thousand football fields! Like all other fungi, the honey fungus has eukaryotic cells with cell walls. Fungi are heterotrophs that feed by absorbing food through their cell walls. Most of the honey fungus is unseen underground. The cells of fungi are arranged into hyphae, or threadlike tubes. Hyphae, like those shown in **Figure 11**, give fungi structure and allow them to spread over large areas. Hyphae also grow into food sources and release chemicals. Food is broken down by the chemicals and then absorbed by the hyphae. Some fungi act as decomposers and consume dead organisms, while others are parasites that attack living hosts.

Fungal Reproduction

Fungi occasionally send up reproductive structures called fruiting bodies. Some fruiting bodies are the familiar mushrooms that you eat or see growing in damp environments. Fruiting bodies produce spores that are carried by wind or water to new locations. Each spore that lands in the right conditions can then start a new fungal colony. Fungi can also reproduce sexually when hyphae from two colonies grow close together and trade genetic information.

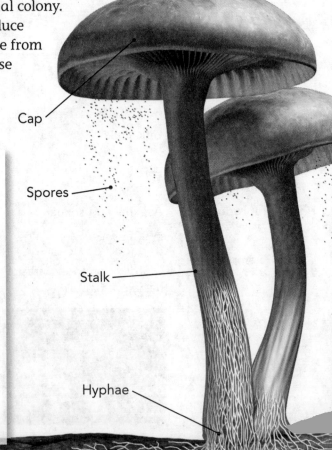

Cap

Spores

Stalk

Hyphae

Structure of a Honey Mushroom

Figure 11 The part of a mushroom you can see above ground is tiny compared to the network of hyphae underground.

Hypothesize What is a possible relationship between the fungus and the tree root?

....

....

☑ **READING CHECK** **Determine Central Ideas** What is the purpose of fungal spores?

....

....

Roles of Fungi

Fungi come in many forms and have varying lifestyles. We depend on fungi for many services. **Figure 12** explores some of the ways that fungi are helpful and harmful. At the same time, fungi can destroy our property and food and make us sick. You've probably heard of *athlete's foot* and *ringworm*. These are both common rashes—mild skin infections caused by fungi in the environment. They are easily treated. Some fungi, however, can cause serious diseases. In fact, more people die each year from fungal infections than from malaria and certain common cancers. There are no vaccines to prevent fungal infections.

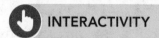

INTERACTIVITY

Use research to develop medicine needed for someone that is ill.

Fungi: Friend or Foe?

Figure 12 ✏️ Circle or highlight evidence of harm in the image descriptions.

1. **Analyze Systems** Why would a fungus growing on a rock need a partner to provide it food?

....

....

2. **Construct Explanations** Why would fungi be better than seeds at absorbing water?

....

....

Mycorrhiza

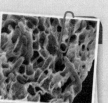

Grows around plant seeds and roots.

Brings water to plant and eats plant sugars.

Helps plants grow.

Penicillium Mold

Grows on food products.

Spoils food.

Produces chemicals used in antibiotics.

Some produce poisons or cause allergic reactions.

Shiitake Mushroom

Grows on and consumes dead logs.

Provides nutritious food.

Breaks down dead wood and makes nutrients available for living things.

Lichen

Forms partnership with autotrophic algae or bacteria.

Provides water, shelter, and minerals, while partner provides food.

Produces chemicals used in dyes, perfumes, and deodorant.

Provides food for animals in harsh environments.

Yeast

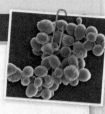

Eats carbohydrates, turning them into alcohols and carbon dioxide.

Helps to bake bread and make beverages.

Causes diaper rash and yeast infections.

Destroys stored foods.

Fungi Files

1. **Apply Concepts** What is most unusual about parasites?

....

....

....

2. **Explain Phenomena** Refer back to **Figure 12.** Explain why trees that have relationships with mycorrhizae are less common in dry climates.

....

....

....

....

3. **Construct Arguments** Could you have two or more viral infections at the same time? Explain, using evidence to support your argument.

....

....

....

....

....

4. **Classify** Which of these taxonomic groups are most closely related to each other: Fungi, Archaea, Bacteria, Protista? Explain.

....

....

....

....

....

5. **Develop Models** ✎ Draw a Venn Diagram to compare and contrast bacteria, viruses, and fungi.

Quest CHECK-INS

In this lesson, you learned about the characteristics of viruses, bacteria, protists, and fungi. You also discovered how some of these living and nonliving things interact with nature and people.

Integrate Information When developing a classification system, do you think identifying similarities or identifying differences is more helpful? Explain.

....

....

....

....

👆 INTERACTIVITIES

- Discovering Rainforest Organisms
- Multicellular Rainforest Organisms

Go online to classify organisms as unicellular or multicellular.

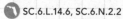
SC.6.L.14.6, SC.6.N.2.2

A Disease Becomes a Cure

Viruses make you sick when they work their way into healthy cells. They can do serious damage as a result. But some scientists are taking advantage of a virus's ability to invade cells to make people better.

The Challenge: To use viruses to deliver targeted therapy to cells.

Cancer therapies battle cancer cells, but they often damage healthy cells in the process. This can lead to serious side effects, from severe nausea to hair loss. Scientists are looking for better methods to target diseased cells while leaving healthy ones alone.

To tackle this problem, scientist James Swartz looked to nature for inspiration. Viruses, he realized, are great at targeting specific cells. He and his team re-engineered a virus by removing the disease-causing properties, leaving a hollow shell that might carry medicine inside. Next, they altered the spiky surface of the virus and attached tiny "tags" to it. The tags send the virus to sick cells to deliver medicine.

Swartz and his team still have to do a lot of research and testing to see whether this improved delivery system works. If it does, they'll have engineered a virus that works in reverse—infecting you with medicine rather than disease.

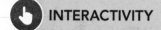

INTERACTIVITY

Explore how viruses are engineered to solve problems.

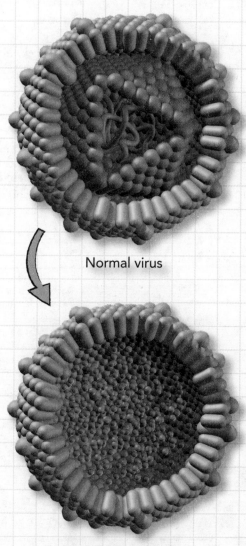

Normal virus

Re-engineered virus

The redesigned protein coat in the middle section of this virus removed the disease-causing properties, leaving the protein able to carry medicine. The spiky virus surface contains tags to direct the virus to the correct cells.

DESIGN CHALLENGE Can you engineer a virus to perform a specific function? Go to the Engineering Design Notebook to find out!

337

☑TOPIC 7 Review and Assess

1 Living Things

SC.6.L.14.A, SC.6.L.14.D

1. What are the basic building blocks of all living things?
   A. food
   B. energy
   C. cells
   D. water

2. Which terms best illustrate homeostasis?
   A. food, water
   B. stimulus, response
   C. growth, development
   D. sweating, shivering

3. **Critique** At lunch, your friend stated that her apple was a living thing, because if she put a piece under the microscope, she'd see cells. How will you respond?

   ....
   ....
   ....
   ....
   ....
   ....

4. **Plan an Investigation** Design a controlled experiment to demonstrate that birds do not spontaneously generate on birdfeeders.

   ....
   ....
   ....
   ....
   ....

2 Classification Systems

SC.6.L.15.1

5. **Explain Phenomena** Some sharks and dolphins are about the same size and shape, and they live in the same habitats. But dolphins are mammals, and sharks are fish. What is this phenomenon, and how does it occur?

   ....
   ....
   ....

6. **Make Models** Develop a taxonomic key that a person could use to identify the following animals: hawk, alligator, duck, snake

   hawk   alligator   duck   snake

7. **Evaluate Reasoning** Substitute the animal below for the hawk in Question 6. Revise your key.

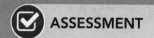
③ Viruses, Bacteria, Protists, and Fungi

 SC.6.L.14.6

8. Which of the following groups is always heterotrophic?

A. Domain Archaea
B. Domain Bacteria
C. Kingdom Fungi
D. Kingdom Protista

9. **Explain Phenomenon** You observe many mushrooms growing in a circle. How many organisms are you likely seeing? Explain.

....

....

....

....

10. **Apply Scientific Reasoning** Explain how a vaccine can prevent you from getting ill from a virus without making you ill.

....

....

....

....

....

....

11. **Explain** Why is *diversity* a good word to use to describe protists?

....

....

....

....

12. **Develop Models** Both bacteria and viruses can only be seen with microscopes. Both can cause illness. They have little else in common. Sketch thumbnails of a slide show you could use to describe the differences to fourth graders. Include bullet points of ways bacteria and viruses differ in classification, reproduction, shapes and structures, and causing disease. Include at least two diagrams.

Science Assessment Practice

Circle the letter of the best answer.

While hiking in Three Rivers State Park, you observe small white wildflowers growing along the trail. Taking a closer look, you notice a few different types of flowers. One of these flowers you have never seen before in Florida. To help you identify the flowers, you consult a field guide. **Use the taxonomic key to answer Questions 1–2.**

Key to White Wildflowers		
1	a	Five petals .... Go to 2
	b	Seven petals ....Starflower (*Trientalis borealis*)
2	a	Petals single pieces .... Go to 3
	b	Petal deeply divided.....................Chickweed (*Stellaria media*)
3	a	Wide round petals........ Common strawberry (*Fragaria virginiana*)
	b	Narrow elongated petals....... Bowman's root (*Gillenia trifoliata*)

❶ Using the taxonomic key, what is the **best** identification for the flower shown?

A Bowman's root

B chickweed

C common strawberry

D starflower

❷ Based upon the binomial nomenclature system created by Carolus Linnaeus, what is the genus name for the five-petaled flower with narrow, elongated petals?

F *Stellaria*

G *media*

H *Gillenia*

I *trifoliata*

❸ Mosquitoes can spread disease caused by viruses or parasitic protists when they bite. In 2013, there was an outbreak of a serious illness in Martin County, Florida, in which 28 people were infected. What is one way a scientist might have determined whether the outbreak was caused by a virus or a parasitic protist?

A Examined a sample under a microscope to see if it was made of cells

B Grew a sample in a laboratory

C Observed an infected patient and monitored the symptoms

D Observed whether antibiotics killed the disease in a blood sample

❹ The pupils, or dark centers, of your eyes get larger when you move into a dark area. What characteristic of living things does this change demonstrate?

F maintenance of homeostasis

G response to a stimulus

H cellular organization

I growth and development

❺ Scientists once classified fungi in the same kingdom as plants. Based on evidence that fungi have many features that are different from plants, scientists now classify fungi in their own kingdom. Which of the following statements supports that change?

A Fungi are heterotrophs.

B Fungi help make yogurt and sour cream.

C Fungi live in your digestive system.

D Fungi use spores to reproduce.

Bacteria have two ways of sharing genetic material. Those processes are shown below, and two steps of each are labeled. **Use the diagrams to answer Questions 6 through 8.**

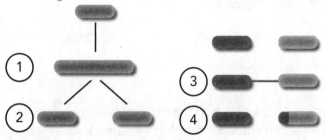

6 One process results in a transfer of genetic material. What is the name of the process, and at which step does the transfer occur?

F binary fission, Step 1

G binary fission, Step 2

H binary fission, Step 3

I conjugation, Step 3

7 Antibiotic resistance spreads when resistant bacteria share genetic material. Which option explains a possible process?

A During binary fission, two parent bacteria pass on resistant genetic material to the next generation.

B During binary fission, one bacterium transfers resistant genetic material to one other bacterium.

C During conjugation, two parent bacteria pass on resistant genetic material to the next generation.

D During conjugation, one bacterium transfers resistant genetic material to another bacterium.

8 Which step shows the bacterium with the newly acquired trait?

F 1

G 2

H 3

I 4

 SC.6.L.15.1

Complete the Quest!

In a group, identify the criteria and constraints for your field guide. Then, create a field guide that will help people identify different organisms at a local nature center.

Identify Limitations What are some of the drawbacks or difficulties in using classification systems in your field guide? How else could you organize living things?

....

....

....

....

....

....

....

....

....

....

....

 **INTERACTIVITY**

Create Your Field Guide

SC.6.L.15.1, SC.6.N.1.1, SC.6.N.2.2

It's Alive!

How can you **gather evidence** to **distinguish living** things from **nonliving** things?

Materials

(per pair)

- hand lens
- samples of living and nonliving things
- prepared slides or microscope pictures of living and nonliving things
- microscope

Safety

Be sure to follow all safety guidelines provided by your teacher. The Safety Appendix of your textbook provides more details about the safety icons.

Background

Before scientists could peer into microscopes, they had very different ideas about what living things were made of. It was a challenge to classify organisms when they couldn't even distinguish between living and nonliving things.

It may seem pretty obvious to you today that a flower is a living thing and a rock is a nonliving thing. But how could you explain this difference to a class of third-grade students in a way they would understand? In this investigation, you will observe samples of living and nonliving things. You will use the data you collect to develop an explanation of how living things can be distinguished from nonliving things.

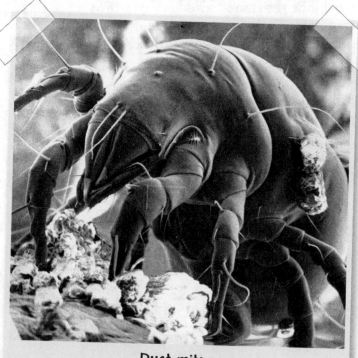

Dust mite

Procedure

1. Work with a partner. At your workstation, you should have a hand lens, a microscope, and paper and pencils for drawing.

2. Discuss with your partner what you should be looking for to help you determine whether your samples are living or nonliving. Then, from the class supplies, choose one sample and the microscope slide or microscope photograph that goes with it. Take them to your station to examine.

3. On a separate paper, make detailed observations of your sample, label it, note whether it is living or nonliving, and describe any structures you observe.

4. Return your sample and select a new one. Continue until you have examined five different samples. You should include three different organisms and two nonliving things, and include at least one fungus and one autotroph.

5. Based on your observations, complete the data table that follows. There may be some spaces that you are not sure how to fill out. If you have time, take another look at the sample(s) in question to gather more evidence.

HANDS-ON LAB

Demonstrate Go online for a downloadable worksheet of this lab.

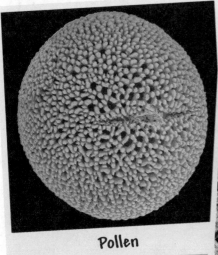

Pollen

Honey

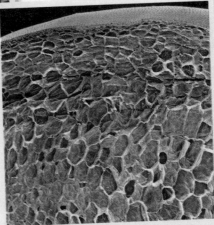

Cross-section of tomato

343

uDemonstrate Lab

Observations

Which Samples Are Living or Nonliving?			
Sample Name	Living or Nonliving?	Observations	Sketches

Analyze and Interpret Data

1. Evaluate Scale Why is the microscope necessary for determining whether a sample is living or nonliving?

....

....

....

....

2. Analyze Properties Compare the appearance of the living samples to the appearance of the nonliving samples. How do you explain the differences in structures?

....

....

....

....

....

3. Apply Concepts Based on what you observed, what are some ways that the living things in this lab could be grouped or organized?

....

....

....

....

4. Construct Explanations How would you explain to a class of third-graders the difference between living things and nonliving things? What are some examples you would give to support your thinking?

....

....

....

....

....

TOPIC
8

Cells and Cell Systems

HANDS-ON LAB

uConnect Explore how an object's
appearance changes when different
tools are used.

SC.6.L.14.1 Describe and identify patterns in the hierarchical organization of organisms from atoms to molecules and cells to tissues to organs to organ systems to organisms.

SC.6.L.14.2 Investigate and explain the components of the scientific theory of cells (cell theory): all organisms are composed of cells (single-celled or multi-cellular), all cells come from pre-existing cells, and cells are the basic unit of life.

SC.6.L.14.3 Recognize and explore how cells of all organisms undergo similar processes to maintain homeostasis, including extracting energy from food, getting rid of waste, and reproducing.

SC.6.L.14.4 Compare and contrast the structure and function of major organelles of plant and animal cells, including cell wall, cell membrane, nucleus, cytoplasm, chloroplasts, mitochondria, and vacuoles.

SC.6.L.14.5 Identify and investigate the general functions of the major systems of the human body (digestive, respiratory, circulatory, reproductive, excretory, immune, nervous, and musculoskeletal) and describe ways these systems interact with each other to maintain homeostasis. (Also **SC.6.N.1.1** and **SC.6.N.3.4**)

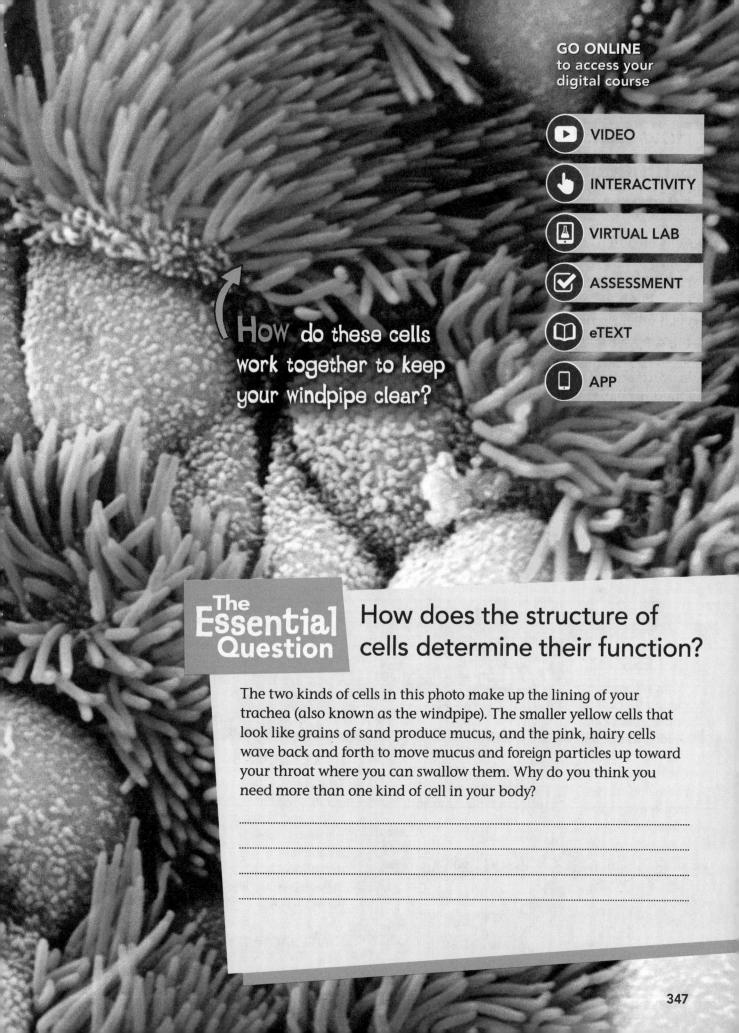

GO ONLINE
to access your
digital course

VIDEO

INTERACTIVITY

VIRTUAL LAB

ASSESSMENT

eTEXT

APP

HOW do these cells work together to keep your windpipe clear?

The Essential Question

How does the structure of cells determine their function?

The two kinds of cells in this photo make up the lining of your trachea (also known as the windpipe). The smaller yellow cells that look like grains of sand produce mucus, and the pink, hairy cells wave back and forth to move mucus and foreign particles up toward your throat where you can swallow them. Why do you think you need more than one kind of cell in your body?

....

....

....

....

Quest KICKOFF

How can you design a model exhibit for a science museum?

Cells are often called "the building blocks of life." But that makes us think of wooden or plastic blocks that simply sit next to each other or stack neatly. In fact, cells have moving parts. And they interact with each other. To help people understand impossible-to-see processes such as these, museum staff—both scientists and engineers—try to engage and educate visitors with easy-to-see and hands-on models. In this problem-based Quest activity, you will plan and design a science exhibit on cells. By applying what you learn in each lesson, digital activity, and hands-on lab, you will gather information that will assist you in creating your exhibit. Then, in the Findings activity, you assemble, organize, and present your exhibit.

👆 **INTERACTIVITY**

Cells on Display

⚓ **SC.6.L.14.4** Compare and contrast the structure and function of major organelles of plant and animal cells, including cell wall, cell membrane, nucleus, cytoplasm, chloroplasts, mitochondria, and vacuoles. (Also **SC.6.N.1.5** and **SC.6.N.3.4**)

NBC LEARN ▶ **VIDEO**

After watching the Quest Kickoff video on how museum models are planned and built, think about the qualities of a good science museum display. Record your thoughts in the graphic organizer.

Qualities of a Science Museum Display	
Good Qualities	**Bad Qualities**

IN LESSON 1
What will your exhibit teach the public about cell theory? Consider the challenges of explaining and modeling things that are hard to observe.

Quest CHECK-IN

IN LESSON 2
What do cells look like? How can you represent different cell parts? Design and build a model cell.

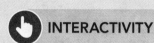
HANDS-ON LAB

Make a Cell Model

Quest CHECK-IN

IN LESSON 3
What cell parts are involved in active and passive transport? Create an animation that shows how materials enter and leave the cell.

👆 **INTERACTIVITY**

Put Your Cells in Motion

IN LESSON 4
Why is cell division important? Think about how to incorporate information about cell division into your exhibit.

The Body Fantastic exhibit at the Odyssium, a science museum in Edmonton, Alberta, Canada.

Quest CHECK-IN

IN LESSON 5

Why is it important to understand how cells work? Research a disease with a cause or cure that is related to cells or cell function and present your findings.

⟩ INTERACTIVITY

The Importance of Cells

IN LESSON 6

Why does a healthy body depend on healthy, functioning cells? Consider what you want the public to learn from your exhibit.

Quest FINDINGS

Complete the Quest!

Determine the best way to present your museum exhibit. Then share your exhibit with museum guests. Evaluate and compare the different exhibits.

⟩ INTERACTIVITY

Reflect on Your Museum Exhibit

Structure and Function of Cells

Guiding Questions

- What evidence is there that cells make up all living things?
- How do cells determine the structure of living things?

Connections

Literacy Determine Central Ideas

Math Represent Quantitative Relationships

 SC.6.L.14.2 Investigate and explain the components of the scientific theory of cells (cell theory): all organisms are composed of cells (single-celled or multi-cellular), all cells come from pre-existing cells, and cells are the basic unit of life.

SC.6.L.14.3 Recognize and explore how cells of all organisms undergo similar processes to maintain homeostasis, including extracting energy from food, getting rid of waste, and reproducing. (Also **SC.6.N.1.3** and **SC.6.N.3.4**).

Vocabulary

cell
microscope
cell theory

Academic Vocabulary

distinguish

 VOCABULARY APP

Practice vocabulary on a mobile device.

Quest CONNECTION

Think about the different methods you can use to communicate information to people about something they cannot see.

Connect It !

✏️ **Circle the different structures you observe in the photograph.**

Cause and Effect With microscopes, we can see the cells inside us and around us. What reactions do you think people had when they first learned that they were surrounded by tiny living organisms?

....

....

....

Cells

What do a whale, a rose, bacteria, a ladybug, and you have in common? You are all living things, or organisms. All are made of **cells**, the basic unit of structure and function in living things. Cells form the parts of an organism and carry out its functions. The smallest organisms, such as the bacteria in **Figure 1,** are made of one cell, while the largest organisms may have trillions of cells.

Cell Structure The structure of an object refers to what it is made of and how its parts are put together. For example, the structure of a car depends on how materials such as plastic, metal, and rubber are arranged. The structure of a living thing is determined by the amazing variety of ways its cells are put together.

Cell Function A single cell has the same needs as an entire organism. For a cell to stay alive, it must perform biological functions. Those functions include obtaining energy, bringing in nutrients and water, and getting rid of wastes. Most organisms have bodies with many different cells that work together to help the organism to stay alive, grow, and reproduce. For example, cells in your circulatory system move blood around your body. This blood provides you with fresh oxygen and removes the waste product carbon dioxide. Cells in your heart pump blood to every part of you. Your body's cells work together to keep you alive.

✅ **READING CHECK** **Determine Central Ideas** How is a single cell similar to an elephant?

....

....

....

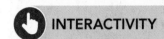

INTERACTIVITY

Explore the function of different cell types in unicellular and multicellular organisms.

Cells Are Everywhere
Figure 1 Suppose you take a swab from someone's tongue. This is what you might see under the microscope. These cells are all bacteria of different shapes and sizes and with different functions.

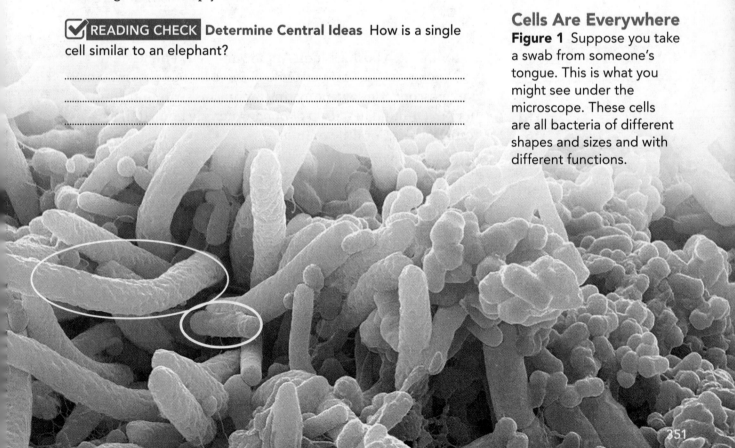

VIDEO

Learn more about the scientists who helped to develop the cell theory.

Cell Theory

It wasn't until the 1600s that scientists realized living organisms are made of cells. The invention of the **microscope**, an instrument that makes small objects look larger, made this discovery possible. The technology of the microscope led to new knowledge of how life is organized. As this technology improved over time, scientists were able to gather new information about cells and how they function. Scientists put all these discoveries together to develop a theory about cells.

Observing Cells In the mid-1600s, English scientist Robert Hooke built his own microscopes to learn about nature. He made drawings of what he saw when he looked at the bark of cork oak trees (**Figure 2**). Hooke thought that the empty spaces he observed in the tree bark looked like tiny rooms, so he named them "cells." Tree bark, however, contains only dead cells.

Early Cell Observations

Figure 2 ✏ Hooke drew what he saw through his microscope in great detail. Draw a circle around one of Hooke's "cells."

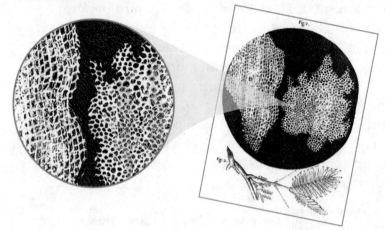

In 1674, Dutch businessman Anton van Leeuwenhoek (LAY von hook) was the first person to observe living cells through a microscope. He saw many tiny organisms swimming and hopping around in a drop of pond water. He named them "animalcules," or little animals.

By 1838, Matthias Schleiden, a scientist working with plants, noticed that all plants are made of cells. A year later, Theodor Schwann came to the conclusion that animals are made of animal cells. The timeline in **Figure 3** shows how the improvement of the microscope furthered the study of cells.

Before Schleiden and Schwann's suggestion that organisms are made up of cells, not much was known about the structure of organisms. These two scientists are credited with the development of the cell theory. Each scientist proposed a hypothesis (plural: hypotheses), a possible answer to a scientific question. Their hypotheses, supported through the observations and experiments of other scientists, led to a theory about cells and all living things.

Literacy Connection

Determine Central Ideas How did early modern scientists learn about cells without performing experiments?

....

....

....

....

....

Microscopes & Cell Theory

1650

Robert Hooke studies bark and fossils with microscopes and coins the term "cells".

1663

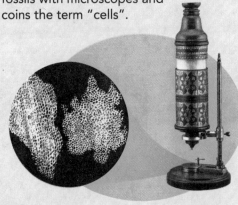

Anton van Leeuwenhoek observes living microorganisms under the microscope.

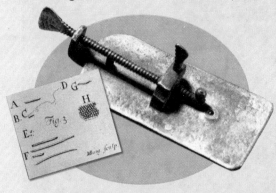

1674

1675

1825

Matthias Schleiden concludes that all plants are made of cells.

1838

1839

Theodor Schwann reaches the conclusion that all animals are made of cells.

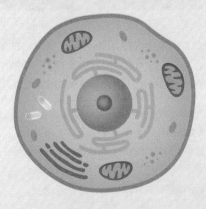

1850

1855

Rudolf Virchow proposes that cells are only made from other cells.

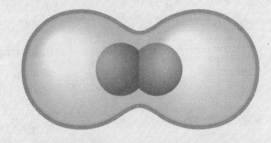

Scientists developed several types of electron microscopes that are 5,000 times more powerful than light microscopes.

1875

1925

Magnifying the Power of Discovery

Figure 3 This timeline shows how technology and science advance together.

1930s

Infer Why didn't Robert Hooke recognize that cells are alive?

....

....

....

1950

353

Giant Cells

Figure 4 Bubble algae, or sea pearls, look like rubber balls. The bubble shown in this life-sized photo is a single cell! Some scientists consider eggs to be single cells as well. An ostrich egg is 15 cm long and a human egg is about the size of the period at the end of this sentence.

HANDS-ON LAB

Investigate Observe objects using a microscope.

Principles of Cell Theory One of the most important ideas in biology, **cell theory** is a widely accepted explanation of the relationship between cells and living things. According to this theory:

• All living things are made of cells.
• Cells are the basic units of structure and function in living things.
• All new cells are produced from existing cells.

Even though living things differ greatly from one another, they are all made of one or more cells. Cells are the basic unit of life. Most cells are tiny. But some, like those shown in **Figure 4**, can be surprisingly large. The cell theory holds true for all living things, no matter how big or how small they are. Organisms can be made of one cell or of many cells. We can study how one-celled organisms remove wastes to sustain life. Then we can use this information to understand how multi-celled organisms carry out the same task. And, because all new cells are produced from existing cells, scientists can study cells to learn about growth and reproduction.

☑ READING CHECK Cite Textual Evidence According to cell theory, how are bubble algae, or sea pearls, made?

....

....

Microscopes The cell theory could not have been developed without microscopes. The microscopes we use today have the same function as those used 200 years ago—to view tiny specimens. The advanced technology in the modern microscope, however, provides far greater detail for much closer observations. Light microscopes focus light through lenses to produce a magnified image. Electron microscopes are more complex. To create an image, electron microscopes use beams of electrons that scan the surface of the specimen. Look at the two different images of the same cells in **Figure 5**. Both types of microscopes do the same job in different ways, and both rely on two important properties—magnification and resolution.

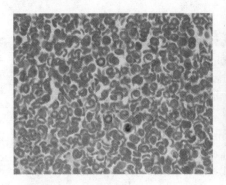 

Different Views

Figure 5 Red blood cells look very different when viewed using a light microscope (left) and an electron microscope (right).

Apply Concepts How could scientists today use current technologies to further support the cell theory?

....

....

....

....

....

....

....

Plan It !

Plastic or Wood?

Two students in a science classroom are debating about whether the tables are made of wood or plastic. As the teacher passes by, she suggests, "Use cell theory to find the truth!"

Plan an Experiment Propose a scientific investigation to determine whether the tables are wooden or plastic. Include your hypothesis, what steps the students should take, and any materials they might need to carry out the procedure.

....

....

....

....

....

....

....

....

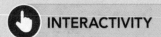

INTERACTIVITY

Explore how to use a microscope to observe specimens under different magnifications.

Magnification The compound light microscope you see in **Figure 6** magnifies an image using two lenses at once. One lens is fixed in the eyepiece. A second lens, called the objective, is located on the revolving nosepiece. A compound microscope usually has more than one objective lens. Each objective lens has a different magnifying power. By turning the nosepiece, you select the lens with the magnifying power you need. A glass rectangle called a slide holds a thin sample to be viewed. A light shines up and passes through the slide and the sample. The light then passes through the lens in the nosepiece and the eyepiece lens. Each lens magnifies the sample. Finally, the light reaches your eye and you get to see the sample in detail!

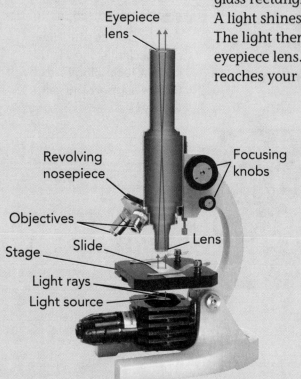

Eyepiece lens

Revolving nosepiece

Focusing knobs

Objectives

Stage

Slide

Lens

Light rays

Light source

Compound Light Microscope

Figure 6 This microscope has a 10X lens in the eyepiece. The revolving nosepiece holds three different objective lenses: 4X, 10X, and 40X.

Apply Which magnification would you select to look at a penny? Which would you select to look at a sample of pond water?

....

Academic Vocabulary

The verb *distinguish* has more than one meaning: "to manage to recognize something you can barely see" or "to point out a difference." What distinguishes technology from science?

....

....

....

....

Resolution A microscope image is useful when it helps you to see the details of an object clearly. The higher the resolution of an image, the better you can **distinguish** two separate structures that are close together, for example. Better resolution shows more details. In general, for light microscopes, resolution improves as magnification increases. Electron microscopes provide images with great resolution and high magnification. As you can see in **Figure 7**, greater resolution and higher magnification makes it relatively easy to study tiny objects.

☑ READING CHECK **Summarize Text** How does the resolution of a microscope help you to observe different structures of the cell?

....

....

....

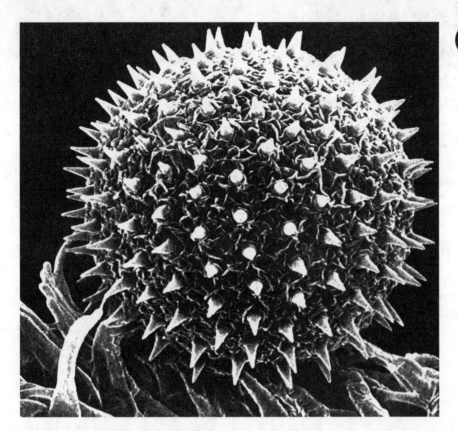

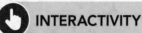
INTERACTIVITY

Investigate a sample to determine if it is living.

Extreme Close-Up

Figure 7 These plant pollen grains are magnified thousands of times.

Observe Look closely at the image. Describe some of the details you can distinguish at this very high resolution.

....

....

....

Math Toolbox

Getting the Right Magnification

The total magnification of the image from a microscope equals the magnifications of the two lenses multiplied together. If the objective lens magnifies the object 10 times, and the eyepiece lens also magnifies the object 10 times, the total magnification of the microscope is 10 x 10, or 100 times (expressed as "100X"). The image you see will be 100 times larger than the actual sample.

1. Write an Expression Calculate the total magnification of a microscope with eyepiece lens 10X and objective lens 4X.

....

2. Evaluate Scale If you use that microscope to view a human hair that is 0.1 mm across, how large will the hair appear in the image?

....

3. Represent Quantitative Relationships ✏ Draw a human hair at actual size, and at the size that it would appear in the the microscope image.

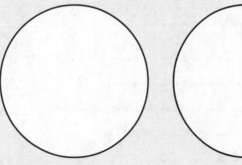

life-sized   magnified

☑ LESSON 1 Check

SC.6.L.14.2, SC.6.L.14.3

1. **Describe** What are the three key points of cell theory?

....

....

....

....

2. **Apply Concepts** Scientists discover new kinds of life in the deep ocean every year. What does cell theory tell them must be true about every new organism? What must be true about every cell in those organisms?

....

....

....

....

....

3. **Construct Explanations** Use evidence to explain how advancements in technology influenced cell theory.

....

....

....

....

....

4. **Relate Structure and Function** Compare and contrast the structure and function of a unicellular organism to that of a multicellular organism.

....

....

....

....

....

....

....

5. **Synthesize Information** Hooke and van Leeuwenhoek made their discoveries around the same time. More than 150 years later, Schleiden, Schwann, and Virchow all made breakthroughs within a few years of each other. Analyze the facts in the text and **Figure 3** and form two hypotheses about the sudden development of the cell theory after that long pause.

....

....

....

....

....

....

6. **Use Models** ✏ In the first circle, draw a small, simple picture of something that is big enough to see without magnification. In the second circle, draw it again under 5X magnification. If it is too big to fit in the circle, draw only the part of the object that fits inside.

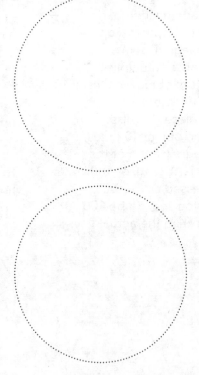

SC.6.L.14.3

Viewing cells through a "Thermal Lens"

This T-cell attacks cancer cells.

Cells have complex functions. Researchers have been trying to figure out how to target cells as a way to deliver drugs and medicines. The mid-infrared photothermal microscope is a new technology that lets scientists peer directly into living cells.

Until now, research into how cells use chemicals has been limited. Infrared imaging techniques could only use samples of dried tissue, a group of similar cells with a specific function. Because the water in live cells kept the infrared signals from passing all the way through the sample, scientists could not get detailed images. The new imaging technology works by shining a laser onto the surface of the tissue. This creates heat and a phenomenon called a 'thermal lens' effect, much like a mirage seen over a road on a hot day. The result is a detailed three-dimensional image of the cell.

Using the photothermal microscope will be essential for understanding how cancer treatment drugs get to and affect cancer cells. Now scientists can learn more about the chemistry of living systems and find better ways to treat many diseases.

New technologies like the mid-infrared photothermal microscope lets researchers see how various drug treatments affect cancer cells such as the one shown here on the left.

MY DISCOVERY

Investigate other conditions and diseases that could be better understood or treated using the new photothermal microscope.

2 Cell Structures

Guiding Questions

- What are some special structures within a cell?
- How do the different parts of a cell help it function?
- How are animal cells different from plant cells?

Connection

Literacy Integrate with Visuals

 SC.6.L.14.4 Compare and contrast the structure and function of major organelles of plant and animal cells, including cell wall, cell membrane, nucleus, cytoplasm, chloroplasts, mitochondria, and vacuoles.

SC.6.L.14.1 Describe and identify patterns in the hierarchical organization of organisms from atoms to molecules and cells to tissues to organs to organ systems to organisms. (Also **SC.6.N.1.1** and **SC.6.N.3.4**)

Vocabulary

organelle
cell wall
cell membrane
cytoplasm
nucleus
mitochondria
chloroplast
vacuole

Academic Vocabulary

structure
function

 VOCABULARY APP

Practice vocabulary on a mobile device.

Quest CONNECTION

Think about how you can incorporate and represent the different cell structures in your exhibit.

Connect It!

✎ **Circle three different structures inside this plant cell.**

Describe This plant cell has been sliced in half and you are looking into one of the halves. How would you describe the structure of the cell?

....

....

....

....

Parts of a Cell

Humans, mushrooms, and plants are all made of many parts. If you've ever taken apart a flower, a leaf, or a nut, you've seen that it also contains smaller parts. You could keep dividing the plant up into parts until you got all the way down to the individual cells. As you learned in your study of the cell theory, cells are the smallest functional units of living organisms. But within each cell there are working structures that help the cell function like an entire organism. Each **organelle** is a tiny cell structure that carries out a specific function within the cell. You can see that the cell in **Figure 1** may have many of the same organelles, but different organelles have a different **structure**. This is because each of the different organelles has a different **function**. Also, some organelles are found only in plant cells, some only in animal cells, and some are found in both plant and animal cells. Bacteria are unicellular organisms that do not contain as many different types of organelles as plant or animals cells. Together, the set of organelles in a cell keeps the cell functioning and contributing to the whole organism.

Academic Vocabulary

Have you heard the terms *structure* and *function* used before? Using what you already know, identify some structures in your classroom. What function does each structure have?

....

....

....

....

....

....

Working as a Team
Figure 1 Many structures, or organelles, in this plant cell work together to help the cell survive. The cells, in turn, work together to help the plant survive and grow.

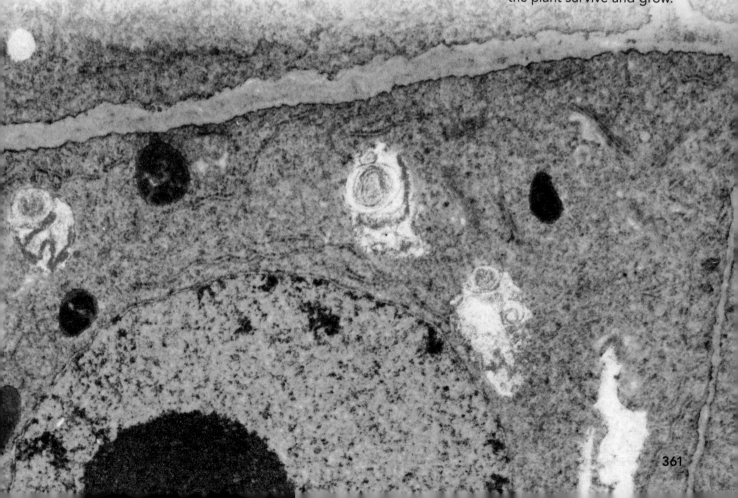

Plant and Animal Cell Differences

Figure 2 These illustrations show typical structures found in plant and animal cells. The functions of some organelles are also included.

1. **Interpret Diagrams** 🖊 Fill in the functions of the cell wall and the cell membrane in the boxes provided.

2. **Identify** 🖊 Draw a circle around the structure *inside* the plant cell that is not inside the animal cell.

3. **Use an Analogy** How would you describe the shape of the plant cell compared to the shape of the animal cell?

....
....
....
....
....
....
....
....

Plant Cell

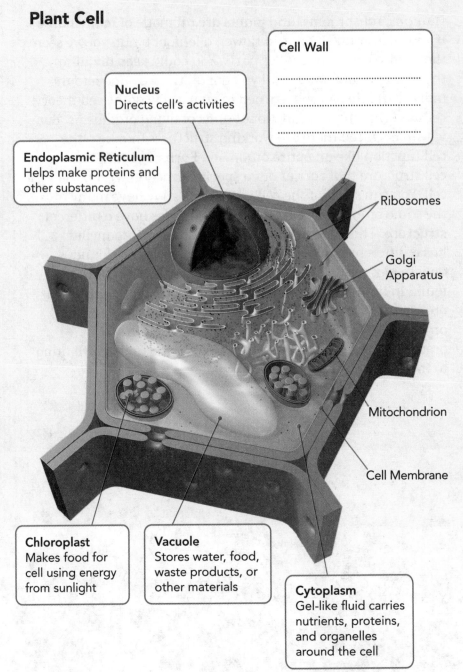

Cell Wall
....
....
....

Nucleus
Directs cell's activities

Endoplasmic Reticulum
Helps make proteins and other substances

Ribosomes

Golgi Apparatus

Mitochondrion

Cell Membrane

Chloroplast
Makes food for cell using energy from sunlight

Vacuole
Stores water, food, waste products, or other materials

Cytoplasm
Gel-like fluid carries nutrients, proteins, and organelles around the cell

Cell Wall The rigid supporting layer that surrounds the cells of plants and some other organisms is the **cell wall**. While plants, protists, fungi, and some bacteria have cell walls, the cells of animals do not have cell walls. One function of the cell wall is to help protect and support the cell. The cell walls of plant cells are made mostly of a strong material called cellulose. The cell walls of fungi are made of chitin, the same material that forms the hard, outer skeleton of insects. Observe in **Figure 2** that there are small holes, or pores, in the plant cell wall. Pores allow materials such as water and oxygen to pass through the cell wall.

Animal Cell

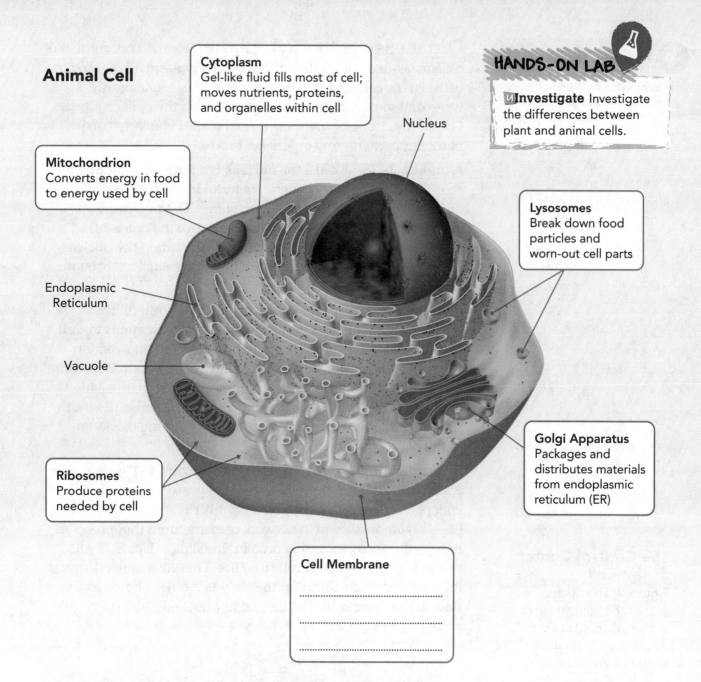

Cytoplasm
Gel-like fluid fills most of cell; moves nutrients, proteins, and organelles within cell

Nucleus

HANDS-ON LAB

☑**Investigate** Investigate the differences between plant and animal cells.

Mitochondrion
Converts energy in food to energy used by cell

Lysosomes
Break down food particles and worn-out cell parts

Endoplasmic Reticulum

Vacuole

Ribosomes
Produce proteins needed by cell

Golgi Apparatus
Packages and distributes materials from endoplasmic reticulum (ER)

Cell Membrane

....

....

....

Cell Membrane The **cell membrane** is a thin, flexible barrier that surrounds a cell and controls which substances pass into and out of a cell. All cells have a cell membrane. In plant cells, the cell membrane is a fluid-like layer between the cell and the cell wall. As you can see in **Figure 2**, animal cells do not have a cell wall, so the cell membrane is the outermost layer. For all cells without a cell wall, the cell membrane forms the border between the cell and its environment. Think about how a dust mask allows you to breathe, but keeps harmful particles outside your body. One of the functions of the cell membrane is similar to that of a dust mask—it prevents harmful materials from entering the cell. Everything a cell needs, such as food particles, water, and oxygen, enters through the cell membrane. Waste products leave the same way.

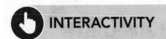
Organelles in the Cytoplasm Most of a cell consists of a clear, gel-like fluid called cytoplasm. **Cytoplasm** fills the region between the cell membrane and the nucleus. Made mostly of water and some salt, the cytoplasm holds all the cell's organelles. Constantly circulating, the clear fluid of the cytoplasm carries nutrients, proteins, and organelles around the cell.

Nucleus In some cells, the **nucleus** is a large oval organelle that contains the cell's genetic material in the form of DNA and controls many of the cell's activities. The nucleus is one of the largest of the cell's organelles. Notice in **Figure 3** that the nucleus is surrounded by a membrane called the nuclear envelope. Materials pass into and out of the nucleus through pores in the nuclear envelope.

Thin strands of genetic material called chromatin fill the nucleus. This genetic material contains the instructions for cell function. For example, chromatin helps to store information that will later make sure leaf cells grow and divide to form more leaf cells. Also in the nucleus is a dark, round structure called the nucleolus. The nucleolus produces dot-like ribosomes that produce proteins. Proteins are important building blocks for many parts of the body.

Endoplasmic Reticulum and Ribosomes In **Figure 3**, you can see a structure like a maze of passageways. The endoplasmic reticulum (en doh PLAZ mik rih TIK yuh lum), or ER, is an organelle with a network of membranes that processes many substances, including proteins and lipids. Lipids, or fats, are an important part of cell structure. They also store energy. Ribosomes dot some parts of the ER, while other ribosomes float in the cytoplasm. The ER and its attached ribosomes make proteins for use in the cell.

The Control Center of the Cell

Figure 3 The nucleus acts as the control center of the cell. Folds of the endoplasmic reticulum (ER) surround the nucleus.

1. **Identify** 🖊 On the electron microscopy photo, label the nucleus, nuclear envelope, and ER.

2. **Apply Concepts** 🖊 Why is the nucleus called the cell's "control center"?

....

....

....

....

....

....

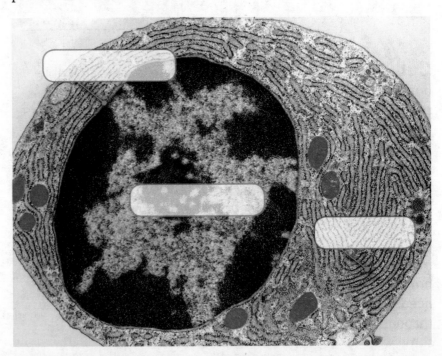

Golgi Apparatus As proteins leave the ER, they move to the Golgi apparatus, a structure that looks like flattened sacs and tubes. Considered the cell's warehouse, the Golgi apparatus receives proteins and other newly formed materials from the ER, packages them, and distributes them to other parts of the cell or to the outside of the cell.

Mitochondria Floating in the cytoplasm are rod-shaped structures. Look again at **Figure 2**. **Mitochondria** (myt oh KAHN dree uh; singular: mitochondrion) convert energy stored in food to energy the cell can use to live and function. They are the "powerhouses" of the cell.

Chloroplasts The **chloroplast** is an organelle in the cells of plants and some other organisms that captures energy from sunlight and changes it to an energy form that cells can use in making food. The function of the chloroplast is to make food, in the form of sugar, for the cell. Plant cells on the leaves of plants typically contain many green chloroplasts. Animal cells do not have chloroplasts because animals eat food instead of making their own food from sunlight.

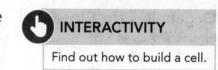

INTERACTIVITY

Find out how to build a cell.

☑ READING CHECK **Determine Conclusions** Suppose there is a drought and a plant cannot get enough water. What happens to the cytoplasm and the organelles in the plant cells?

....

....

Model It!

The Substance of Life
Earth is often called the water planet because water covers 75 percent of its surface. Cytoplasm, a jel-like fluid, is about 80 percent water. Cytoplasm has three important functions: it gives the cell form, it houses the other organelles in the cell, and it stores chemicals that the cell needs.

Develop Models What could you use to model cytoplasm? What would you use to represent each organelle? List the items you would use.

....

....

....

....

Organelles Up Close

Figure 4 Advanced microscopes capable of very high magnification allow scientists to see organelles in very fine detail. The actual images are not colored. All of these images have been colorized to help you see details.

1. **Interpret Diagrams** Fill in the blank under each image with the name of the organelle.

2. **Classify** ✏️ For each organelle, fill in the small circle with A if it is found only in animal cells, P if it is found only in plant cells, or B if it is found in both kinds of cells.

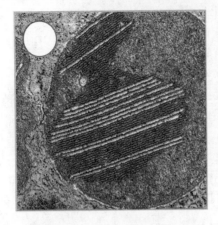

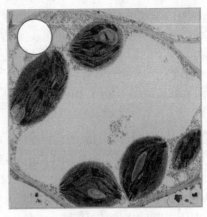

....

....

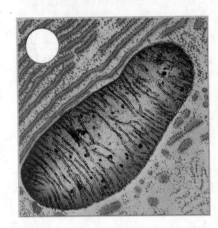

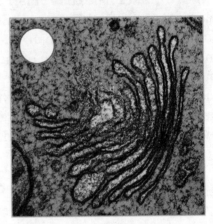

....

....

VIDEO

Take a tour of the major structures of a cell.

Lysosomes You can think of lysosomes as a cell's recycling centers. Refer to the animal cell in **Figure 2**. Notice the small, round organelles? These are called lysosomes (LY suh sohmz). Lysosomes contain substances that break down large food particles into smaller ones. Lysosomes also break down old cell parts and release the materials so they can be used again.

Vacuoles Plant cells often have one or more large, water-filled sacs floating in the cytoplasm along with the other organelles shown in **Figure 4**. In some animals cells these sacs are much smaller. This structure is a **vacuole** (VAK yoo ohl), a sac-like organelle that stores water, food, or other materials needed by the cell. In addition, vacuoles store waste products until the wastes are removed. In some plants, vacuoles also perform the function of digestion that lysosomes perform in animal cells.

✅ **READING CHECK** **Integrate with Visuals** Use **Figure 2** to describe the main differences between lysosomes and vacuoles.

....

....

....

Cells Working Together

A unicellular organism must perform every function for the survival, growth, and reproduction of the organism. A bacterium is one example of a unicellular organism that performs all the functions that sustain life. When the only cell that makes up the bacterium dies, the entire organism dies. In a multicellular organism, there are many different types of cells with different functions, and they often look quite different from one another.

Specialized Cells Multicellular organisms are more complex than unicellular organisms. Because they are more complex, they are composed of different types of cells that perform different functions. One type of cell does one kind of job, while other types of cells do other jobs. For example, red blood cells are specialized to deliver oxygen to cells throughout your body. However, they would not travel through your body without the specialized cells of the heart, which send them to other cells needing oxygen. Just as specialized cells differ in function, they also differ in structure. **Figure 5** shows specialized cells from plants and animals. Each type of cell has a distinct shape. For example, a nerve cell has thin, thread-like extensions that reach toward other cells. These structures help nerve cells transmit information from one part of your body to another. The nerve cell's shape would not help a red blood cell fulfill its function.

INTERACTIVITY

Investigate the functions of different specialized cells.

Literacy Connection

Integrate with Visuals Which image in **Figure 5** shows you evidence that the cells are relaying information to each other? What does it remind you of?

....

....

....

....

Functions of Specialized Cells

1. Animal cells that bend and squeeze easily through narrow spaces	2. Animal cells that relay information to other cells	3. Plant root cells that absorb water and minerals from the soil	4. Plant cells that make food

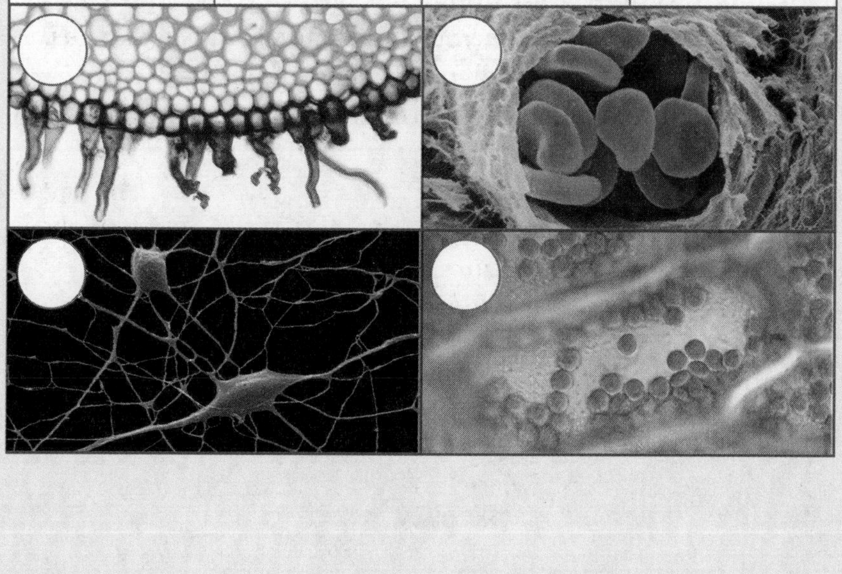

The Right Cell for the Job

Figure 5 Different cells carry out different functions.

1. **Draw Conclusions** ✏ Match each function to a cell. Write the number of the function in the corresponding image.

2. **Consider Limitations** Recall the animal cell in **Figure 2**. Why is that model not a true representation of different types of animal cells?

....

....

....

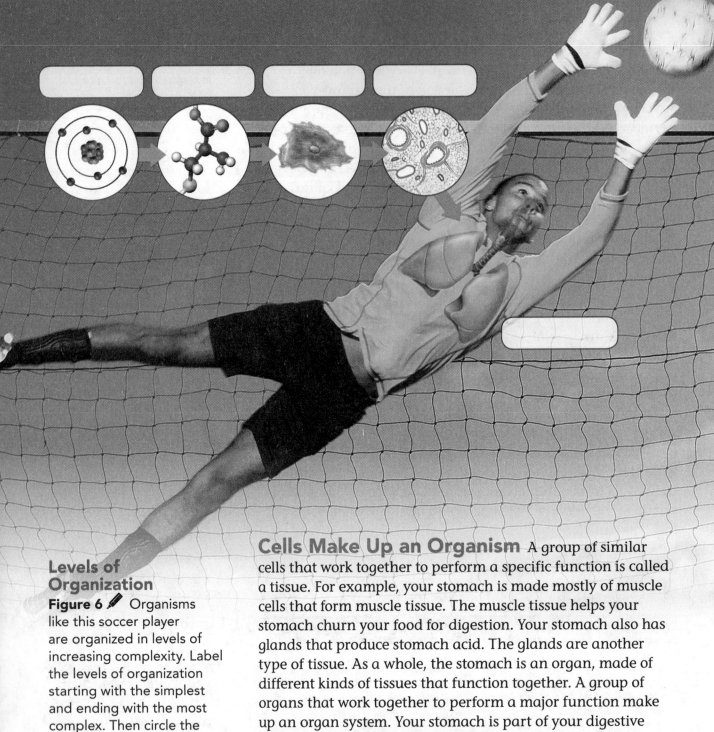

Levels of Organization

Figure 6 ✏ Organisms like this soccer player are organized in levels of increasing complexity. Label the levels of organization starting with the simplest and ending with the most complex. Then circle the organ system.

📖 **Make Meaning**
Consider a time when you worked on a team. In your science notebook, describe how members of your team had special skills that helped you to work together to solve a problem or overcome a challenge.

Cells Make Up an Organism A group of similar cells that work together to perform a specific function is called a tissue. For example, your stomach is made mostly of muscle cells that form muscle tissue. The muscle tissue helps your stomach churn your food for digestion. Your stomach also has glands that produce stomach acid. The glands are another type of tissue. As a whole, the stomach is an organ, made of different kinds of tissues that function together. A group of organs that work together to perform a major function make up an organ system. Your stomach is part of your digestive system, which breaks down your food into useful substances. **Figure 6** shows how the body builds up complex structures from atom to molecule to cell to tissue to organ to organ system.

☑ **READING CHECK** **Determine Central Ideas** Could a single part of a multicellular organism survive on its own? Explain.

....

....

....

✅LESSON 2 Check

 SC.6.L.14.1, SC.6.L.14.4

1. Analyze Structure What is the yellow structure, and what role does it play in a cell?

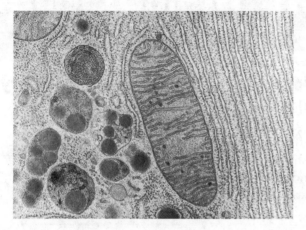

....

....

2. Explain Phenomena Why do cells need so many different organelles and structures?

....

....

3. Apply Concepts Are there more tissues or more organs in your body? Explain.

....

....

....

4. Apply Scientific Reasoning Does the cell shown have a cell wall, a cell membrane, or both? Explain your reasoning.

....

....

....

5. Provide Critique Your friend joked that a cell is like his little brother's bathtub with tub toys floating in it. Critique his analogy.

....

....

....

....

....

Quest CHECK-IN

In this lesson, you learned about the different structures of plant and animal cells and how they function.

Develop Models How can a model help visitors to the exhibit better understand cell structures and their functions?

....

....

....

....

....

HANDS-ON LAB

Make a Cell Model

Go online for a downloadable worksheet of this lab. Design and build a model of a plant cell.

Obtaining and Removing Materials

Guiding Question

• What is the primary role of the cell membrane in cell function?

Connections

Literacy Integrate with Visuals

Math Analyze Proportional Relationships

SC.6.L.14.3 Recognize and explore how cells of all organisms undergo similar processes to maintain homeostasis, including extracting energy from food, getting rid of waste, and reproducing (Also **SC.6.N.1.5** and **SC.6.N.3.4**).

Vocabulary

selectively
    permeable
diffusion
osmosis
endocytosis
exocytosis

Academic Vocabulary

maintain

 VOCABULARY APP

Practice vocabulary on a mobile device.

Quest CONNECTION

Consider how your exhibit can illustrate the processes that bring materials into the cell and take other materials out of the cell.

Connect It!

✏ **Circle the area on the photo where you think the skunk spray odor will be strongest.**

Hypothesize How do you think it's possible for you to detect skunk spray from inside your house or from inside a moving car?

....

....

....

Moving Materials Into and Out of Cells

INTERACTIVITY

Discuss how objects move in and out of an area.

One evening you are out walking near your home. You spy something moving around on the ground. Look at **Figure 1**: Is it a black and white cat? As you move closer to get a better look, the animal fluffs up and raises its tail. It's a skunk! You hurriedly turn around and go in the other direction. You know that if you get sprayed by a skunk, people will be able to smell the stink from far away. Odor molecules will travel through the air to be inhaled by everyone around you.

Cells rely on the movement of surrounding gases, liquids, and particles to supply them with nutrients and materials. In order to live and function, cells must let certain materials enter and leave. Oxygen and water and particles of food must be able to move into a cell, while waste materials must move out. The same mechanism that lets materials in and out of a cell also lets those skunk spray molecules—the chemical makeup of odor—seep into the specialized cells in your nose that perceive smell.

Stinky Defense

Figure 1 When a skunk starts to feel threatened, you better watch out! Being sprayed is a miserable experience, and the smell travels fast through the air through the process of diffusion. Diffusion also carries useful molecules to the cells of every living organism.

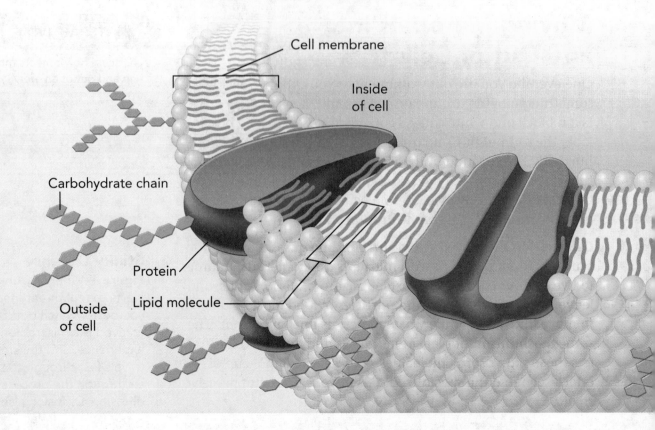

Cell membrane

Inside of cell

Carbohydrate chain

Protein

Lipid molecule

Outside of cell

A Selective Barrier

Figure 2 Carbohydrates, proteins, and lipids are important molecules that make up the structure of the cell membrane. They help move materials into and out of the cell through the cell membrane.

Make Models In what way is the cell membrane like a security guard?

....

....

....

....

....

....

Function of the Cell Membrane Every cell is

surrounded by a cell membrane that lets substances in and out. This movement allows the cell to maintain homeostasis (a stable internal environment) and get all the chemicals needed to support life. The cell membrane is not rigid, but flexible. In **Figure 2**, you can see that different types of molecules play important roles in helping materials move across the cell membrane.

A permeable membrane allows liquids and gases to pass through it. Some materials move freely across the cell membrane. Others move less freely or not at all. The cell membrane is **selectively permeable**, which means some substances can cross the membrane, while others cannot. Substances that move into and out of a cell do so by means of one of two processes: passive transport or active transport.

Passive Transport Moving materials across the cell

membrane sometimes requires no energy. At other times, the cell has to use its own energy. Consider this analogy: If you pour a bucket of water down a slide, the water flows down easily with no effort on your part. Your role is passive. Now, suppose you have to push that same water back up the slide. You would have to use your own energy to move the water. The movement of dissolved materials across a cell membrane without using the cell's energy is called passive transport.

Diffusion Molecules are always moving. As they move, they bump into one another. Crowded, or concentrated, molecules collide more often. Collisions cause molecules to push away from one another. Over time, as molecules continue colliding and moving apart, they spread evenly throughout the space and become less concentrated. **Diffusion** (dih FYOO zhun) is the process by which molecules move from an area of higher concentration to an area of lower concentration. Consider a cell in the lining of your lungs. The cell is in contact with the air that you breathe. The air outside the cell has a higher concentration of oxygen. What happens? Oxygen moves easily into the cell. The diffusion of oxygen into the cell does not require the cell to use any of its energy. Diffusion is a form of passive transport. **Figure 3** shows how insects use spiracles instead of lungs to diffuse oxygen into their cells.

✅ READING CHECK **Write Informative Text** Why is it important for a cell membrane to be selectively permeable?

....

....

....

....

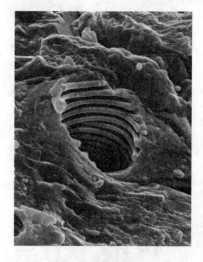

No Lungs Necessary
Figure 3 Spiracles are holes in the exoskeleton, or outer shell, of insects, that allow oxygen to enter and diffuse into the cells of the insect. Spiracles connect to air passages that lead into all parts of the insect.

Relate Function and Structure ✏ Circle the area where air can enter the insect's body.

Math Toolbox

Breathing Without Lungs

The largest insects ever discovered were giant dragonflies that lived 300 million years ago. These dragonflies had a wingspan of 67 cm! Today the largest dragonfly has a wingspan of about 20 cm. The giant dragonflies existed at a time when the oxygen level in the atmosphere was about 35 percent, compared to 21 percent today. Use this information to answer the following questions.

1. **Analyze Proportional Relationships** What is the percentage size difference between the giant dragonfly and the modern dragonfly?

....

2. **Infer** Refer back to the spiracles in **Figure 3**. What do you think the relationship is between the spiracles, insect size, and air oxygen levels?

....

....

....

....

Model It!

Raisins No More

Figure 4 Raisins are simply dried grapes—most of the water is removed. The cells of raisins are dead but still very high in sugar. If you soak raisins in water, the cells will take up water by the process of diffusion.

Develop Models Use the grape cell shown below as a reference. In the empty circles, first draw a raisin cell and then draw what the cell looks like after soaking the raisin in water overnight.

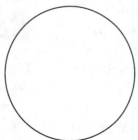
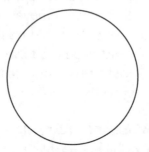

Osmosis Like oxygen, water passes easily into and out of a cell across the cell membrane. **Osmosis** is the diffusion of water molecules across a selectively permeable membrane. Many cellular processes depend on osmosis to bring them the water they need to function. Without enough water, most cells will die. Because it requires no energy from the cell, osmosis is a form of passive transport.

Osmosis can have important effects on cells and entire organisms. The soaked raisins in **Figure 4** are lighter in color and appear plumper due to a healthy flow of water both into and out of their cells. Under certain conditions, osmosis can cause water to move out of the cells more quickly than it moves in. When that happens, the cytoplasm shrinks and the cell membrane pulls away from the cell wall. If conditions do not change, the cells can die.

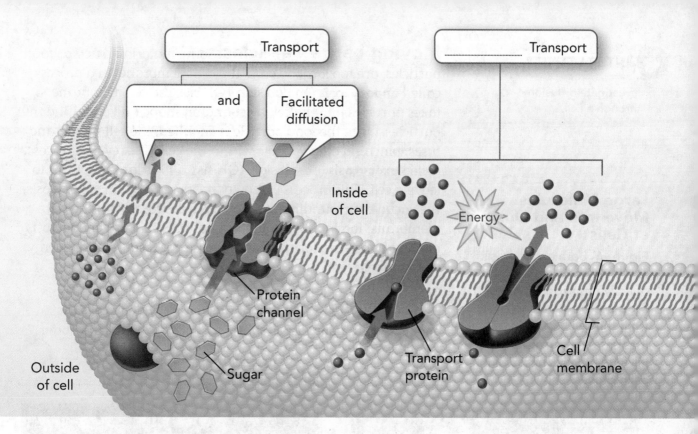

_____ Transport

_____ and

Facilitated diffusion

_____ Transport

Inside of cell

Energy

Protein channel

Transport protein

Cell membrane

Sugar

Outside of cell

Facilitated Diffusion Oxygen, carbon dioxide, and water freely diffuse across the cell membrane. Some molecules, such as sugar, cannot easily cross the cell membrane. In a process called facilitated diffusion, proteins in the cell membrane form channels through which the sugars can pass. The word _facilitate_ means "to make easier." As shown in **Figure 5**, these proteins provide a pathway for the sugars to diffuse. The proteins function much the way downspouts guide water that flows from the roof of a house to the ground. Facilitated diffusion uses no cell energy and is a form of passive transport.

Active Transport
During diffusion, molecules move randomly in all directions. A few molecules move by chance from areas of low concentration to areas of high concentration, but most molecules move toward areas of lower concentration. In many cases, cells need the concentration of a molecule inside the cell to be higher than the concentration outside the cell. In order to **maintain** this difference in the concentration of molecules, cells use active transport. Cells supply the energy to do this work—just as you would supply the energy to pedal your bike uphill. Active transport is the movement of materials across a cell membrane using cellular energy. As in facilitated diffusion, proteins within the cell membrane play a key role in active transport. Using the cell's energy, transport proteins "pick up" specific molecules passing by the cell and carry them across the membrane. Calcium, potassium, and sodium are some substances that are carried into and out of cells by active transport.

Crossing the Cell Membrane
Figure 5 Molecules move into and out of a cell by means of passive or active transport.

Interpret Diagrams ✏
Complete the labels. Fill in the missing words.

Academic Vocabulary
To maintain means to keep in an existing state. When have you had to maintain something?

....

....

....

HANDS-ON LAB

☐**Investigate** Model the way that water moves into and out of a cell.

Large Molecules Move Into and Out of Cells

Figure 6 Both endocytosis and exocytosis are forms of active transport. These processes require energy from the cell.

Interpret Diagrams
Fill in the blanks by labeling each process shown below.

Moving Large Particles Some materials, such as food particles, are too large to cross the cell membrane. In a process called **endocytosis** (en doh sigh TOH sis), the cell membrane takes particles into the cell by changing shape and engulfing the particles. Once the food particle is engulfed, the cell membrane fuses, pinching off a vacuole within the cell. The reverse process, called **exocytosis** (ek soh sigh TOH sis), allows large particles to leave a cell. This process is shown in **Figure 6**. During exocytosis, the vacuole surrounding the food particles fuses with the cell membrane, forcing the contents out of the cell. Both endocytosis and exocytosis are forms of active transport that require energy from the cell.

✓ **READING CHECK** **Draw Conclusions** Why don't cells use endocytosis to transport all substances across the cell membrane?

....

....

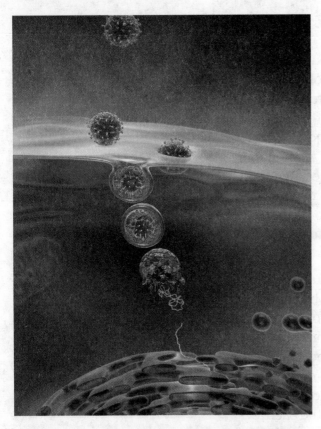

Large Molecules Entering the Cell
Large food particles are close to the cell. In order to bring food into the cell, the membrane wraps itself around a particle and draws it into the cytoplasm.

....

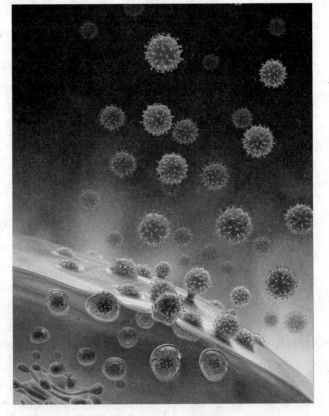

Large Molecules Leaving the Cell
Vacuoles carrying large particles of waste move toward the cell membrane. The vacuoles fuse with the membrane in order to push the waste particles out of the cell.

....

SC.6.L.14.3

1. Explain Phenomena What general roles does the cell membrane play in maintaining homeostasis?

....

....

2. Revise Simulations How would a vacuole from the soaked raisin cell in your **Figure 4** model look if you soaked it in extremely salty water? Explain.

....

....

....

....

3. Apply Scientific Reasoning Could disease-causing bacteria get inside a cell without damaging the cell membrane? Explain.

....

....

....

....

....

4. Compare and Contrast ✏ Fill in the Venn diagram below with the following terms: exocytosis, diffusion, endocytosis, osmosis

Into Cell   Out of Cell

5. Analyze Systems Describe one process in your household that is similar to endocytosis and one that is similar to exocytosis. How do they maintain your house's "homeostasis"?

....

....

....

....

....

Quest CHECK-IN

In this lesson, you learned about the cell membrane and how cells take in the substances they need in order to function. You also learned how cells remove waste products through cellular processes.

Relate Structure and Function Consider which structures of the cell membrane function to help materials move into and out of the cell. How can you best model this information in your animation?

....

....

....

👆 INTERACTIVITY

Put Your Cells in Motion

Go online to plan an animation that shows the ways materials enter and leave the cell. Then create your animation for the exhibit.

4 Cell Division

Guiding Questions

- What are the four functions of cell division?
- Which structures in a cell help it to reproduce?

Connections

Literacy Summarize Text

Math Analyze Quantitative Relationships

SC.6.L.14.3 Recognize and explore how cells of all organisms undergo similar processes to maintain homeostasis, including extracting energy from food, getting rid of waste, and reproducing. (Also **SC.6.N.3.4** and **SC.6.N.1.5**)

Vocabulary

cell cycle
interphase
replication
mitosis
cytokinesis

Academic Vocabulary

sequence

 VOCABULARY APP

Practice vocabulary on a mobile device.

Quest CONNECTION

Think about the role that cell division plays in a healthy, functioning cell, and consider how you can incorporate this information into your exhibit.

Connect It!

✏ **Using the x-ray image as a guide, place a circle on the biker to show where the broken bone is.**

Construct Explanations Where will the bike rider's body get new cells to repair the broken bones?

....

....

The Functions of Cell Division

The bike rider in **Figure 1** really took a tumble! Thankfully, he was wearing a helmet and only suffered a broken arm and a scraped elbow. His body will immediately begin to repair the bones, muscles, and skin. Where will his body get so many new cells to repair the damage? Recall that cells can only be produced by other cells. The new cells will come from older cells that divide in two, over and over again, until there are enough healthy cells to restore full function. Similarly, cell division can replace aging cells and those that die from disease.

Cell division also allows an organism to grow larger. A tiny fertilized egg cell splits into two, two into four, and so on, until a single cell becomes a multicellular organism. Another function of cell division is reproduction. Many single-celled organisms, such as yeasts, reproduce simply through cell division. Other organisms reproduce when cell division leads to the growth of new structures. For example, a strawberry plant can grow new stems and roots. These structures then break away from the parent plant and become a separate plant. Most organisms reproduce when specialized cells from two different parents combine, forming a new cell. This cell then undergoes many divisions and grows into a new organism.

✓ **READING CHECK** **Determine Central Ideas** What are four functions of cell division?

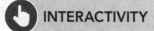**Reflect** Think of a time when you injured yourself. In your Science Notebook, describe the appearance and feeling of the injury when it first happened and then how the injured area changed as your body healed.

INTERACTIVITY

Reflect on where you think cell division is occurring in your body.

Cell Division to the Rescue

Figure 1 As soon as you break a bone, your body sets to work repairing it. Many new cells are produced to clean up the mess and produce new tissues.

Phases of the Cell Cycle

Figure 2 The series of diagrams represents an entire cell cycle.

Interpret Diagrams What happens to the cell's genetic information during the cell cycle?

....

....

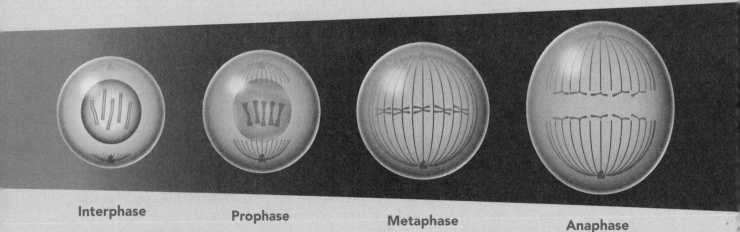

Interphase　　Prophase　　Metaphase　　Anaphase

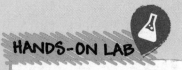

HANDS-ON LAB

✍Investigate Model how a cell divides.

Academic Vocabulary

Cell division follows a careful sequence of events. Describe the sequence of events on one of your typical school days.

....

....

....

....

....

The Cell Cycle

Most of the time, cells carry out their regular functions, but everything changes when a cell gets the signal to divide. At that point, the cell must accomplish several tasks to be ready for the big division into two "daughter cells." **Figure 2** summarizes those tasks.

First, the cell must grow in size and double its contents. This phase is called interphase. Next, the cell must divide up its contents so that the two daughter cells will have roughly equal contents. This second phase is called mitosis, and it has several stages.

Finally, the cell's cytoplasm physically divides in two in a phase called cytokinesis. The regular **sequence** of events in which the cell grows, prepares for division, and divides to form two daughter cells is known as the **cell cycle**. After the division is complete, each of the daughter cells begins the cycle again.

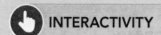

INTERACTIVITY

Explore the cell cycle and learn why living things go through the cell cycle.

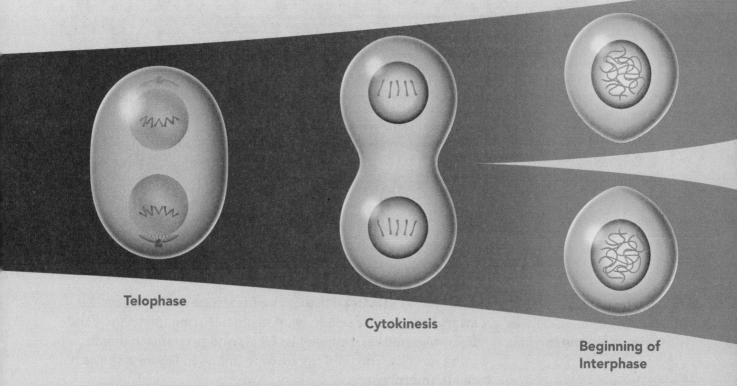

Telophase

Cytokinesis

Beginning of Interphase

Dividing Cells

Every cell division produces two daughter cells. You can see in the diagram that after one division, the single cell has become two cells.

🖊 Fill in the last two circles to show the results from two more cell divisions.

| 0 Divisions | 1 Division | 2 Divisions | 3 Divisions |

1. **Analyze Quantitative Relationships** How does the number of cells increase with each new division of the cells?

....

2. **Calculate** How many cells would there be after five divisions?

....

3. **Hypothesize** Do you think all human cells divide at the same rate throughout life? Explain your reasoning.

....

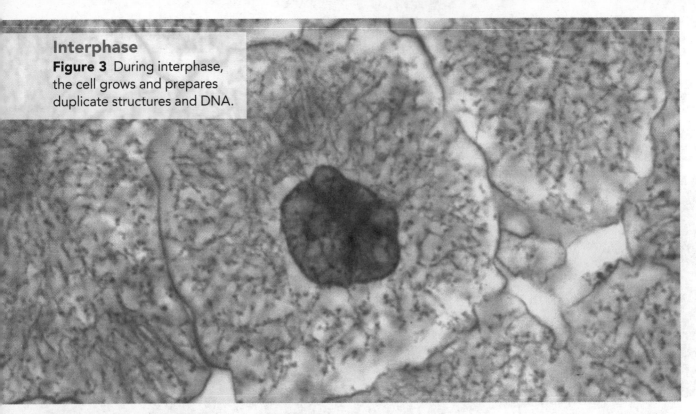

Interphase

Figure 3 During interphase, the cell grows and prepares duplicate structures and DNA.

INTERACTIVITY

Discover how bones heal after they are broken.

VIDEO

Find out more about how cell division allows living things to grow.

Stage 1: Interphase The first stage of the cell cycle is **interphase**, before cell division begins. During interphase, the cell grows, makes a copy of its DNA, and prepares to divide into two cells. The light microscope image in **Figure 3** shows a cell in interphase.

Growing Early in interphase, a cell grows to its full size and produces the organelles that both daughter cells will need. For example, plant cells make more chloroplasts. All kinds of cells make more ribosomes and mitochondria. Cells also make more enzymes, substances that speed up chemical reactions in living things.

Replication Recall that chromatin in the nucleus holds all the genetic information that a cell needs to carry out its functions. That information is in a complex chemical substance called DNA (deoxyribonucleic acid). In a process called **replication**, the cell makes a copy of the DNA in its nucleus before cell division. DNA replication results in the formation of threadlike structures called chromosomes. Each chromosome inside the nucleus of the cell contains two identical sets of DNA, called chromatids.

Preparing for Division Once the DNA has replicated, preparation for cell division begins. The cell produces structures that will help it to divide into two new cells. In animal cells, but not plant cells, a pair of centrioles is duplicated. The centrioles help later with dividing the DNA between the daughter cells. At the end of interphase, the cell is ready to divide.

Stage 2: Mitosis

Once interphase ends, the second stage of the cell cycle begins. During **mitosis** (my TOH sis), the cell's nucleus divides into two new nuclei and one set of DNA is distributed into each daughter cell. Scientists divide mitosis into four parts, or phases: prophase, metaphase, anaphase, and telophase.

During prophase, DNA condenses into separate chromosomes. Recall that during replication, chromosomes formed. The two chromatids that make-up the chromosome are exact copies of identical DNA. The nuclear membrane that surrounds the DNA begins to break apart. In metaphase, the chromosomes line up along the center of the cell. The chromatids that will go to each daughter cell are lined up on that side of the cell. Next, in anaphase, fibers connected to the centrioles pull the chromatids apart into each side of the cell. The final phase of mitosis is telophase. During telophase, the chromatids are pulled to opposite ends of the cell. The nuclear membrane reforms around the DNA to create two new nuclei. Each nucleus contains a complete, identical copy of DNA. Test your knowledge of the phases of mitosis in **Figure 4**.

✓ READING CHECK **Summarize Text** What are the three things that a cell has to complete in order to be ready for cell division?

....

....

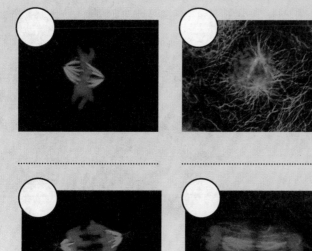

....

....

Scrambled Mitosis

Figure 4 These dividing cells have been marked with a dye that glows under fluorescent light. The dye makes it easy to see the DNA, stained blue, and fibers, stained green. The pictures are in the wrong order.

Identify 🖊 Label each phase of mitosis in the space provided. Then, write the numbers 1 to 4 in the circles to show the correct order of the phases in mitosis.

383

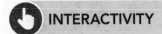
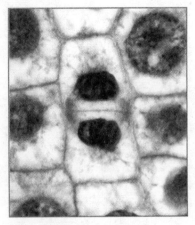

Plant Cytokinesis

Figure 5 One of these plant cells is dividing.

Identify ✏ Find the cell that is dividing. Place an *X* on each daughter cell and trace the cell plate.

Stage 3: Cytokinesis The final stage of the cell cycle is called **cytokinesis** (sy toh kih NEE sis). This stage completes the process of cell division. During cytokinesis, the cell's cytoplasm divides, distributing the organelles into each of the two new daughter cells. Cytokinesis usually starts at about the same time as telophase. When cytokinesis is complete, each daughter cell has the same number of chromosomes as the parent cell. Next, each cell enters interphase and the cell cycle begins again.

Cytokinesis in Animal Cells During cytokinesis in animal cells, the cell membrane squeezes together around the middle of the cell. The cytoplasm pinches into two cells. Each daughter cell gets about half of the organelles of the parent cell.

Cytokinesis in Plant Cells Cytokinesis is somewhat different in plant cells. A plant cell's rigid cell wall cannot squeeze together in the same way that a cell membrane can. Instead, a structure called a cell plate forms across the middle of the cell, as shown in **Figure 5**. The cell plate begins to form new cell membranes between the two daughter cells. New cell walls then form around the cell membranes.

☑ READING CHECK **Determine Conclusions** What would happen if cytokinesis did not occur?

....

....

Question It!

A Two-Celled Organism?
Two students examining a sample of lake water find an unusual-looking organism.

Develop Questions What kinds of questions would you have if you saw the organism shown here? List three questions and two resources you could use to help you to answer them.

....

....

....

....

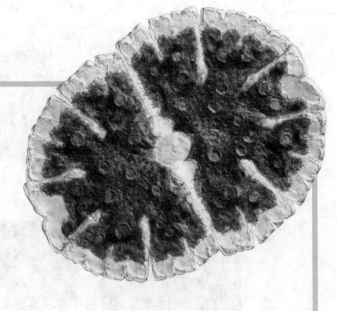

☑ LESSON 4 Check

SC.6.L.14.3

1. Explain Why is it important for the cells in your body to go through the cell cycle?

....

....

....

2. Draw Conclusions If a single-celled organism is unable to undergo cell division, which of its life functions is affected?

....

....

....

3. Apply Concepts When you look at cells under a microscope, how can you recognize cells that are dividing?

....

....

....

....

4. Predict Examine the photo of a cell cycle phase below. Then draw, label, and describe the phase that follows it.

5. Form a Hypothesis What would happen to a cell that didn't replicate its DNA before cell division?

....

....

....

6. Develop Models How could you direct a group of people to model the movements of the phases of the cell cycle? Write directions below for each movement. Label the phases in your steps. (Hint: **Use Figure 2** for reference.)

5 Body Organization

Guiding Questions

- How do groups of cells form interacting subsystems in the body?
- How do the structures of specialized organs relate to their functions in the body?

Connections

Literacy Support Author's Claim

Math Identify Equivalent Expressions

SC.6.L.14.1 Describe and identify patterns in the hierarchical organization of organisms from atoms to molecules and cells to tissues to organs to organ systems to organisms.
SC.6.L.14.5 Identify and investigate the general functions of the major systems of the human body (digestive, respiratory, circulatory, reproductive, excretory, immune, nervous, and musculoskeletal) and describe ways these systems interact with each other to maintain homeostasis. (Also **SC.6.N.1.1** and **SC.6.N.3.4**)

Vocabulary

tissue
organ
organ system

Academic Vocabulary

organized

 VOCABULARY APP

Practice vocabulary on a mobile device.

Quest CONNECTION

Consider the importance of cells and how they contribute to the proper functioning of organs and organ systems.

Connect It!

✏ **Circle an instrument panel that the co-pilot might control. The co-pilot sits on the right side.**

Use an Analogy If an airplane has parts that function like a person's parts, then what part of the body does the pilot represent? Explain your reasoning.

....

....

....

Organization of the Body

Driving a car safely requires constant attention, even in the best road conditions. Controlling an airplane is even more demanding. For a plane to fly safely to its destination, all of its systems must be in good working order. The plane's steering system, brake system, lights, tires, and jet engines are all vital to a safe flight. The pilot and the co-pilot must be skilled at operating the instrument panels shown in **Figure 1**. They have to be able to steer the plane safely through all sorts of conditions. At times, they must fly the plane while relying on the instruments and screens in the cockpit, because they cannot see where the plane is headed.

Like an airplane, your body is **organized** into systems that work together. For example, your digestive and circulatory systems work together to help the cells in your body get the energy they need to function. When you walk up the stairs or ride a bike, your nervous, skeletal, and muscular systems are working together to move your body. Each system is made up of smaller parts, with the smallest being the cells that form the basic units of every living thing. Just as an airplane cannot function properly without its landing gear or its electrical system, the same is true for your body: You need each of your systems so that you can survive and grow.

☑ READING CHECK **Support Author's Claim** How is the human body similar to an airplane?

....

....

HANDS-ON LAB

Examine the levels of organization in a multicellular organism.

Academic Vocabulary

What steps do you take to get organized for an upcoming project?

....

....

....

....

All Systems Go

Figure 1 All systems in an airplane, including the pilot and co-pilot, must function properly in order to operate the plane.

Levels of Organization

The smooth functioning of your body depends on its organization. Recall that the levels of organization in the human body are atoms, molecules, cells, tissues, organs, and organ systems. All cells are made of atoms and molecules. All tissues are made up of cells. Organs are made of different kinds of tissues. And an organism is made of different organ systems working together.

Cells and Tissues You are alive because specialized cells are performing their functions throughout your body. Recall that cells have organelles, which means "little organs." Organelles are actually groups of complex molecules that keep a cell alive and help it to function. A **tissue** is a group of similar cells that perform the same function. Muscle tissue, for example, contracts, or shortens, to make parts of your body move. Nerve tissue carries electrical signals from the brain all over the body and back again. Connective tissue, such as bone and fat, provides support for your body and attaches all of its parts together. Skin, the largest organ in the human body, has epithelial (ep uh THEE lee ul) tissue that protects your insides from damage. Epithelial tissue covers the inner and outer surfaces of your body.

Math Toolbox
Counting Cells in the Body

Scientists and mathematicians have wondered about the number of cells in the human body for centuries. Estimates of the number of cells have ranged from 100 billion to 1 quadrillion, or a 1 followed by 15 zeros! It's easier to write one quadrillion using exponents: 1×10^{15} where the exponent 15 is the number of zeros.

A team of European scientists recently completed a new estimate of the human cells in an average person. Their estimate is about 37 trillion cells per person.

Name	Number	Written with Power of Ten Exponent
million	1,000,000	1×10^{6}
billion	1,000,000,000	1×10^{9}
trillion	1,000,000,000,000	1×10^{12}
quadrillion	1,000,000,000,000,000	1×10^{15}

1. Identify Equivalent Expressions How do you write 37 trillion as a number and using the power of ten exponent?

....

2. Analyze Quantitative Relationships How does the new European estimate compare to the smallest and largest estimates of other research groups?

....

Organs and Systems

Organs and Systems Your kidneys, heart, brain, and skin are all organs. An **organ** is a body structure composed of different kinds of tissues that work together. Each organ has a specific function in the body. Because its structure is more complex, the job of an organ is usually more complex than that of a tissue. For example, kidneys remove waste from your blood and form urine. Each kidney contains muscle, connective, and epithelial tissues. In addition, nervous tissue connects to the kidney and helps to control its function. Look at **Figure 2** to see where the different kinds of tissue are found in the kidney. Each tissue contributes in a different way to the kidney's job of filtering blood.

Every organ is part of an **organ system**, which is a group of organs that work together, performing major functions. For example, your kidneys are part of your excretory system. The excretory system also includes the skin, lungs, and liver.

✓ READING CHECK **Summarize Text** What type of cells work together to make a tissue?

....

....

....

HANDS-ON LAB

☑**Investigate** Consider how the structures of cells and tissues relate to their functions in the body.

Many Tissues Make an Organ

Figure 2 Kidneys filter blood to remove waste and excess water.

Explain Phenomena What might happen to a kidney if the muscle tissue does not function properly?

....

....

....

....

Epithelial tissue in the renal cortex gives the kidney structure and protects the nephrons that filter the blood.

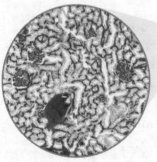

Nerve cells help the kidney pump and filter blood.

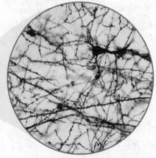

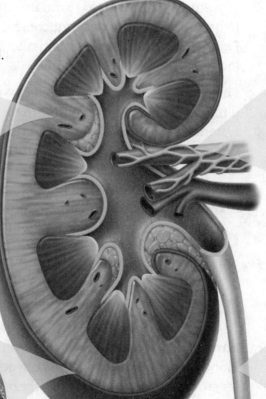

Renal capsule covering connective and fat tissues also protects the kidney.

Muscle cells in the ureter drain urine to the bladder.

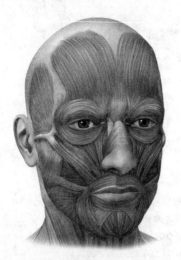

Make a Face

Figure 3 A multitude of facial muscles allows for a variety of expressions.

Interpret Diagrams

✎ Draw an X on the muscles involved in blinking your eyes.

 VIDEO

Find out how your body is like an orchestra.

Human Organ Systems

Eleven major organ systems keep the human body running smoothly. All of the systems work together to support proper functioning.

Control Systems To function properly, each part of your body must be able to communicate with other parts of your body. Your body communicates using the nervous system, which is made up of the brain, spinal cord, and nerves. The nervous system sends information through nerve cells to control your actions.

Many body functions are controlled through the endocrine system, a collection of glands that produces important chemicals. The chemicals in turn affect your energy level, body temperature, digestion, and even your moods!

Structural Systems Three organ systems work to shape, move, and protect your body. The skeletal system includes your bones and connective tissues. The main functions of the skeletal system support your body, protect your organs, make blood cells, and store minerals. Connective tissues cushion the bones and attach bones to muscles.

The muscular system includes 650 muscles that control your movements, help you to stand up straight, and allow you to breathe. The muscles that control your face are shown in **Figure 3**. The muscular system also keeps your blood and your food moving through your body.

The integumentary system protects your body from outside damage. Skin, hair, and nails are all parts of the integumentary system. Oil and sweat glands under the skin help to keep your skin waterproof and your temperature comfortable. Your skin is attached to muscles, which are anchored to bones by connective tissue. Together, these three systems provide your shape and allow you to move your body in many ways.

Oxygen and Transport Systems The respiratory system brings in oxygen and moves out carbon dioxide by way of the lungs. As you breathe in fresh air, oxygen diffuses into the red blood cells. When you breathe out, carbon dioxide diffuses back into the air.

The circulatory system carries oxygen-rich blood to all the parts of your body. Your heart pumps the blood through your blood vessels. Blood cells pass oxygen to your cells and pick up carbon dioxide. Your veins then bring the blood back to your heart and lungs. The circulatory system also transports nutrients, wastes, and disease-fighting cells all over your body through your bloodstream.

Food and Waste Processing Systems Food you put into your mouth begins a journey through your digestive system. Your esophagus squeezes the food down into the stomach, where the food is crushed and broken down by acids. Next, the food travels into the intestines. Useful substances pass through the intestinal walls into the blood. The liver and pancreas produce substances that help to break down food. So do trillions of bacteria that live in your intestines. Some parts of the food cannot be digested. Those parts pass out of your body as waste. You can think of the digestive system as a long tube that runs through your body. Food passes through the tube and back out into the world without ever entering the tissues of your body.

The excretory system gets rid of waste products and toxic substances in your body. Kidneys produce urine, sweat glands in your skin make sweat, and lungs release wastes from the body into the air. Meanwhile, the liver breaks down toxic chemicals into substances that the kidneys can pull out of your blood.

☑ READING CHECK **Determine Conclusions** What would happen if your organ systems stopped functioning properly?

....

....

Literacy Connection

Support Author's Claim
Is it true that the human body can make its own chemicals? Cite evidence from the text.

....

....

....

....

Model It!

What? No Bones?

Figure 4 Most of the known animals on Earth are invertebrates. These organisms lack the backbone found in humans, birds, reptiles, and other vertebrates.

Develop Models ✏ Choose a kind of invertebrate— snail, insect, worm, octopus, water bear (shown here), and spider are just a few. Consider how an animal maintains its structure with no bones. Then sketch a diagram to explain how your animal moves with no bones connected to its muscles.

Organ Systems in the Human Body

Figure 5 The structures of different body systems all work together to allow you to grow, obtain energy, move, stay healthy, and reproduce.

Analyze Systems ✏ Use the key on the right to label each body system. There may be more than one function for each system.

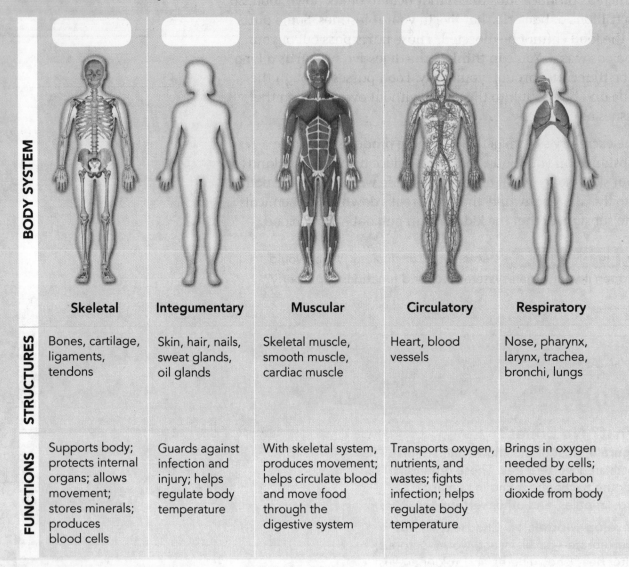

	Skeletal	Integumentary	Muscular	Circulatory	Respiratory
STRUCTURES	Bones, cartilage, ligaments, tendons	Skin, hair, nails, sweat glands, oil glands	Skeletal muscle, smooth muscle, cardiac muscle	Heart, blood vessels	Nose, pharynx, larynx, trachea, bronchi, lungs
FUNCTIONS	Supports body; protects internal organs; allows movement; stores minerals; produces blood cells	Guards against infection and injury; helps regulate body temperature	With skeletal system, produces movement; helps circulate blood and move food through the digestive system	Transports oxygen, nutrients, and wastes; fights infection; helps regulate body temperature	Brings in oxygen needed by cells; removes carbon dioxide from body

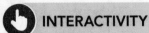 **INTERACTIVITY**

Explore the structures and functions of different body systems.

Defense System The immune system is your defense system against infections. Lymph nodes and lymph vessels trap bacteria and viruses. "Swollen glands" are lymph nodes that have grown larger to fight off an infection. White blood cells produced inside your bones also attack and destroy bacteria and other causes of disease. As shown in **Figure 5** above, many different organs work together to help to fight off invading disease organisms.

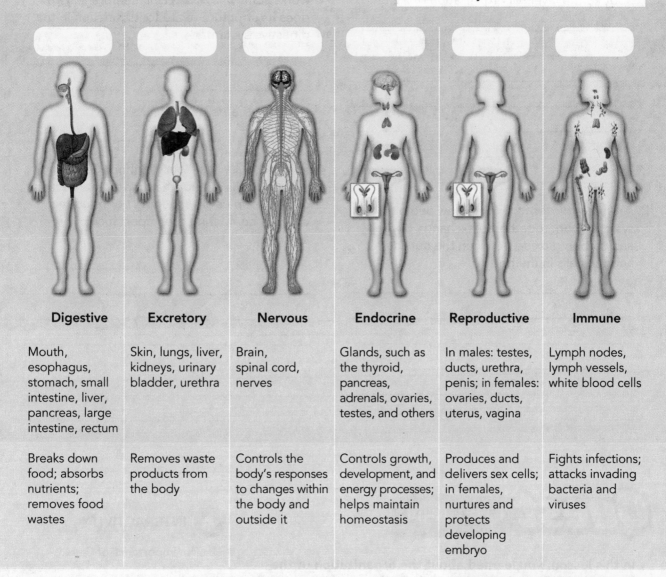

KEY
A Structural Support System
B Oxygen and Transport System
C Food and Waste Processing System
D Defense System
E Reproductive System
F Control System

Digestive	Excretory	Nervous	Endocrine	Reproductive	Immune
Mouth, esophagus, stomach, small intestine, liver, pancreas, large intestine, rectum	Skin, lungs, liver, kidneys, urinary bladder, urethra	Brain, spinal cord, nerves	Glands, such as the thyroid, pancreas, adrenals, ovaries, testes, and others	In males: testes, ducts, urethra, penis; in females: ovaries, ducts, uterus, vagina	Lymph nodes, lymph vessels, white blood cells
Breaks down food; absorbs nutrients; removes food wastes	Removes waste products from the body	Controls the body's responses to changes within the body and outside it	Controls growth, development, and energy processes; helps maintain homeostasis	Produces and delivers sex cells; in females, nurtures and protects developing embryo	Fights infections; attacks invading bacteria and viruses

Reproductive System The reproductive system is responsible for producing sperm and eggs and (in females) for nurturing the fetus until birth. Male reproductive organs include the testes (also known as testicles) and the penis. Female reproductive organs include the ovaries, uterus, and vagina. A cell can reproduce itself to make a new cell, but it takes a whole organ system to create a new human.

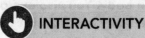 **INTERACTIVITY**

Explain how the human body is organized and how different body systems work together.

✓ READING CHECK **Cite Textual Evidence** Identify an example of how multiple body systems work together to perform a specific function.

....

....

SC.6.L.14.1, SC.6.L.14.5

1. Distinguish Relationships How would you relate the levels of organization in the human body to the levels of organization of a city?

....

....

....

....

....

....

2. Analyze Systems Explain how two body systems work together to exchange oxygen and carbon dioxide between the outside air and the cells in the body.

....

....

....

....

....

....

3. Relate Structure and Function The thin layer of epithelial tissue in the small intestines works somewhat like a cell membrane. How does its structure relate to its function in the digestive system?

....

....

....

....

4. Evaluate Claims Your neighbor Gabe just said that cells are not that important, because organs keep us alive. Support or refute his claim by comparing the importance of organs and cells.

....

....

....

....

....

....

Quest CHECK-IN

In this lesson, you learned about the organization of the human body. You also explored the different systems of the human body and how they interact.

Apply Concepts How do healthy cells contribute to a properly functioning body? How do you think you can communicate this information in your exhibit?

....

....

....

....

👆 INTERACTIVITY

The Importance of Cells

Go online to find out more about a medical condition that directly involves cells or cell function. Then construct an exhibit that explains to visitors why this topic is important.

Artificial SKiN

👆 **INTERACTIVITY**

Identify criteria, constraints, and materials that need to be considered when building an artificial limb.

How do you help people who suffer due to severely damaged skin? You engineer new skin for them! Bioengineers may have solved a big problem.

The Challenge: To grow artificial skin that functions like the real thing.

Until recently, using artificial skin presented doctors with challenges and risks. Without hair follicles and oil glands, the skin could not function properly to help maintain homeostasis, the process that keeps internal conditions in the body stable. But new developments in cell research and bioengineering may have overcome this obstacle.

To make the artificial skin, bioengineers took cells from the mouths of mice. After treating the cells with chemicals, the scientists were able to form random clumps of a mix of cell types that you might find in a newly fertilized egg.

When researchers placed these cells into other mice, the cells gradually changed into specialized tissue. Once this happened, the scientists transplanted them out of those mice and into the skin tissue of other mice. Here the tissues developed normally as integumentary tissue, with hair follicles and oil glands. They also discovered that the implanted tissues made normal connections with the surrounding nerve and muscle tissues, allowing the different body systems to interact normally.

This artificial skin (genetically modified to "glow" green) is able to function just like real skin. It can grow hair and is able to sweat.

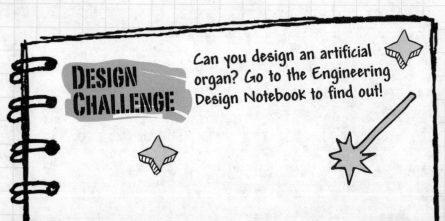

DESIGN CHALLENGE

Can you design an artificial organ? Go to the Engineering Design Notebook to find out!

LESSON
6 Systems Interacting

Guiding Questions

- How do organ systems interact to carry out all the necessary functions for an organism's growth and survival?
- How do organ systems interact to maintain homeostasis?

Connection

Literacy Cite Textual Evidence

SC.6.L.14.5 Identify and investigate the general functions of the major systems of the human body (digestive, respiratory, circulatory, reproductive, excretory, immune, nervous, and musculoskeletal) and describe ways these systems interact with each other to maintain homeostasis. (Also **SC.6.N.1.1** and **SC.6.N.3.4**)

Vocabulary

stimulus
response
gland
hormone
stress

Academic Vocabulary

interactions
stable

 VOCABULARY APP

Practice vocabulary on a mobile device.

Quest CONNECTION

Think about how systems interact and why one body system is dependent on the functioning of healthy cells in other body systems.

Connect It!

In the space provided on the image, list the body systems that you think are involved in skateboarding.

Predict If one of these body systems were to stop interacting with the other systems, would this activity still be possible? Explain.

....

....

....

Systems Working Together

All the systems in the human body work together to perform all the necessary functions for life. Cells need oxygen provided by the respiratory system and carried by the circulatory system. Organs carry out commands from the nervous system. And every part of the body changes its activities based on signals from the endocrine system.

Movement How is the skateboarder in **Figure 1** able to do what she does? **Interactions** between the skeletal, muscular, and nervous systems make it possible. Skeletal muscles are attached to the bones of the skeleton and provide the force that moves bones. Muscles contract and relax. When a muscle contracts, it shortens and pulls on the bones to which it is attached.

Try standing on one leg and bending the other leg at the knee. Hold that position. You can feel that you are using the muscles at the back of your thigh. Your nervous system controls when and how your muscles act on your bones.

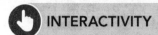

INTERACTIVITY

Explore how joints function in the human body.

Academic Vocabulary

What kinds of interactions are there between people in your neighborhood?

....

....

....

....

Poetry in Motion
Figure 1 We can accomplish impressive feats when all the body's systems are working together properly.

Literacy Connection

Cite Textual Evidence
The central idea of this text is that the body is organized into systems that interact with each other. As you read, underline evidence that organ systems interact with each other.

Controlling Body Functions The nervous system has two ways of controlling body functions: electrical signals from nerves and chemical signals from the endocrine system. Both methods help you to respond to your environment.

Transporting Materials All cells need oxygen and nutrients, and they need to get rid of carbon dioxide and other wastes. But most cells are locked into position with no way to move in search of food. So how can they stay alive? The answer is that blood vessels from the circulatory system carry nutrients to and waste from the cells in the body. Blood vessels divide into smaller and smaller branches until the tiniest, called capillaries, are only as wide as one blood cell. Capillaries, visible in **Figure 2**, pass near every cell in the body.

Blood picks up oxygen from the lungs and food molecules from the intestines and delivers them to needy cells. At the same time, blood collects carbon dioxide and waste from the cells. The carbon dioxide is returned to the lungs to be released into the air. Waste products are filtered from the blood by the kidneys in the excretory system and passed out of the body in urine.

✓ READING CHECK **Determine Meaning** Why do the capillaries have to be so small?

....

....

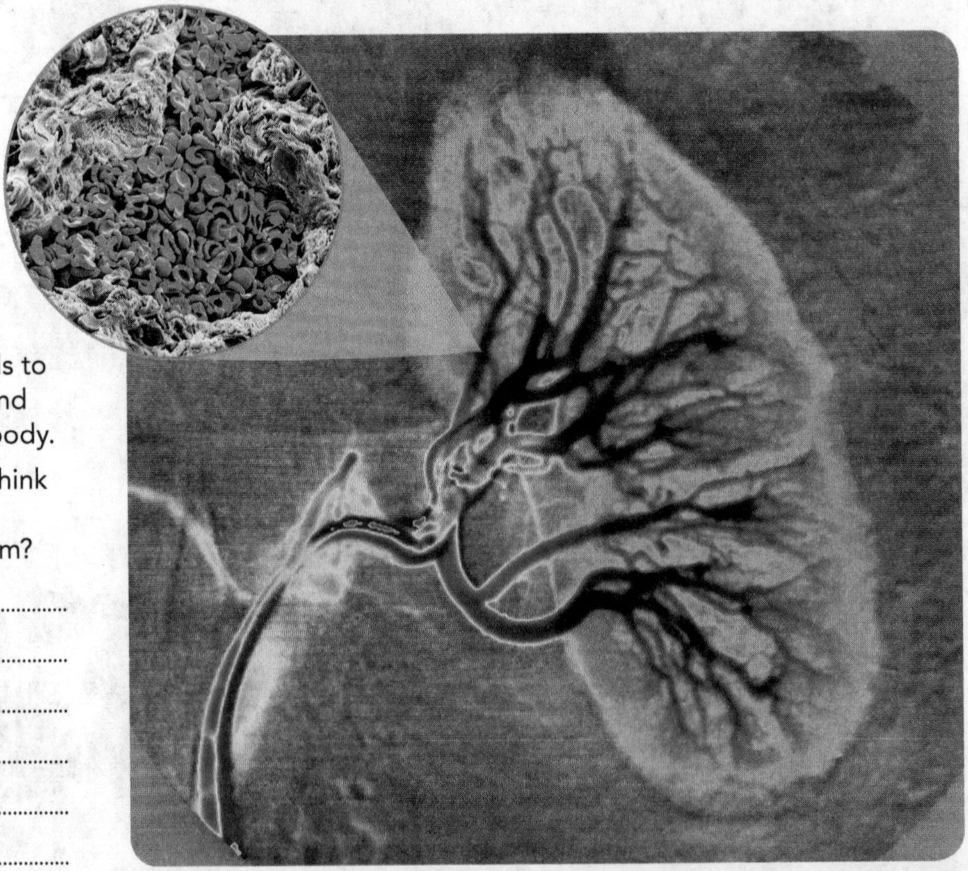

Special Delivery
Figure 2 Blood cells, like those shown in the inset, travel through a network of blood vessels to transport materials to and from every part of the body.

Predict How do you think a blocked blood vessel would affect an organism?

....

....

....

....

....

Stimulus and Response Your eyes, ears, skin, nose, and taste buds all send information about your environment to your nervous system. Your senses let you react to loud noises, hot objects, and the odor of your favorite food. Any change or signal in the environment that can make an organism react in some way is called a **stimulus** (plural: stimuli). A **response** is an action or change in behavior that occurs as a result of a stimulus. Responses are directed by your nervous system but often involve other body systems as well. Your muscular and skeletal systems help you reach for food, and your digestive system releases saliva before the food even reaches your mouth. **Figure 3** shows an example of stimulus and response used in an American Sign Language expression.

 INTERACTIVITY

Investigate how different body systems work together.

Plan It

Reaction Time
The time that passes between a stimulus and a response is the reaction time. A short reaction time could save you from a fall or a burn, and it might help you beat video games.

Plan Your Investigation Plan an investigation to measure reaction times under different conditions. Choose two or three factors that you suspect may influence reaction time, such as time of day, type of stimulus, environmental conditions, or state of mental alertness. How could you display your results?

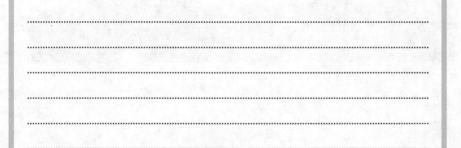

....
....
....
....
....
....
....
....
....
....
....
....
....

Don't Burn Your Mouth
Figure 3 The American Sign Language expression for *hot* shows a reaction to hot food.

Apply Concepts Use the terms *stimulus* and *response* to explain what the sign is expressing.

....
....
....
....

HANDS-ON LAB

Investigate Identify the body systems used to perform specific actions.

Hormonal Control

Hormonal Control The endocrine system uses chemical signals instead of nerves to control body functions. The endocrine system is made up of many **glands**, organs that produce and release chemicals either through tiny tubes called ducts or directly into the bloodstream. For example, when something startles you, your adrenal glands send signals that prepare you to fight or run away. Your heart pumps faster, your lungs let in more air, and your ability to feel pain decreases. The pupils of your eyes even grow larger and allow in more light. You are ready for action.

The chemical produced by an endocrine gland is called a **hormone**. Hormones are carried through your body by the circulatory system. These chemicals affect many body processes. One hormone interacts with the excretory system and the circulatory system to control the amount of water in the bloodstream. Another hormone interacts with the digestive system and the circulatory system to control the amount of sugar in the bloodstream. Hormones also affect the reproductive systems of both males and females. **Figure 4** shows some of the effects of hormones on boys during puberty.

✓ **READING CHECK** **Cite Textual Evidence** What text on this page supports the idea that the endocrine system functions differently from the nervous system?

....

....

....

Hormones and Puberty

Figure 4 Hormones can have dramatic and long-lasting effects.

Make Observations Identify some of the changes you see between the before-puberty and after-puberty pictures.

....

....

....

Interacting Systems

Figure 5 This swimmer's body systems work together as she pushes herself to excel.

Apply Concepts   Read the descriptions of functions happening in the swimmer's body. Then identify the main systems involved.

Food from the swimmer's breakfast has been broken down into nutrients and is delievered to cells.

....

....

The swimmer's brain interprets what her eyes see and directs her movements.

....

....

....

Carbon dioxide moves rapidly out of the swimmer's lungs. Cell wastes move into her blood and are filtered by her kidneys.

....

....

....

The swimmer's arms reach out to pull her through the water.

....

....

Hormones move through the swimmer's bloodstream, stimulating her body systems to work harder.

....

....

The swimmer's breathing rate and heart rate increase, supplying more oxygen to her muscle cells.

....

....

Cooling Down

Figure 6 The woman in the first image is using several different ways to warm up.

Apply Concepts Identify some ways the woman in the second drawing might cool her body and maintain a constant body temperature.

....

....

....

Homeostasis

Academic Vocabulary

Stable is a common word to describe something that hasn't changed much and isn't expected to change much in the future. Make a list of some things you have heard described as stable.

....

....

....

....

What happens when you go outside in the cold? Does your body temperature fall to meet the outside temperature? It does not, and that's a very good thing! Your body only functions well around 37°C. It is vitally important for your body to maintain that temperature. Whether the weather is below freezing or roasting hot, your body's temperature must stay **stable** and remain close to 37°C.

Each organism requires specific conditions to function. Maintaining those conditions is necessary for life to continue. Remember that the condition in which an organism's internal environment is kept stable in spite of changes in the outside environment is called homeostasis.

Regulating Temperature When your body temperature starts to fall too low, as shown in **Figure 6**, your nervous system sends out signals to your other systems to take action to warm you up. Your skin, which is part of the integumentary system, develops goosebumps. Your muscles cause you to shiver. You tend to move your large muscles to generate heat. All of these actions help to raise your temperature back to normal.

 VIDEO

Find out how a house's heating system is like your body.

Keeping Balance Structures in your inner ear sense the position of your head. They send this information to your brain, which interprets the signals. If your brain senses that you are losing your balance, then it sends messages to your muscles to move in ways that help you stay steady. **Figure 7** shows the cycle of how your body keeps its balance.

Meeting Energy Needs When the cells in your body need more energy, hormones from the endocrine system signal the nervous system to make you feel hungry. After you eat, other hormones signal your brain to make you feel full.

Maintaining Water Balance All the chemical reactions that keep you alive take place within the watery environment of your cells. If your body needs more water, then your nervous system causes you to feel thirsty. Your senses, muscles, and skeleton take you to a source of water. After you have had enough water, your nervous system causes your thirst to end. Soon after, the water passes through your digestive system to your circulatory system and from there into your cells. Water balance is restored!

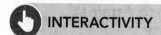 **INTERACTIVITY**

Explain how body systems interact to maintain homeostasis.

Maintaining Homeostasis
Figure 7 Interactions among your ears, brain, and muscular system make up the balance cycle.

Sequence ✏ Fill in the missing steps to create a diagram of the thirst cycle.

☑ READING CHECK
Translate Information What role does the nervous system play in maintaining homeostasis? Explain.

....

....

....

....

....

....

....

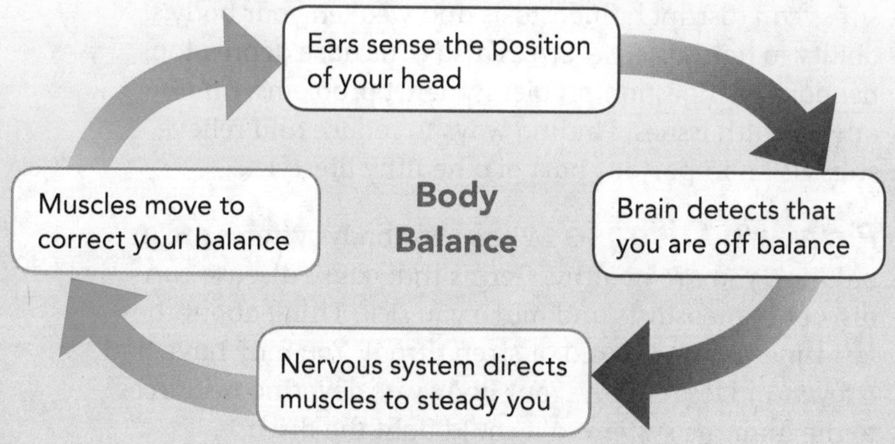

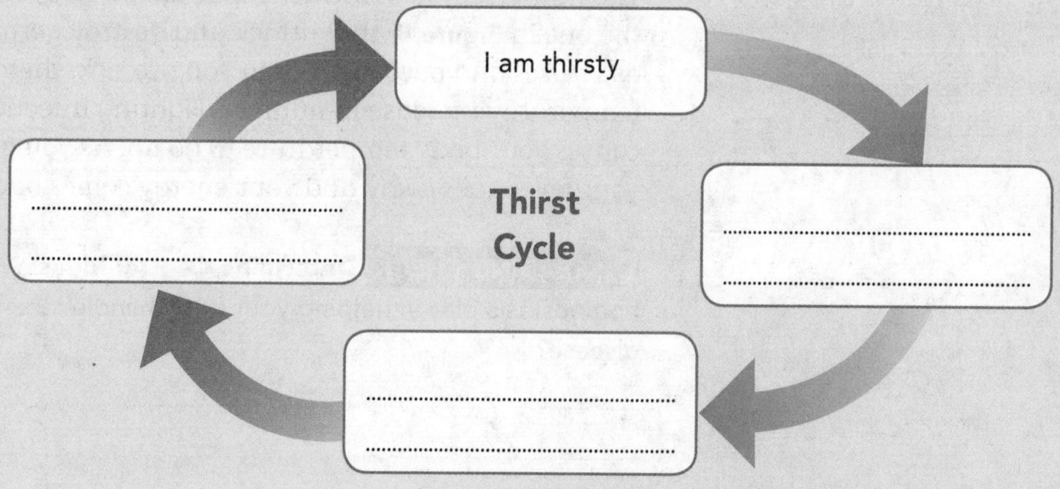

Body Balance

- Ears sense the position of your head
- Brain detects that you are off balance
- Nervous system directs muscles to steady you
- Muscles move to correct your balance

Thirst Cycle

- I am thirsty
- [blank]
- [blank]
- [blank]

Defense Against Disease

Figure 8 The green cell is an immune cell. It engulfs the orange and blue bacteria cells, and destroys them.

Apply Concepts How do you think the immune system is affected by stress?

....

....

....

....

....

....

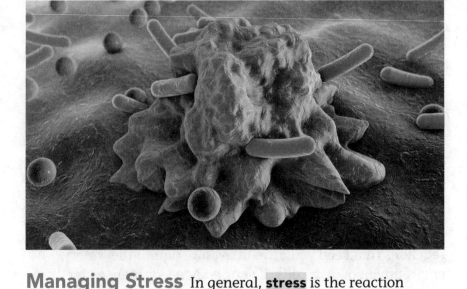

INTERACTIVITY

Analyze symptoms to see what body systems are affected by an illness.

VIDEO

Go inside the world of a medical illustrator.

Managing Stress In general, **stress** is the reaction of a person's body to potentially threatening, challenging, or disturbing events. Each person experiences stress differently. One person may enjoy taking on the challenge of a math test, while someone else might freeze with fear.

Some stress is unavoidable. If stress is over quickly, then the body returns to its normal, healthy condition. However, too much stress for too long a time can be unhealthy. Ongoing stress can disrupt homeostasis and weaken your body's ability to fight disease. Stress also can cause depression, headaches, digestion problems, heart problems, and other health issues. Finding ways to reduce and relieve stress is an important part of a healthy lifestyle.

Fighting Disease When your body systems are in balance, you are healthy. Germs that cause disease can disrupt homeostasis and make you sick. Think about the last time you had a cold or strep throat. You may have had a fever and less energy. Your body was devoting resources to the immune system so it could fight the disease.

The immune system includes specialized cells, such as the one in **Figure 8**, that attack and destroy germs, such as viruses and bacteria. When you are sick, these cells temporarily increase in number. Fighting infection sometimes causes your body temperature to go up. As you get well, your fever goes away and your energy comes back.

✓ **READING CHECK** **Determine Central Ideas** What role does homeostasis play in helping your body handle stress and fight disease?

....

....

....

☑ LESSON 6 Check

1. **Define** What is a hormone?

2. **Explain** What are four conditions that need to be stable to maintain homeostasis?

3. **Cause and Effect** Explain how getting sick is both a cause and effect of a lack of homeostasis.

4. **Make Judgments** How does learning about body systems help you make informed decisions about your health?

5. **Explain Phenomena** Suppose you sit in the same position so long that your leg starts to hurt. How do different body systems interact to stop the pain?

6. **Apply Concepts** Write a journal entry (real or fictional) that includes at least five interactions between your skeletal (S), integumentary (I), muscular (M), circulatory (C), respiratory (R), digestive (D), excretory (EX), nervous (N), and/or endocrine (EN) systems. Note every system involved in each interaction.

7. **Identify Limitations** Examine the diagram of the body balance feedback system below. Fill in the box after each process with the codes for each body system involved. (See Question 6 for codes.) Suggest a way this diagram could be improved to help you understand more about balance.

Ears sense the position of your head

Brain detects that you are off balance

Body Balance

Nervous system directs muscles to steady you

Muscles move to correct your balance

AGENTS OF Infection

You may think that doctors and nurses in emergency rooms usually set broken bones and stitch up bad wounds. But they also have to deal with all kinds of infections that can harm people. Knowing how to treat each kind of infection is key to maintaining a healthy population.

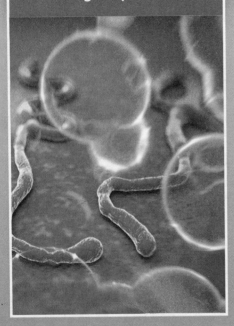

Medical professionals and patients need to take safety precautions, such as hand washing, to prevent the spread of infection.

This bacterium is responsible for causing strep throat.

There are thousands of living and nonliving things that cause infections. The living ones include bacteria, fungi, worms, and single-celled organisms called protists. A bacterium is responsible for strep throat. Ringworm is caused by a fungus. Dysentery can result from a bacterial infection as well as amoebas. The good news about being infected with one of these organisms is that, for the most part, the infections they cause can be cured with medical treatment. There are also a number of ways that you can protect yourself from infections. For example, you can reduce your chances of getting or spreading an infection by washing your hands and by avoiding touching your face if your hands are not clean.

Nonliving viruses also cause infections. Viruses can cause diseases such as HIV, the common cold, and chicken pox. Only a few medications can treat them. A virus is hard to treat because it uses living cells to make copies of itself. These cells are damaged or destroyed when the new virus particles are released. The virus particles then infect other cells. Depending on the type of infection, people may get better over time. Sometimes a viral infection is so severe that symptoms never go away and conditions worsen.

You may have heard of the Zika virus or the flesh-eating bacterium *Vibrio vulnificus*. Each of these causes serious symptoms in people, often requiring hospitalization. Read about some of these infections in the table.

Infectious Agent	Type of Organism	Cause/Transmission	Symptoms	Treatment
Zika	Virus	Mosquito bites or transmission from infected person	Fever, rash, joint pain	There is no specific medicine or vaccine for Zika virus.
Brain-eating *Naegleria fowleri*	Amoeba	Infection occurs most often from diving, water skiing, or other water sports when water is forced into the nose.	Headache, fever, stiff neck, loss of appetite, seizures, coma	A number of drugs kill *N. fowleri* amoebas in the test tube. But even when treated with these drugs, very few patients survive.
Flesh-eating *Vibrio vulnificus*	Bacterium	It releases a toxin that causes the immune system to release white blood cells that destroy the individual's flesh.	Sweats, fever, and chills with red, swollen, blister-like patches on the body	Either the affected tissue has to be amputated, or antibiotics have to be administered.

Use the text and the table to answer the following questions.

1. Compare and Contrast How are viruses different from other infectious agents, such as bacteria and fungi?

....

....

....

2. Construct an Argument Do you think science and medicine will ever be able to discover a cure for Zika? Why or why not?

....

....

....

....

3. Solve Problems What are some steps you can take to prevent getting or spreading an infectious disease?

....

....

....

① Structure and Function of Cells

SC.6. L.14.2, SC.6. L.14.3

1. Which of the following is **not** stated in the cell theory?

A. Cells are the basic units of structure and function in living things.

B. Animal cells are more complex than plant cells.

C. All living things are composed of cells.

D. All new cells are produced from other cells.

2. Analyze Systems Explain the statement "A single cell has the same needs as an entire organism."

....

....

....

....

3. Apply Concepts What would be the first step in proving whether or not the object shown is a living thing? What technology would be most useful in that step?

....

....

....

② Cell Structures

SC.6. L.14.4

4. Which of these structures breaks down sugars to provide energy for cell activities?

A. vacuole   B. endoplasmic reticulum

C. nucleus   D. mitochondrion

5. Construct Explanations All cells have a cell membrane, but plant cells also have a cell wall. What could explain this difference?

....

....

....

6. Determine Differences What are three differences between plant and animal cells?

....

....

....

....

③ Obtaining and Removing Materials

SC.6. L.14.3

7. Which of the following substances moves from an area of higher concentration to an area of lower concentration by a type of diffusion called osmosis?

A. gas   B. sugar

C. food   D. water

8. Relate Structure and Function How does the term "selectively permeable" describe the function of a cell membrane?

....

....

....

9. Predict Without endocytosis and exocytosis, some types of substances would be prevented from crossing the cell membrane. What would be the impact on the cell?

....

....

....

....

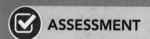
4 Cell Division

SC.6. L.14.3

10. What is the result of cell reproduction?
   A. Two identical daughter cells are created.
   B. One parent cell and one daughter cell are created.
   C. One parent cell and two identical daughter cells are created.
   D. Two identical parent cells are created.

11. Apply Concepts At what point and during what process in the cell cycle does one cell become two?

....

....

....

12. Construct Explanations During which cell cycle stage is a cell plate present? Explain its purpose.

....

....

....

....

....

5 Body Organization

SC.6.L.14.1, SC.6.L.14.5

13. Because the structure of an organ is more complex than the structure of a tissue,
   A. organs are always larger than tissues.
   B. only large animals have organs.
   C. an organ can have more complex functions than a tissue.
   D. a tissue can have more complex functions than an organ.

14. Analyze Systems Compare the functions of four human organ systems to parts of your school.

....

....

....

....

....

....

....

....

....

6 Systems Interacting

SC.6.L.14.5

15. Which system sends signals that make skeletal muscles move?
   A. muscular system   B. digestive
   C. nervous   D. respiratory

16. Lack of homeostasis could **most** directly cause
   A. lack of sleep.
   B. too much anxiety.
   C. extreme thirst.
   D. deep depression.

17. Apply Scientific Reasoning Every time you have a test coming up, you find yourself getting sick! Explain what you think is happening to your body.

....

....

....

....

....

....

Circle the letter of the best answer.

Skin is the largest organ in the human body. Since the 1980s, scientists have been investigating engineered skin—replacement tissue for patients who have lost skin because of severe burns. One method is to take skin cells from a patient and then grow the tissue in a lab environment. Unfortunately, engineered skin has disadvantages. It lacks important structures like hair, oil glands, and sweat glands. **Consider this information as you answer Questions 1–5.**

1 Which option shows levels of organization that **best** represent how engineered skin is used on a person's body?

A new skin cell

B new skin cell, new tissue

C new skin cell, new tissue, new skin organ

D new skin cell, new tissue, new skin organ, new integumentary system

2 How is natural skin such as that shown in the image different from engineered skin?

F It cannot burn.

G It has no hair.

H It cannot stretch and bend.

I It has oil and sweat glands.

3 Which of the following is the **best** example of how homeostasis would be affected if a person with engineered skin were living in a hot climate?

A The person would not feel hot.

B The person would sweat more.

C The person would sweat less.

D The person would get more sunburns.

4 Given what you have learned about engineered skin, which characteristics do its cells **most likely** have?

F The cells undergo the cell cycle.

G The cells have cell walls and cell membranes.

H The cells look like animal cells under a microscope.

I The cells perform all the functions of obtaining and removing materials.

5 A new engineered skin has been developed. The investigator has a hypothesis that it does not have the drawbacks that existing engineered skin has. Which variable should be manipulated in an investigation to collect the **most** useful data?

A humidity

B light

C size of skin graft

D temperature

6 Which organ system is described? *It carries nutrients absorbed from food, it carries oxygen absorbed from the air to cells, and it takes wastes to the lungs and to the kidneys.*

F circulatory system

G digestive system

H excretory system

I respiratory system

SC.6. L.14.1, SC.6. L.14.2, SC.6. L.14.3, SC.6. L.14.4, SC.6. L.14.5

Examine the cell organelle photos below. Then answer Questions 7 and 8.

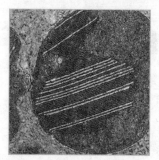 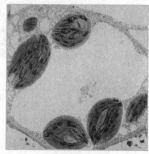

7 The organelle in the left photo can be considered a cell control center. It is a

A cell wall.

B mitochondrion.

C nucleus.

D vacuole.

8 The organelles in the right photo help plant cells transform energy. They are

F cell walls.

G chloroplasts.

H mitochondria.

I vacuoles.

9 What is one difference between the cell of a unicellular organism and a cell of a multicellular organism?

A Only multicellular organisms have specialized cells.

B Only multicellular organisms produce cells from other cells.

C Only unicellular organisms have vacuoles.

D Only unicellular organisms make their own food.

10 Which cell structure does NOT play a role in removing wastes?

F cell membrane **G** lysosome

H chloroplast **I** vacuole

Quest FINDINGS

SC.6.L.14.4, SC.6.N.1.5, SC.6.N.3.4

Complete the Quest!

Determine the best way to present your cell model for the museum exhibit. Then present your exhibit to the class.

Use Models Many museum exhibits rely on models to help teach or inform the public. What are some of the advantages of using models to show objects and processes that cannot be seen with the naked eye? What are some disadvantages?

....

....

....

....

....

....

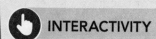 **INTERACTIVITY**

Reflect on Your Museum Exhibit

Design and Build a Microscope

Can you **design** and build your own **microscope** to **examine** small objects?

Background

Have you ever used a magnifying glass to read the date on a small coin more easily? What do you think would happen if you used a second magnifying glass to look through the first magnifying glass?

That's the basic idea behind a compound microscope—using one lens to look through a second lens to get a better view of small objects. This view often gives scientists the ability to understand how the structure of an organism helps with its function. In this activity, you will design and build your own microscope to examine small objects.

Materials

(per pair)

- book
- 2 hand lenses; one low-power and one high-power
- metric ruler
- cardboard tubes
- tape
- scissors
- rubber bands
- other common materials for building your microscope

Safety

Be sure to follow all safety guidelines provided by your teacher. The Safety Appendix of your textbook provides more details about the safety icons.

Herald Moth The wings on this Herald moth allow it to fly. Viewing the moth's wings up close could explain how the wing's structure enables the moth to fly.

Procedure

Part 1: Define the Problem

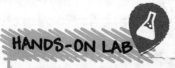

HANDS-ON LAB

⋈ Demonstrate Go online for a downloadable worksheet of this lab.

1. Work with a partner to explore how lenses can be used to magnify objects. Using only your eyes, examine words in a book. Then use the high-power lens to examine the same words. Draw your observations in the space provided.

2. Hold the high-power lens 5 to 6 cm above the words in the book. Keep the high-power lens about the same height above the words. Hold the low-power lens above the high power lens.

3. Move the high-power lens up and down until the image is in focus and upside down. Once the image is in focus, experiment with raising and lowering both lenses. Your goal is to produce the highest magnification while keeping the image in clear focus.

4. Measure and record the distance between the book and the high-power lens, and between the two lenses. Draw your observations through both lenses together.

Part 2: Design a Solution

5. Using this information, design your own compound microscope. Think of creative ways to use the available materials. Your microscope should meet all the criteria shown.

6. Sketch your design. Obtain your teacher's approval for your design. Then construct your microscope.

Part 3: Test and Evaluate Your Solution

7. Test your microscope by examining printed words or a printed photograph. Then, examine other objects such as a leaf or onion skin. Record your observations. Did your microscope meet the criteria listed in Step 5?

8. Examine microscopes made by other students. Based on your tests and your examination of other microscopes, identify ways you could improve your microscope.

Your microscope should:

- contain one low-power lens and one high-power lens
- allow the distance between the two lenses to be easily adjusted
- focus to produce a clear, enlarged, and upside-down image of the object

Part 1: Research and Investigate

Sketch what you observed:

eyes only   high-powered lens   both lenses

Measurements:

....

....

Part 2: Design and Build

Sketch of proposed microscope design:

Part 3: Evaluate and Redesign

Observations: Ideas to improve microscope:

....

....

....

....

....

....

Analyze and Interpret Data

1. **Evaluate Your Solution** When you used two lenses, how did moving the top lens up and down affect the image? What was the effect of moving the bottom lens up and down?

   ....

   ....

   ....

2. **Make Observations** Compare the images you observed using one lens with the image from two lenses. What do you think accounts for these differences?

   ....

   ....

   ....

3. **Apply Scientific Reasoning** How do you think that the compound microscope contributed to the development of the cell theory? Use evidence from your investigation.

   ....

   ....

   ....

4. **Use Models** How did modeling a microscope with the two lenses in Part 1 help you determine the design and function of your microscope? What types of limitations did you encounter as you designed and built your prototype?

   ....

   ....

   ....

   ....

5. **Engage in Argument** Imagine you are living in the year 1675. Write a letter to a scientific magazine that will convince scientists to use your new microscope rather than the single-lens variety used by Van Leeuwenhoek. Support your points with evidence from your investigation.

   ....

   ....

   ....

   ....

SC.6.N.1.1

Tools of Science

Science Processes

Science provides us with ways to answer questions and to solve problems, like finding new energy sources or treating illnesses. Scientists learn how to ask questions that can be answered through the processes of investigation and experimentation.

Scientists rely not only on tools such as rulers or clocks to measure things, but also on processes such as making observations and predictions. The table shows some of the processes that scientists use as tools to learn about the natural world.

Process	Definition
qualitative observation	using one or more of the senses to gather information that relies on descriptions
quantitative observation	using one or more of the senses to gather information that relies on numbers or amounts
inference	explaining or interpreting things observed
prediction	a statement about the future based on evidence
evaluation	reaching a conclusion based on observations
classification	grouping together items that are alike
investigation	making an in-depth study of a subject

Measurement

The process of quantitative observation involves using numbers and units to make measurements. Measurements are useful for sharing information among scientists, but only if everyone uses the same methods and units of measurement. This is why scientists developed a standard system of measurement. It is called the International System of Units, or SI. Scientists use this system for measuring properties such as length (in meters or centimeters), mass (in kilograms), and time (in seconds).

Reflect Use the ruler shown to collect data about the salamander. Record your measurements and explain why your data are useful for sharing with other students.

Math Tools

Scientists use math in many ways to interpret data that include numbers. Math tools such as estimating or finding the average of a set of values help scientists to analyze information and to make sure measurements are accurate.

Scientists also evaluate whether or not the data they collect make sense or seem reasonable. Sometimes a measurement does not fit with the rest of the data. You should not ignore anomalous or unexpected data because they may indicate mistakes in procedures.

Interpret Data Determine whether each set of data seems reasonable. Record any anomalous data you identify.

Data Collected	Anomalous Data
Number of teeth in five different adult crocodiles: 60, 62, 63, 64, 101	
Daily high air temperature for three days: 27°C, 26°C, 28°C	
Average time students in three classes can hold their breath: 1 minute 35 seconds, 1 minute 20 seconds, 3 minutes 45 seconds	
Distance a car moves: 1.5 meters, 12 meters, 1.8 meters, 2.0 meters	

Graphs

A graph is another tool that scientists use to organize and interpret large sets of data. Types of graphs include circle graphs, bar graphs, and line graphs. Graphs often make viewing and displaying data easier. They provide a way to spot relationships and trends in the data more easily, which then enables scientists to make inferences and predictions.

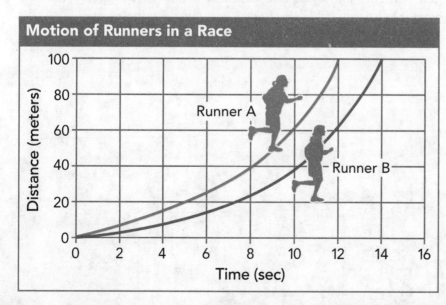

Motion of Runners in a Race

Make Meaning
Identify the variables shown in the graph. Then analyze the information in the graph to make a prediction about which runner will most likely travel 200 meters faster to win the race. Explain your prediction.

SC.6.N.1.1, SC.6.N.1.2, SC.6.N.1.3, SC.6.N.1.4

Gathering Knowledge

Science Experiments

Scientific inquiry is the process by which scientists study and explain the natural world. This process varies. It usually begins with making observations and gathering information about a particular question. Based on this information, a scientist develops a hypothesis—a possible answer to his or her question.

To test a hypothesis, you might conduct a controlled experiment. In an experiment, you collect, organize, and analyze data. Then you draw a conclusion and share your data with other scientists so that they can verify the results.

An important part of performing a controlled experiment is identifying the variables. Variables are factors that can affect the results of an experiment. Often the hypothesis is in the form of a prediction that includes both the independent and dependent variables. The independent variable is the factor purposely changed to test a hypothesis. The dependent variable is the factor that may change in response to the independent variable.

For example, if you wanted to investigate the effect that temperature has on how fast a rock breaks apart, then your hypothesis might be, "If the temperature increases, then the rate of weathering will increase." The rate of weathering is the dependent variable because it may change when the temperature changes. The temperature is the independent variable because it is the factor you change during the experiment.

Make Meaning
Flamingoes consume a varied diet of algae, insects, and crustaceans. Suppose that you wanted to conduct a controlled experiment to determine what part of the diet causes white flamingo feathers to turn pink. What would your hypothesis statement be? What are the independent and dependent variables?

Communicating Results

Scientists share ideas and communicate results in many ways. By working together, scientists can come up with new questions and work out how best to solve a problem. Scientists communicate by sharing their ideas and results, giving talks at scientific meetings, and publishing articles in journals.

By sharing the procedures, data, and conclusions of their investigations, scientists can repeat each other's investigations. Before research gets published, other scientists review it to check the data and conclusions. This review process prevents unreliable results from being published.

Reflect Suppose you conduct an experiment to find out how sunlight affects plant cells. Explain why that investigation and your results should be repeatable by other students in your class.

Other Types of Investigations

Not all investigations are controlled experiments. Studies about organisms, such as owls, often involve observational research. In this type of investigation, researchers make observations without interfering. One benefit is that direct observation often leads to new ideas for study. Also, the data collected represent real-world events rather than those created in a lab, as in many experiments. One drawback is that observational research can take a long time to complete.

Another type of investigation is opinion-based research, in which researchers ask people questions. The questions are often about people's opinions or feelings. This type of investigation is useful for learning about ways of thinking or emotions.

Construct Explanations Identify the two types of scientific investigations and explain the difference between them. Then describe a benefit and a limitation of each type of investigation.

Student observes western burrowing owls to find out how they get food

Type of Investigation:

....

How it differs from other investigation:

....

....

Benefit: ....

....

Limitation: ....

....

Student controls variables to see how friction affects skateboard speed

Type of Investigation:

....

How it differs from other investigation:

....

....

Benefit: ....

....

Limitation: ....

....

SC.6.N.1.5, SC.6.N.2.1

Scientific Thinking

Characteristics of Scientific Thinking

It's important for scientists to keep an open mind. They must draw conclusions based on what their data show, not based on their own opinions, hopes, or predictions. This is difficult because it is part of human nature to want your predictions to be correct. Often, scientists must revise their hypotheses based on the results of their investigations. This is an important part of scientific inquiry.

Another part of scientific inquiry is creativity, which involves coming up with new ways to solve problems or to produce new things. Scientists must be creative when they design experiments, brainstorm solutions, and come up with explanations that fit the evidence they gather.

Write About It In 1888, inventor Charles Brush built a wind turbine in his back yard. The 144-blade fan mounted atop a 60-foot tower provided electricity for Brush's mansion. Explain why you think his invention did or did not involve creativity.

Scientists do need to be creative and open-minded about new ideas. But, they also need to be skeptical, or doubtful, of conclusions and explanations presented without enough evidence to support them. Scientists generally consider whether an idea seems reasonable based on what they already know to be true about the topic.

Even though the data in a study may point to a certain conclusion, the way a scientist interprets the data may be influenced by biases. Biases are likes or dislikes that may affect how people interpret information. For example, if someone is a dedicated cat owner, then he or she may interpret information about diseases that can be transmitted from cats to humans differently than does a colleague who does not own cats. Bias occurs when a certain result is more likely to occur because the experiment was designed to support that result.

Scientific Reasoning

Reasoning is a logical way of thinking used to solve a problem. It often involves collecting data and interpreting results based on evidence in the data.

Objective thinking is based on facts. It includes information not influenced by emotions or judgments. Subjective thinking is based on opinions and personal feelings that cannot be proven true or false. Saying something tastes good is an example of subjective thinking. Scientific conclusions should be based only on facts evaluated using objective thinking.

There are two main types of scientific reasoning—inductive and deductive. Inductive reasoning involves making a generalization from a specific observation. Suppose you observe worms on a sidewalk after a rainstorm. You might use inductive reasoning to infer that rain drives worms out of the soil and onto sidewalks.

Deductive reasoning is useful for testing a hypothesis because it is a way to explain observations. For example, you might know that dark clouds and strong winds are features of thunderstorms. If you look outside and see dark clouds and objects blown by the wind, you might conclude that a thunderstorm is nearby.

If you draw a conclusion without enough data, your reasoning might lead to an incorrect conclusion. This is called faulty reasoning. For example, you might conclude that it always rains in Miami because it rained the two times you visited the city. However, your reasoning is faulty.

Make Meaning
Suppose a friend tells you that rainy weather causes colds because it rained every day last week and now she is sick. How can you apply scientific reasoning to explain to your friend that she is incorrect?

Apply Concepts Look at the table and decide whether the statements are based on objective or subjective thinking.

Statement	Objective or Subjective Thinking?
There are more than 3,000 species of spiders in North America.	
Most of Earth's fresh water occurs as ice.	
Studying global ocean currents is more important than studying global winds.	
Some cheeses taste stronger than others.	

SC.6.N.2.2, SC.6.N.2.3

What Scientists Do

Source of Scientific Knowledge

Scientific knowledge is built on facts collected through observation and experimentation. New evidence and advances in technology can lead to new interpretations and discoveries.

Reflect Suppose you are a paleontologist who discovers a fossilized insect that does not look like any known insect. Would you disregard all previous knowledge about insect species when faced with this new evidence? Explain.

For example, scientists used to think that nothing could live at the bottom of the ocean. However, in 1977, scientists found colonies of tube worms living at 2,000 meters below the ocean surface. New technology allowed the scientists to go deeper than ever before, making this discovery possible. Based on new observations, scientists now know many organisms live on the ocean floor. Scientific knowledge is durable, or lasting, because it adjusts to new evidence.

Careers

The hundreds of science careers you might choose from are based on three main fields of science: life science, earth and space science, and physical science. Life science is the study of all living things, including plants, animals, and microscopic organisms. Earth and space science includes the study of Earth and its place in the universe. It includes specialties such as geology and astronomy. Physical science involves the study of processes that direct the world around you. It includes topics such as forces, energy, and chemistry.

There are also many other careers that require some knowledge of science. Farmers need to understand soil properties to grow crops. Electricians must understand electricity to make sure electrical appliances work.

Classify Read about each scientist in the table. Determine which field of science reflects each scientist's interests and goals.

Scientist	Life, Earth/Space, or Physical Science?
Jane Goodall is best known for her study of wild chimpanzees in Tanzania.	
Nicola Tesla was a scientist/engineer who studied electrical energy.	
Charles Lyell was an English scientist who investigated river erosion.	

Backgrounds of Scientists

Scientists come from all over the world and from different backgrounds. They are men and women with varied talents and interests. Their interests drive their curiosity to answer questions about the natural world.

Some scientists are inspired by a life-changing event or an experience that leads them to ask questions. But they all use good observation skills and have the ability to apply scientific reasoning to solve problems.

For example, Marie Maynard Daly, the first African American woman to earn a Ph.D. in chemistry, developed an interest in science as a young woman. She was an avid reader, and her family encouraged her to pursue her interests. She was further inspired to earn her Ph.D. by her father, who had to drop out of college because he couldn't afford to finish.

Scientists Working Together

Scientists benefit when they work together to share ideas, resources, and information. If you were a scientist studying the impacts of pollution on the Atlantic Ocean, you would need the help of many other scientists to gather and interpret data. Some of the types of people you might need to communicate with are named in the diagram.

Research teams are often made up of many different kinds of scientists. They also include many nonscientists, such as guides and technicians.

Write About It If you became a scientist, what types of things would you be most interested in studying? How do you think your life experiences might influence your interests and goals? How might students in other parts of the world be influenced by their life experiences?

Make Meaning Imagine that you and your team plan to visit and study the glaciers of Antarctica. Draw a diagram like the one shown. Include at least four different scientists and one nonscientist you will need to help with the investigation.

Scientists Working Together

Meteorologists study the ocean's effect on weather.

Geochemists study the properties of ocean water.

Marine zoologists study aquatic animal life.

Atlantic Ocean Study

Marine botanists study aquatic plants and algae.

Geologists study coastal erosion and landforms.

Oceanographers study ocean currents.

SC.6.N.3.1, SC.6.N.3.2, SC.6.N.3.3, SC.6.N.3.4

Communicating Scientific Knowledge

Scientific Laws

A driver observing the speed limit obeys a rule set by the government to keep people safe. This rule is a societal law. Scientific laws, on the other hand, are not legal rules that people must follow. They are statements that describe scientific principles, or what you can always expect under certain conditions in the natural world. Scientific laws are based on repeated observations and experimental results.

Scientific laws describe *what* will happen or how it will happen without trying to explain *why* it happens. For example, every time you throw an apple in the air, you know that it will always fall back down to Earth. This observed pattern—that the apple always falls back down—is an example of Newton's law of universal gravitation. This law states that the force of gravity acts between all objects in the universe.

Based on this law, you know gravity acts between Earth and the apple. The law does not attempt to explain why gravity does this, but focuses on describing a repeatable pattern that anyone can observe. Other examples of scientific laws are shown in the table.

Make Meaning

Explain what a scientific law is. Then give an example of one and explain how it differs from a law that says you must have a valid driver's license to drive a car.

Scientific Law	What It Says
Newton's law of universal gravitation	The force of gravity acts between all objects in the universe.
Newton's first law of motion	An object at rest will remain at rest, and an object moving at a constant velocity will continue moving at a constant velocity, unless it is acted upon by an unbalanced force.
Newton's second law of motion	Acceleration depends on the object's mass and the net force acting on the object.
law of conservation of energy	In a chemical reaction, energy cannot be created or destroyed, but it can change from one form to another.

Scientific Theories

Have you ever heard people say they have a theory to explain why something happens? They might have a theory that the traffic is slow because of a traffic accident. Everyday theories, called claims, are different from scientific theories. Scientific theories are thoroughly tested, accurate descriptions that predict why something happens in nature. They are widely accepted by scientists and are based on observations and data that support them.

One example is cell theory, which explains how cells and living things are related. This theory is well supported by data collected by many scientists. Therefore, it is accepted as true.

Scientific theories are different from scientific laws. Scientific theories explain why a process occurs. Scientific laws describe what happens, but they do not explain why it happens.

Scientific Models

Have you ever tried to picture how much of Earth's surface is covered by water? A globe can help you. It is a model of Earth that shows features of the surface. A model represents a simple or complex object or process.

Models can be pictures, diagrams, maps, or three-dimensional objects, such as a globe. They can also be mathematical equations, computer programs, and written descriptions. Scientists use many types of models to gain understanding and to share ideas. They use models to make predictions and to show complex systems, such as weather systems.

Make Meaning
Explain what a scientific theory is and how it differs from a claim. Give an example of each.

Write About It
These globes are both examples of three-dimensional models. How are these models similar? How are they different?

Safety Symbols

These symbols warn of possible dangers in the laboratory and remind you to work carefully.

 Safety Goggles Wear safety goggles to protect your eyes in any activity involving chemicals, flames or heating, or glassware.

 Lab Apron Wear a laboratory apron to protect your skin and clothing from damage.

 Breakage Handle breakable materials, such as glassware, with care. Do not touch broken glassware.

 Heat-Resistant Gloves Use an oven mitt or other hand protection when handling hot materials, such as hot plates or hot glassware.

 Plastic Gloves Wear disposable plastic gloves when working with harmful chemicals and organisms. Keep your hands away from your face, and dispose of the gloves according to your teacher's instructions.

 Heating Use a clamp or tongs to pick up hot glassware. Do not touch hot objects with your bare hands.

 Flames Before you work with flames, tie back loose hair and clothing. Follow your teacher's instructions about lighting and extinguishing flames.

 No Flames When using flammable materials, make sure there are no flames, sparks, or other exposed heat sources present.

 Corrosive Chemical Avoid getting acid or other corrosive chemicals on your skin or clothing or in your eyes. Do not inhale the vapors. Wash your hands after the activity.

 Poison Do not let any poisonous chemical come into contact with your skin, and do not inhale its vapors. Wash your hands when you are finished with the activity.

 Fumes Work in a well-ventilated area when harmful vapors may be involved. Avoid inhaling vapors directly. Test an odor only when directed to do so by your teacher, and use a wafting motion to direct the vapor toward your nose.

 Sharp Object Scissors, scalpels, knives, needles, pins, and tacks can cut your skin. Always direct a sharp edge or point away from yourself and others.

 Animal Safety Treat live or preserved animals or animal parts with care to avoid harming the animals or yourself. Wash your hands when you are finished with the activity.

 Plant Safety Handle plants only as directed by your teacher. If you are allergic to certain plants, tell your teacher; do not do an activity involving those plants. Avoid touching harmful plants such as poison ivy. Wash your hands when you are finished with the activity.

 Electric Shock To avoid electric shock, never use electrical equipment around water, when the equipment is wet, or when your hands are wet. Be sure cords are untangled and cannot trip anyone. Unplug equipment not in use.

 Physical Safety When an experiment involves physical activity, avoid injuring yourself or others. Alert your teacher if there is any reason you should not participate.

 Disposal Dispose of chemicals and other laboratory materials safely. Follow the instructions from your teacher.

 Hand Washing Wash your hands thoroughly when finished with an activity. Use soap and warm water. Rinse well.

 General Safety Awareness When this symbol appears, follow the instructions provided. When you are asked to develop your own procedure in a lab, have your teacher approve your plan.

Using a Laboratory Balance

A laboratory balance is an important tool in scientific investigations. Different kinds of balances are used in the laboratory to determine the masses and weights of objects. You can use a triple-beam balance to determine the masses of materials that you study or experiment with in the laboratory. An electronic balance, unlike a triple-beam balance, is used to measure the weights of materials.

The triple-beam balance that you may use in your science class is probably similar to the balance depicted in this Appendix. To use the balance properly, you should learn the name, location, and function of each part of the balance.

Triple-Beam Balance

The triple-beam balance is a single-pan balance with three beams calibrated in grams. The back, or 100-gram, beam is divided into ten units of 10 grams each. The middle, or 500-gram, beam is divided into five units of 100 grams each. The front, or 10-gram, beam is divided into ten units of 1 gram each. Each gram on the front beam is further divided into units of 0.1 gram.

Apply Concepts What is the greatest mass you could find with the triple-beam balance in the picture?

....

Calculate What is the mass of the apple in the picture?

....

The following procedure can be used to find the mass of an object with a triple-beam balance:

1. Place the object on the pan.

2. Move the rider on the middle beam notch by notch until the horizontal pointer on the right drops below zero. Move the rider back one notch.

3. Move the rider on the back beam notch by notch until the pointer again drops below zero. Move the rider back one notch.

4. Slowly slide the rider along the front beam until the pointer stops at the zero point.

5. The mass of the object is equal to the sum of the readings on the three beams.

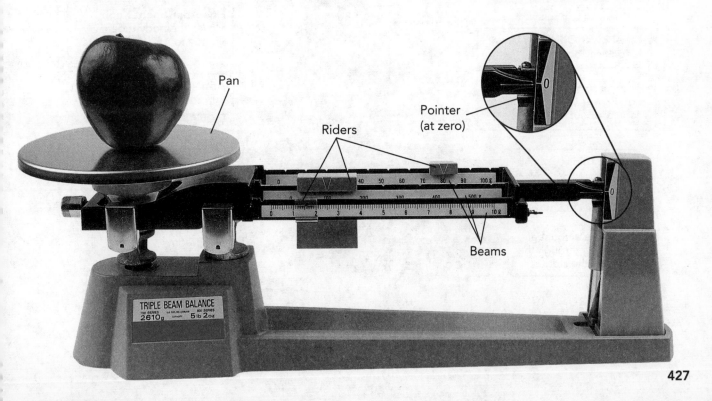

Pan

Riders

Pointer (at zero)

Beams

TRIPLE BEAM BALANCE
700 SERIES   800 SERIES
2610g   5 lb 2 oz

Using a Microscope

The microscope is an essential tool in the study of life science. It allows you to see things that are too small to be seen with the unaided eye.

You will probably use a compound microscope like the one you see here. The compound microscope has more than one lens that magnifies the object you view.

Typically, a compound microscope has one lens in the eyepiece (the part you look through). The eyepiece lens usually magnifies 10×. Any object you view through this lens will appear 10 times larger than it is.

A compound microscope may contain two or three other lenses called objective lenses. They are called the low-power and high-power objective lenses. The low-power objective lens usually magnifies 10×. The high-power objective lenses usually magnify 40× and 100×.

To calculate the total magnification with which you are viewing an object, multiply the magnification of the eyepiece lens by the magnification of the objective lens you are using. For example, the eyepiece's magnification of 10× multiplied by the low-power objective's magnification of 10× equals a total magnification of 100×.

Use the photo of the compound microscope to become familiar with the parts of the microscope and their functions.

The Parts of a Microscope

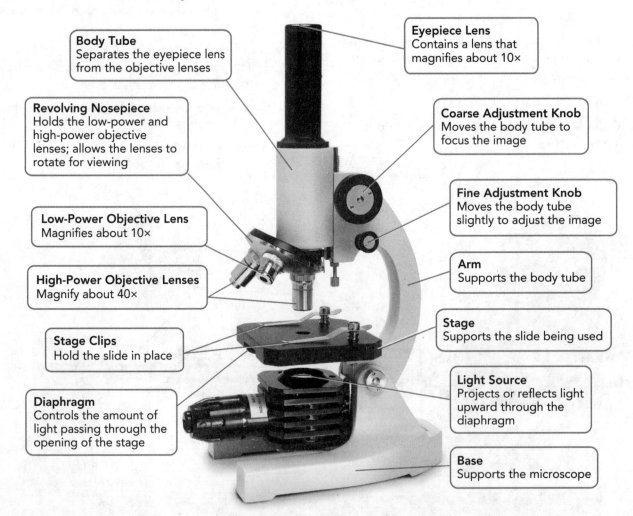

Body Tube
Separates the eyepiece lens from the objective lenses

Revolving Nosepiece
Holds the low-power and high-power objective lenses; allows the lenses to rotate for viewing

Low-Power Objective Lens
Magnifies about 10×

High-Power Objective Lenses
Magnify about 40×

Stage Clips
Hold the slide in place

Diaphragm
Controls the amount of light passing through the opening of the stage

Eyepiece Lens
Contains a lens that magnifies about 10×

Coarse Adjustment Knob
Moves the body tube to focus the image

Fine Adjustment Knob
Moves the body tube slightly to adjust the image

Arm
Supports the body tube

Stage
Supports the slide being used

Light Source
Projects or reflects light upward through the diaphragm

Base
Supports the microscope

Using the Microscope

Use the following procedures when you are working with a microscope.

1. To carry the microscope, grasp the microscope's arm with one hand. Place your other hand under the base.

2. Place the microscope on a table with the arm toward you.

3. Turn the coarse adjustment knob to raise the body tube.

4. Revolve the nosepiece until the low-power objective lens clicks into place.

5. Adjust the diaphragm. While looking through the eyepiece, adjust the mirror until you see a bright white circle of light. **CAUTION:** Never use direct sunlight as a light source.

6. Place a slide on the stage. Center the specimen over the opening on the stage. Use the stage clips to hold the slide in place. **CAUTION:** Glass slides are fragile.

7. Look at the stage from the side. Carefully turn the coarse adjustment knob to lower the body tube until the low-power objective almost touches the slide.

8. Looking through the eyepiece, very slowly turn the coarse adjustment knob until the specimen comes into focus.

9. To switch to the high-power objective lens, look at the microscope from the side. Carefully revolve the nosepiece until the high-power objective lens clicks into place. Make sure the lens does not hit the slide.

10. Looking through the eyepiece, turn the fine adjustment knob until the specimen comes into focus.

Making a Wet-Mount Slide

Use the following procedures to make a wet-mount slide of a specimen.

1. Obtain a clean microscope slide and a coverslip. **CAUTION:** Glass slides and coverslips are fragile.

2. Place the specimen on the center of the slide. The specimen must be thin enough for light to pass through it.

3. Using a plastic dropper, place a drop of water on the specimen.

4. Gently place one edge of the coverslip against the slide so that it touches the edge of the water drop at a 45° angle. Slowly lower the coverslip over the specimen. If you see air bubbles trapped beneath the coverslip, tap the coverslip gently with the eraser end of a pencil.

5. Remove any excess water at the edge of the coverslip with a paper towel.

Periodic Table of Elements

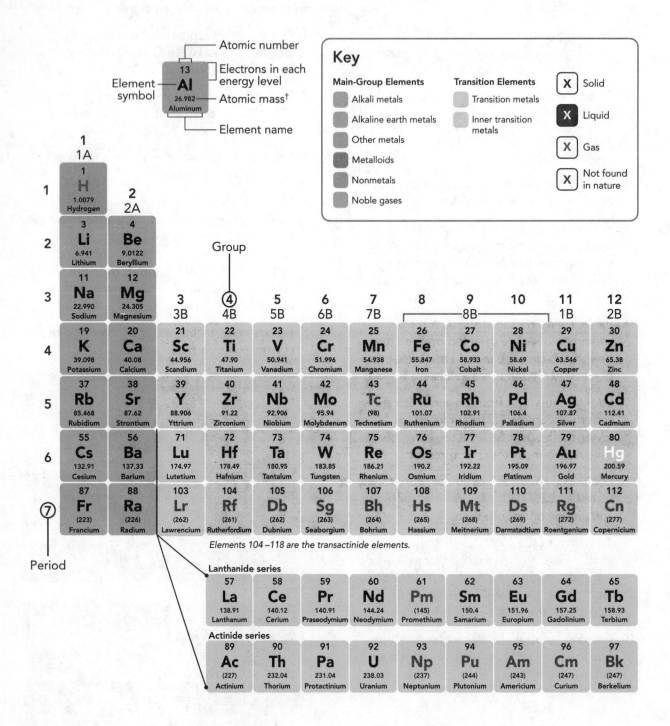

Elements 104–118 are the transactinide elements.

| 18 |
| 8A |

| 2 |
| He |
| 4.0026 |
| Helium |

| 13 | 14 | 15 | 16 | 17 |
| 3A | 4A | 5A | 6A | 7A |

5	6	7	8	9	10
B	C	N	O	F	Ne
10.81	12.011	14.007	15.999	18.998	20.179
Boron	Carbon	Nitrogen	Oxygen	Fluorine	Neon

13	14	15	16	17	18
Al	Si	P	S	Cl	Ar
26.982	28.086	30.974	32.06	35.453	39.948
Aluminum	Silicon	Phosphorus	Sulfur	Chlorine	Argon

31	32	33	34	35	36
Ga	Ge	As	Se	Br	Kr
69.72	72.59	74.922	78.96	79.904	83.80
Gallium	Germanium	Arsenic	Selenium	Bromine	Krypton

49	50	51	52	53	54
In	Sn	Sb	Te	I	Xe
114.82	118.69	121.75	127.60	126.90	131.30
Indium	Tin	Antimony	Tellurium	Iodine	Xenon

81	82	83	84	85	86
Tl	Pb	Bi	Po	At	Rn
204.37	207.2	208.98	(209)	(210)	(222)
Thallium	Lead	Bismuth	Polonium	Astatine	Radon

113	114	115	116	117	118
Nh	Fl	Mc	Lv	Ts	Og
(284)	(289)	(288)	(292)	(294)	(294)
Nihonium	Flerovium	Moscovium	Livermorium	Tennessine	Oganesson

66	67	68	69	70
Dy	Ho	Er	Tm	Yb
162.50	164.93	167.26	168.93	173.04
Dysprosium	Holmium	Erbium	Thulium	Ytterbium

98	99	100	101	102
Cf	Es	Fm	Md	No
(251)	(252)	(257)	(258)	(259)
Californium	Einsteinium	Fermium	Mendelevium	Nobelium

GLOSSARY

432

A

acceleration The rate at which velocity changes. (67)

air mass A huge body of air that has similar temperature, humidity, and air pressure at any given height. (203)

alluvial fan A wide, sloping deposit of sediment formed where a stream leaves a mountain range. (275)

anticyclone A high-pressure center of dry air. (208)

aquifer An underground layer of rock or sediment that holds water. (132)

atmosphere The relatively thin layer of gases that forms Earth's outermost layer. (108)

B

bacteria Single-celled organisms that lack a nucleus; prokaryotes. (330)

binomial nomenclature The classification system in which each organism is given a unique, two-part scientific name indicating its genus and species. (317)

biosphere The parts of Earth that contain living organisms. (108)

C

cell The basic unit of structure and function in living things. (306, 351)

cell cycle The series of events in which a cell grows, prepares for division, and divides to form two daughter cells. (380)

cell membrane A thin, flexible barrier that surrounds a cell and controls which substances pass into and out of a cell. (363)

cell theory A widely accepted explanation of the relationship between cells and living things. (354)

cell wall A rigid supporting layer that surrounds the cells of plants and some other organisms. (362)

chemical energy A form of potential energy that is stored in chemical bonds between atoms. (26)

chemical weathering The process that breaks down rock through chemical changes. (254)

chloroplast An organelle in the cells of plants and some other organisms that captures energy from sunlight and changes it to an energy form that cells can use in making food. (365)

classification The process of grouping things based on their similarities. (317)

climate The average annual conditions of temperature, precipitation, winds, and clouds in an area. (231)

coastline A line that forms the boundary between the land and the ocean or a lake. (119)

condensation The change in state from a gas to a liquid. (128, 194)

conduction The transfer of energy from one particle of matter to another. (156)

continental glacier A glacier that covers much of a continent or large island. (284)

convection The transfer of thermal energy by the movement of a fluid. (156)

convergent evolution The process by which unrelated organisms evolve similar characteristics. (323)

Coriolis effect The effect of Earth's rotation on the direction of winds and currents. (165)

cryosphere The portion of the hydrosphere that is frozen, including all the ice and snow on land, plus sea and lake ice. (108)

current A large stream of moving water that flows through the oceans. (171)

cyclone A swirling center of low air pressure. (208)

cytokinesis The final stage of the cell cycle, in which the cell's cytoplasm divides, distributing the organelles into each of the two new daughter cells. (384)

cytoplasm The thick fluid region of a cell located inside the cell membrane (in prokaryotes) or between the cell membrane and nucleus (in eukaryotes). (364)

D

deflation The process by which wind removes surface materials. (266)

delta A landform made of sediment that is deposited where a river flows into an ocean or lake. (119, 275)

deposition Process in which sediment is laid down in new locations. (263)

dew point The temperature at which condensation begins. (194)

diffusion The process by which molecules move from an area of higher concentration to an area of lower concentration. (373)

domain The most basic level of organization in the classification of organisms. (318)

drought A long period of low precipitation. (225)

dune A hill of sand piled up by the wind. (119)

E

El Niño An abnormal climate event that occurs every two to seven years in the Pacific Ocean, causing changes in winds, currents, and weather patterns for one to two years. (174)

elastic potential energy The energy of stretched or compressed objects. (19)

electrical energy The energy of electric charges. (27)

electromagnetic energy The energy of light and other forms of radiation, which travels through space as waves. (27)

electromagnetic wave 1. A wave made up of a combination of a changing electric field and a changing magnetic field. 2. A wave that can transfer electric and magnetic energy through the vacuum of space. (151)

endocytosis The process by which the cell membrane takes particles into the cell by changing shape and engulfing the particles. (376)

energy The ability to do work or cause change. (5, 109)

erosion The process by which water, ice, wind, or gravity moves weathered particles of rock and soil. (253)

evaporation The process by which molecules at the surface of a liquid absorb enough energy to change to a gas. (127, 193)

evolution Change over time; the process by which modern organisms have descended from ancient organisms. (322)

exocytosis The process by which the vacuole surrounding particles fuses with the cell membrane, forcing the contents out of the cell. (376)

F

flood An overflowing of water in a normally dry area. (225)

flood plain The flat, wide area of land along a river. (273)

force A push or pull exerted on an object. (6, 57)

friction The force that two surfaces exert on each other when they rub against each other. (58)

front The boundary where unlike air masses meet but do not mix. (205)

G

genus A taxonomic category that names a group of similar, closely-related organisms. (317)

geosphere The densest parts of Earth, including the crust, mantle, and core. (108)

glacier Any large mass of ice that moves slowly over land. (283)

gland An organ that produces and releases chemicals either through ducts or into the bloodstream. (400)

gravitational potential energy Potential energy that depends on the height of an object. (18)

gravity The attractive force between objects; the force that moves objects downhill. (58)

greenhouse effect The trapping of heat near a planet's surface by certain gases in the planet's atmosphere. (154)

groundwater Water that fills the cracks and spaces in underground soil and rock layers. (277)

H

homeostasis The condition in which an organism's internal environment is kept stable in spite of changes in the external environment. (402)

hormone 1. A chemical that affects growth and development. 2. The chemical produced by an endocrine gland. (400)

host An organism that provides a source of energy or a suitable environment for a parasite to live with, in, or on. (328)

humidity The amount of water vapor in a given volume of air. (195)

humus Dark-colored organic material in soil. (257)

hurricane A tropical storm that has winds of about 119 kilometers per hour or higher. (222)

hydrosphere The portion of Earth that consists of water in any of its forms, including oceans, glaciers, rivers, lakes, groundwater and water vapor. (108)

I

ice age Time in Earth's history during which glaciers covered large parts of the surface. (284)

inertia The tendency of an object to resist a change in motion. (76)

interphase The first stage of the cell cycle that takes place before cell division occurs, during which a cell grows and makes a copy of its DNA. (382)

J

jet stream Band of high-speed winds about 10 kilometers above Earth's surface. (167, 203)

K

kinetic energy Energy that an object has due to its motion. (15)

L

La Niña A climate event in the eastern Pacific Ocean in which surface waters are colder than normal. (174)

land breeze The flow of air from land to a body of water. (163)

landform A feature on the surface of Earth, such as a coastline, dune, or mountain. (115)

law of conservation of energy The rule that energy cannot be created or destroyed. (36)

loess A wind-formed deposit made of fine particles of clay and silt. (267)

longshore drift The movement of water and sediment down a beach caused by waves coming in to shore at an angle. (290)

M

mass movement Any one of several processes by which gravity moves sediment downhill. (264)

GLOSSARY

mechanical energy Kinetic or potential energy associated with the motion or position of an object. (23)

mechanical weathering The type of weathering in which rock is physically broken into smaller pieces. (254)

meteorologist A scientist who studies the causes of weather and tries to predict it. (211)

microscope An instrument that makes small objects look larger. (352)

mitochondria Rod-shaped organelles that convert energy in food molecules to energy the cell can use to carry out its functions. (365)

mitosis The second stage of the cell cycle, during which the cell's nucleus divides into two new nuclei and one set of DNA is distributed into each daughter cell. (383)

motion The state in which one object's distance from another is changing. (5, 55)

mountain A landform with high elevation and high relief. (118)

multicellular Consisting of many cells. (307)

N

net force The overall force on an object when all the individual forces acting on it are added together. (59)

newton A unit of measure that equals the force required to accelerate 1 kilogram of mass at 1 meter per second per second. (57)

nuclear energy The potential energy stored in the nucleus of an atom. (24)

nucleus In cells, a large oval organelle that contains the cell's genetic material in the form of DNA and controls many of the cell's activities. (364)

O

occluded Cut off, as in a front where a warm air mass is caught between two cooler air masses. (207)

organ A body structure that is composed of different kinds of tissues that work together. (389)

organ system A group of organs that work together to perform a major function. (389)

organelle A tiny cell structure that carries out a specific function within the cell. (361)

organism A living thing. (305)

osmosis The diffusion of water molecules across a selectively permeable membrane. (374)

P

parasite An organism that benefits by living with, on, or in a host in a parasitism interaction. (333)

plucking The process by which a glacier picks up rocks as it flows over the land. (285)

potential energy The energy an object has because of its position; also the internal stored energy of an object, such as energy stored in chemical bonds. (17)

power The rate at which one form of energy is transformed into another. (10)

precipitation Any form of water that falls from clouds and reaches Earth's surface as rain, snow, sleet, or hail. (128, 196)

protist A eukaryotic organism that cannot be classified as an animal, plant, or fungus. (333)

R

radiation The transfer of energy by electromagnetic waves. (156)

reference point A place or object used for comparison to determine whether an object is in motion. (55)

relative humidity The percentage of water vapor in the air compared to the maximum amount of water vapor that air can contain at a particular temperature. (195)

replication The process by which a cell makes a copy of the DNA in its nucleus before cell division. (382)

response An action or change in behavior that occurs as a result of a stimulus. (306, 399)

river A natural stream of water that flows into another body of water, such as an ocean, lake, or another river. (119)

runoff Water that flows over the ground surface rather than soaking into the ground. (271)

S

sand dune A deposit of wind-blown sand. (267)

sea breeze The flow of cooler air from over an ocean or lake toward land. (163)

sediment Small, solid pieces of material that come from rocks or the remains of organisms; earth materials deposited by erosion. (263)

selectively permeable A property of cell membranes that allows some substances to pass across it, while others cannot. (372)

slope The steepness of a graph line; the ratio of the vertical change (the rise) to the horizontal change (the run). (65)

soil The loose, weathered material on Earth's surface in which plants can grow. (257)

species A group of similar organisms that can mate with each other and produce offspring that can also mate and reproduce. (317)

speed The distance an object travels per unit of time. (63)

spontaneous generation The mistaken idea that living things arise from nonliving sources. (308)

stimulus Any change or signal in the environment that can make an organism react in some way. (306, 399)

storm A violent disturbance in the atmosphere. (219)

storm surge A "dome" of water that sweeps across the coast where a hurricane lands. (223)

stream A channel through which water is continually flowing downhill. (272)

stress The reaction of a person's body to potentially threatening, challenging, or disturbing events. (404)

surveying A process in which mapmakers determine distances and elevations using instruments and the principles of geometry. (120)

T

taxonomy The scientific study of how living things are classified. (318)

thermal energy The total kinetic and potential energy of all the particles of an object. (25, 155)

thunderstorm A small storm often accompanied by heavy precipitation and frequent thunder and lightning. (221)

till The sediments deposited directly by a glacier. (286)

tissue A group of similar cells that perform a specific function. (388)

topography The shape of the land determined by elevation, relief, and landforms. (115)

tornado A rapidly whirling, funnel-shaped cloud that reaches down to touch Earth's surface. (224)

transpiration The process by which water is lost through a plant's leaves. (127)

tributary A stream or river that flows into a larger river. (272)

U

unicellular Made of a single cell. (307)

uniformitarianism The geologic principle that the same geologic processes that operate today operated in the past to change Earth's surface. (253)

V

vaccine A substance used in a vaccination that consists of pathogens that have been weakened or killed but can still trigger the body to produce chemicals that destroy the pathogens. (328)

vacuole A sac-like organelle that stores water, food, and other materials. (366)

valley glacier A long, narrow glacier that forms when snow and ice build up in a mountain valley. (284)

velocity Speed in a given direction. (66)

virus A tiny, nonliving particle that enters and then reproduces inside a living cell. (328)

W

water cycle The continual movement of water among Earth's atmosphere, oceans, and land surface through evaporation, condensation, and precipitation. (127, 193)

watershed The land area that supplies water to a river system. (130)

weight A measure of the force of gravity acting on an object. (89)

well A hole sunk into the ground to reach a supply of water. (132)

wind The horizontal movement of air from an area of high pressure to an area of lower pressure. (161)

work Force exerted on an object that causes it to move. (7)

INDEX

INDEX Page numbers for key terms are printed in boldface type.

ACKNOWLEDGEMENTS

Photographs

Photo locators denoted as follows: Top (T), Center (C), Bottom (B), Left (L), Right (R), Background (Bkgd)

Front Cover: Lava: Doug Perrine/Nature Picture Library
Back Cover: Notes/papers: Marinello/DigitalVision Vectors/Getty Images

Front Matter

iv: Tanarch/Shutterstock; vi: David Jones/PA Images/Alamy Stock Photo; vii: Matteo Arteni/Shutterstock; viii: Mark Whitt Photography/Getty Images; ix: UniversalImagesGroup/Getty Images; x: switas/Getty Images; xi: Robert Harding/Alamy Stock Photo; xii: Martin Harvey/Getty Images; xiii: NIBSC/Science Photo Library/Getty Images; xiv: Brian J. Skerry/National Geographic/Getty Images; xv: Steve Byland/Shutterstock

Topic 1

xvi: David Jones/PA Images/Alamy Stock Photo; 002: Jeffrey Coolidge/Getty Images; 004: Derek Watt/Alamy Stock Photo; 008: Hero Images/Getty Images; 009 BC: Steven May/Alamy Stock Photo; 009 BL: WavebreakMediaMicro/Fotolia; 009 BR: Monkey Business/Fotolia; 010 BL: Ben Schonewille/Shutterstock; 010 BR: Andrey Popov/Shutterstock; 011: Egmont Strigl/imageBROKER/Alamy Stock Photo; 012 TCL: Ariel Skelley/Blend Images/Getty Images; 012 TL: B Christopher/Alamy Stock Photo; 014: AFP/Getty Images; 017: Feng Yu/Fotolia; 018: Anatoliy Gleb/Fotolia; 021: Sportpoint/Fotolia; 022: fhm/Moment/Getty Images; 023: Steve Byland/Shutterstock; 025: Paul Vinten/Fotolia; 026: Toa55/Shutterstock; 031 B: John Lund/Marc Romanelli/Blend Images/Getty Images; 031 TR: Hero Images Inc./Alamy Stock Photo; 032: Holger Thalmann/Cultura RM/Alamy Stock Photo; 034 BL: Richard Megna/Fundamental Photographs; 034 BR: Kim Karpeles/Alamy Stock Photo; 036: parkerphotography/Alamy Stock Photo; 038: Ian McDonnell/iStock/Getty Images; 040: blackpixel/Shutterstock; 046: Stockbyte/Getty Images

Topic 2

050: Matteo Arteni/Shutterstock; 052: Heiner Heine/imageBROKER/Alamy Stock Photo; 054: Seth K. Hughes/Image Source/Alamy Stock Photo; 056: Marcio Jose Bastos Silva/Shutterstock; 057 CR: WilleeCole Photography/Shutterstock; 057 TCR: Sonya Etchison/Fotolia; 057 TR: dmussman/iStock/Getty Images; 058 BL: gbh007/Getty Images; 058 BR: Monkey Business Images/Shutterstock; 062: Ian Lishman/Juice Images/Getty Images; 064: kuznetsov_konsta/Fotolia; 064: Scott A. Miller/ZUMA Press/Newscom; 065: Jim Zuckerman/Alamy Stock Photo; 066: Emma Yacomen/Alamy Stock Photo; 068 TC: WING/UPPA/Photoshot/Newscom; 068 TL: John Ewing/Portland Press Herald/Getty Images; 068 TR: Jim Cummins/The Image Bank/Getty Images; 072 Bkgrd: hkeita/Shutterstock; 072 CL: BLACKDAY/Shutterstock; 074: lsantilli/123RF; 076 CL: Janet Horton/Alamy Stock Photo; 076 TL: Hero Images Inc/Alamy Stock Photo; 077: Sorin Papuc/Alamy Stock Photo; 078: omgimages/123RF; 079 BL: Janet Horton/Alamy Stock Photo; 079 C: Jiang Dao Hua/Shutterstock; 080: imageBROKER/Alamy Stock Photo; 081 B: D. Trozzo/Alamy Stock Photo; 081 TR: full image/Fotolia; 083 CR: ScofieldZa/Shutterstock; 083 TCR: Barry Blackburn/Shutterstock; 084: kuznetsov_konsta/Fotolia; 088: Robert Daly/OJO Images/Getty Images; 089: Scott Andrews/NASA; 090: Mihajlo Maricic/Alamy Stock Photo; 093 B: Andrey Volodin/Alamy Stock Photo; 093 CR: koya979/Fotolia; 098: Jason O. Watson (Sports)/Alamy Stock Photo; 099: Gary Hamilton/Icon SMI/Icon Sport Media/Getty Images

Topic 3

102: Mark Whitt Photography/Getty Images; 104 Bkgrd: 123RF; 104 TR: tfoxfoto/Getty Images; 106: Samuel Borges/Alamy Stock Photo; 108 BL: Marco Regalia/Alamy Stock Photo; 108 CL: Dorota Wasik/EyeEm/Getty Images; 109 BR: Panther Media GmbH/Alamy Stock Photo; 109 CR: Mario Hoppmann/Shutterstock; 113: seafarer/Shutterstock; 116: David Pearson/Alamy Stock Photo; 117: Stocktrek Images, Inc./Alamy Stock Photo; 120: Charles Gurche/Danita Delimont/Alamy Stock Photo; 122 BR: UniversalImagesGroup/Getty Images; 122 TL: Tetra Images/Alamy Stock Photo; 125 BCR: Songquan Deng/Shutterstock; 125 CR: Everett Collection/Shutterstock; 126: Paul Prescott/Shutterstock; 130: Clint Farlinger/Alamy Stock Photo; 131 CR: Aurora Photos/Alamy Stock Photo; 131 TR: imageBROKER/Alamy Stock Photo; 136: FloridaStock/Shutterstock; 137: Tribune Content Agency LLC/Alamy Stock Photo; 139: Westend61/Getty Images; 142: Sergio Azenha/Alamy Stock Photo; 143: BW Folsom/Shutterstock

Topic 4

146: UniversalImagesGroup/Getty Images; 148: dan_prat/Getty Images; 150: Louise Murray/robertharding/Getty Images; 157: Iakov Kalinin/Shutterstock; 159 Bkgrd: NASA; 160: Ian Brown/Alamy Stock Photo; 162: id1974/123RF; 163 BL: efesenko/Fotolia; 163 BR: Polifoto/Fotolia; 170: Andrey Armyagov/Shutterstock; 174: Stuart Rankin/NOAA; 175: Geraldas Galinauskas/Shutterstock; 178: Kevin Kelley/Getty Images; 184: vermontalm/Fotolia

Topic 5

188: switas/Getty Images; 190: A.T. Willett/Alamy Stock Photo; 192: alexanderkorotun/Fotolia; 195 TCR: David J. Green Technology/Alamy Stock Photo; 195 TR: GIPhotoStock/Science Source; 197 BL: mario beauregard/Fotolia; 197 CL: georgeion88/Fotolia; 197 CR: Nebojsa/Fotolia; 197 TR: Tatiana Belova/Fotolia; 201: Frans Lemmens/Alamy Stock Photo; 202: ValentinValkov/Fotolia; 205: Galyna Andrushko/Fotolia; 208: harvepino/Fotolia; 210: GIS/Fotolia; 212 Bkgrd: solarseven/Shutterstock; 212 BR: Carolina K. Smith MD/Shutterstock; 212 CR: chanelle/Fotolia; 212 TR: Karim Agabi/Science Source; 213: NOAA; 217 Bkgrd: Pavelk/Shutterstock; 217 BR: Science Source; 217 TR: David R. Frazier/Danita Delimont Photography/Newscom; 218: Smith Collection/Gado/Getty Images; 221: stnazkul/123RF; 224: Carlo Allegri/Reuters; 225: Aram Boghosian/The Boston Globe/Getty Images; 228: Juanmonino/Getty Images; 229: Logan Bowles/AP Images; 230: marcaletourneux/Fotolia; 234: Dorling Kindersley/Getty Images; 236: The Whiteview/Shutterstock; 237: Michael Runkel/Alamy Stock Photo; 238: US Geological Survey; 244: Paul Aniszewski/Shutterstock; 245: 123RF

Take Notes